WHEY

TYPES, COMPOSITION AND HEALTH IMPLICATIONS

FOOD SCIENCE AND TECHNOLOGY

Additional books in this series can be found on Nova's website
under the Series tab.

Additional e-books in this series can be found on Nova's website
under the e-books tab.

AGRICULTURE ISSUES AND POLICIES

Additional books in this series can be found on Nova's website
under the Series tab.

Additional e-books in this series can be found on Nova's website
under the e-books tab.

FOOD SCIENCE AND TECHNOLOGY

WHEY

TYPES, COMPOSITION AND HEALTH IMPLICATIONS

RAFAEL MAURO BENITEZ

AND

GUSTAVO M. ORTERO

EDITORS

Nova Science Publishers, Inc.

New York

NOTICE TO THE READER

Library of Congress Cataloging-in-Publication Data

Whey : types, composition and health implications / editors: Rafael Mauro Benitez and Gustavo M. Ortero.
p. cm.
Includes index.
ISBN 978-1-61942-862-1 (hardcover)
1. Whey. I. Benitez, Rafael Mauro, 1962- II. Ortero, Gustavo M.
SF275.W5W56 2012
637'.3--dc23   2011053521

Published by Nova Science Publishers, Inc. † New York

CONTENTS

PREFACE

Whey, the serum or liquid part of milk remaining after separation of the curd, results from the coagulation of milk by acid or proteolytic enzymes. Whey proteins have a relevant nutritional value, and several commercial uses have been developed by the dairy industry. In this book, the authors present topical research in the study of the types, composition and health implications of whey. Included in this compilation are the immune-modulating effects of whey proteins and peptides; the behavior of whey proteins as fat replacers in low-fat food products; up-stream processing methods, general principles and fermentation strategies for microbial productions using whey as a substrate; and the effects of whey protein intake on glucose homeostasis.

Chapter 1 - Whey, a co-product in cheese manufacture, has been traditionally reused by its high content in soluble proteins. Complete, delactosed or low salts content powder whey are commonly used as food ingredients. Whey protein concentrates (WPC) or isolates (WPI) obtained by membrane technology (MT) with different proteins content are in fact one of the most important products in whey processing industries. These products are present in many human foods.

In recent years a number of bioactive peptides present in cheese whey have been described giving this co-product a new extra pharmaceutical and medical interest.

Bioactive peptides have been defined as specific protein fragments that have a positive impact on body functions and can positively affect human health. These biopeptides are inactive within protein sequence and can be released in a proteolysis mainly made by specific enzymes. Main limitations to biopeptides production at the industrial scale are the development of appropriate technologies to fractionate and purify the peptides in economical and competitive processes. From the point of view of human health, real activity of most of them must be still demonstrated and clinical tests must be performed in the next years.

In this chapter a review of possible biopeptides obtained from single whey proteins (mainly alpha-lactalbumin, beta-lactoglobulin and caseinomacropeptide - CMP) as well as from raw whey and WPC is made. The different biological and physiological activities of main peptides described in the literature are also included.

Enzymatic hydrolysis conditions, peptides fractionation by membrane technology, peptides analysis and animal and human trials to demonstrate the biological effects of these products are also reviewed.

Chapter 2 - Whey is an important surplus product of the food industry. Based on the point of view, huge quantities of whey produced worldwide can represent an environmental problem with its disposal, or, due to the fact that whey is rich in fermentable nutrients, it can be considered as an attractive substrate for microbial production of various industrially interesting products. Therefore, this chapter is intended to summarize possible up-stream processing methods, general principles and fermentation strategies for the microbial productions using whey as a substrate. Further, among huge amount of potential products, this review focuses on the production of high value substances and materials which find applications especially in the fields of health care, medicine and pharmacy. At first, many biologically active substances such as vitamins, carotenoids, antibiotics etc. can be produced from whey employing various microorganisms (bacteria, yeasts as well as fungi) and cultivation strategies. Moreover, also number of biopolymers which can be used in form of drug carriers, scaffolds, sutures, adhesives *etc.* can be produced by using whey as a cheap complex substrate. Apart from poly (lactic acid), these materials include bacterial polyesters-polyhydroxyalkanoates and also several polysaccharides such as xanthan, alginate, hyaluronic acid, gellan, pullulan, dextran or chitosan. In addition, the aim of this review is also to provide basic economical consideration of fermentation processes. In conclusion,utilization of whey as a substrate for microbial productions of high value products could result in a very promising process meeting both economic and ecological requirements.

Chapter 3 - Whey proteins are high nutritional quality proteins and are currently used to prepare a number of commercial products claiming effects on consumer health. Whey proteins have potential as a functional food in the management of obesity and its co-morbidities, in detail non insulin dependent diabetes (NIDD or type-2 diabetes) and high blood pressure. Focusing on the effects of whey protein consumption on the insulinemic and glycemic response to meal in both type-2 diabetic and healthy subjects, preclinical and clinical studies suggest that whey protein intake can ameliorate postprandial glucose control and potentiate insulin release.

The insulinotropic effect of whey proteins can be due to their rapid digestion and to the following fast increase in plasma amino acids, in particular in the so called branched-chain amino acids (leucine, isoleucine, valine, threonine). Most likely, the insulinotropic effect of whey occurs by multiple pathways, including the potentiation of incretin activity mediated by small bioactive peptides released during gastrointestinal digestion or during food processing.

Glucose-dependent insulinotropic polypeptide (GIP) and glucagone-like peptide-1 (GLP-1) are gut derived peptides (so called incretin hormones) that are released after food ingestion and potentiate insulin secretion from the islet β-cells in a glucose-dependent manner. They are both rapidly degraded by the aminopeptidase, dipeptidyl peptidase-4 (DPP-4), after termination of feeding. Noteworthy, the use of injected DPP-4 resistant GLP-1 analogs or, alternatively, the use of orally administered inhibitors of DPP-4 activity in order to increase endogenous incretin levels, are the most recent advances in the pharmacological treatment of type-2 diabetes.

As to the mechanism accounting for the positive effect of whey on the incretin system, there is evidence that products of whey protein digestion have the potential to affect incretin degradation through inhibition of intestinal DPP-4, with the outcome of prolonging their insulinotropic effect.

The aim of the present work is to review recent studies dealing with the effects of whey protein intake on glucose homeostasis and to focus on the molecular determinants for such effects contained within whey protein amino acids sequences. Genetic variants of whey proteins among species and within species which might predict differences in their effects on glycemic control will be also discussed.

Chapter 4 - Microbiologically, whey is an interesting product. Traditionally as whey was a waste material in the dairy industry, a by-product of casein and cheese manufacture, the microbiological quality of whey was of little concern. The protein and lactose content of whey is now recognised as a valuable resource and products from the ultrafiltration and reverse osmosis of whey are an integral part of the dairy industry. Maintaining microbiological quality of these whey products to meet customer specifications is challenging. The raw whey leaving the casein or cheese manufacturing plant is often contaminated with bacteria – many originating from the starter cultures used in the manufacture of these products. Changes in the handling of whey have helped improve the quality of products manufactured from whey. However, further challenges exist in the processing of whey which involves large areas of filtration membrane on which biofilm can grow and thence contaminate the product. The composition of the membrane influences biofilm growth, so appropriate selection of membranes may help in controlling biofilm development. Mixed enzyme cleaners and mixed oxidant sanitisers offer the best control of microflora on the membrane surfaces used in whey processing plants.

Chapter 5 - Whey proteins and whey peptides have been known to have physiological as well as nutritional benefits. Until recently, bovine whey proteins and peptides have been mainly studied for their benefits in energy, and muscle performance. Currently, most researches on whey proteins and peptides focus on their benefits for human health. Whey contains various proteins and peptides with physiological functionality. The proteins and peptides found in whey are β-lactoglobulin, α-lactalbumin, immunoglobulins, bovine serum albumin, and lactoferrin, in addition to glycomacropeptide which is made from casein during cheese-making process. Whey proteins and their components have been demonstrated to have immune-modulating properties, that is, the stimulation of innate and adaptive immunities as well as anti-inflammatory effects. Whey proteins also have other benefits, such as anti-oxidant, anti-hypertensive, anti-bacterial, anti-viral and serum lipid-lowering effects. Peptides derived from whey proteins have also been shown to possess various bioactive properties, such as opioid, anti-hypertensive and immune-modulating effects. This review focuses on the immune-modulating potency of whey proteins and peptides which have been well studied, and the recent progress in the authors' laboratory on the anti-inflammatory potency of whey proteins and peptides.

Chapter 6 - The type and composition of whey at dairy plants mainly depends upon the processing techniques resulting from caseins removal during cheese-making. The content and composition of whey proteins from goat, sheep camel, mare and donkey differ consistently from whey protein content in cow milk. Whey proteins proteolysis generates smaller peptides some of which possess beneficial biological activities, and their total content is influenced by whey origin and composition. The industrial exploitation of whey proteins may follow two approaches. From one side, following the principle of sustainable economy and waste recycling the industry could exploit the high amounts of whey by-products as source of valuable peptides. On the other side, a different approach has been pursued through extraction of individual proteins from milk or whey consisting in chitosan addition to milk, acidification, centrifugation and chromatographic separation using anionic resins added in bulk that exploit different Isoelectric points of each whey protein. Whey bioactives are a valuable source of functional proteins that can be exploited in novel formulations, to be assumed through food ingestion. This chapter discusses the beneficial effects and potential applications of different whey isolates originating from different mammal milks, and the approaches to exploitation of whey protein fractions of different whey types.

Chapter 7 - Among identified food allergens, milk exhibits a relevant allergenic potential related to the multiplicity and diversity of the involved proteins. The main whey protein, beta-lactoglobulin, is usually considered to be the major cow's milk allergen. This protein, absent in human milk, is resistant to gastric acid and to proteolytic action, and it has the ability to cross the intestinal mucosa. Food processing can alter the allergenic properties of proteins by hiding, destroying or exposing allergic epitopes through protein structural changes. Some researches have been carried out on the thermal stability of the β-lactoglobulin allergen structure, and a significant reduction in its allergenecity was observed depending on the assayed thermal treatment. The use of microbial transglutaminase can also modify the immunogenicity of food proteins. Recently, it was suggested that the polymerization of β-lactoglobulin catalyzed by transglutaminase might decrease the antigenic response by hiding antigenic sites due to molecular rearrangements. In the authors' recent experiences, β-lactoglobulin aggregates were formed by two different treatments, thermal and enzymatic. In the first one, 55 mg mL^{-1} β-lactoglobulin solutions in 20 mM sodium phosphate buffer pH 6.8, were heated at 85 °C from different periods of time: 1, 3, 5, 7, 10 and 15 min. In the enzymatic method, 25 mg mL^{-1} β-lactoglobulin solutions in 20 mM sodium phosphate buffer pH 8.0, in the presence of 0.07 M cysteine, were incubated with transglutaminase (at a level of 1 U g^{-1} substrate), for different times: 30, 60, 120 and 180 min. Protein structural characterization was analyzed based on electrophoresis, fluorescence, circular dichroism and viscosity studies. Comparing both treatments, it was observed that heating produces a higher degree of unfolding and therefore, a higher index of surface hydrophobicity; less compact and more asymmetrical aggregates, with higher flexibility. These conformational changes can be related to the lesser degree of allergenicity observed, either by the major accessibility to a proteolytic attack, in the case of the unfolding, or by hiding epitopes, in the case of formation of more compact protein aggregates.

Chapter 8 - Whey proteins are used as fat mimetics in low-fat food manufacture in order to improve sensorial quality of the final product. The success of whey proteins as fat replacers lies in the potential capacity of these proteins to imitate the human sensory perception of fat. For example, whey proteins can be incorporated in foods as microparticles. Microparticulated whey proteins have a mean particle size in the order of homogenized fat globules. As a result, the use of whey proteins as fat replacers in low-fat foods (for example cheeses, ice creams, and yogurts) has made it possible to achieve sensory characteristics similar to full-fat products with a reduction in the fat content and beneficial health implications. The present chapter is a brief review about the use of whey proteins as fat replacers in low-fat food products concerning the physicochemical, rheological, and functional properties.

Chapter 9 - Whey proteins and their associated peptides in addition to their nutritional and functional attributes possess immense potential as functional and nutraceutical food ingredients owing to their biological activities. These encompass their antioxidant, chelation, antihypersensitive, anticarcinogenic, hypolipidemic, immune system stimulation, ACE inhibition, antiviral and antibacterial activities. An upsurge in the research activities associated with the investigation of the bioactivity and further corroboration of proven bioactivities of whey proteins and peptides has been evidenced by the scientific community in recent times. Further, the data from clinical studies has already set the pace for use of whey proteins and their associated peptides as functional food ingredients/nutraceuticals. The current chapter provides an overview of the developments with respect to the potentially beneficial human health effects of whey proteins and their peptides. The therapeutic benefits stemming out of the biological activities have also been emphasised with a discussion of the supportive clinical trials.

In: Whey: Types, Composition and Health Implications   ISBN: 978-1-61942-862-1
Editors: Rafael M. Benitez and Gustavo M. Ortero   © 2012 Nova Science Publishers, Inc.

Chapter 1

CHEESE WHEY AS A SOURCE OF ACTIVE PEPTIDES: PRODUCTION, ANALYSIS, PURIFICATION AND ANIMAL AND HUMAN TRIALS

F. A. Riera Rodríguez[*1], *A. Fernández Martínez*[1]
and C. Muro Urista[2]

[1]Department of Chemical Engineering and Environmental Technology.
Oviedo University. Spain
[2]Department of Chemical Engineering and Research.
Instituto Tecnológico de Toluca. México

ABSTRACT

Whey, a co-product in cheese manufacture, has been traditionally reused by its high content in soluble proteins. Complete, delactosed or low salts content powder whey are commonly used as food ingredients. Whey protein concentrates (WPC) or isolates (WPI) obtained by membrane technology (MT) with different proteins content are in fact one of the most important products in whey processing industries. These products are present in many human foods.

In recent years a number of bioactive peptides present in cheese whey have been described giving this co-product a new extra pharmaceutical and medical interest.

Bioactive peptides have been defined as specific protein fragments that have a positive impact on body functions and can positively affect human health. These biopeptides are inactive within protein sequence and can be released in a proteolysis mainly made by specific enzymes. Main limitations to biopeptides production at the industrial scale are the development of appropriate technologies to fractionate and purify the peptides in economical and competitive processes. From the point of view of human health, real activity of most of them must be still demonstrated and clinical tests must be performed in the next years.

In this chapter a review of possible biopeptides obtained from single whey proteins (mainly alpha-lactalbumin, beta-lactoglobulin and caseinomacropeptide - CMP) as well

---

[*] Email: far@uniovi.es

as from raw whey and WPC is made. The different biological and physiological activities of main peptides described in the literature are also included.

Enzymatic hydrolysis conditions, peptides fractionation by membrane technology, peptides analysis and animal and human trials to demonstrate the biological effects of these products are also reviewed.

1. CHEESE WHEY GENERALITIES

Cheese whey is the most important by-product from cheese and casein manufacture. Each kilogram of cheese produced generates between 8 and 9 litres of whey; that means that huge amounts of this product, that contains half of the total milk solids and 20% of the original milk proteins, is produced in world. At small cheese plants, whey continues being a disposal problem due to its high BOD (40,000-60,000 mg O_2/L) and the difficulty of managing small-medium amounts of whey.

In medium and large cheese and casein companies whey is converted in a number of valuable products oriented to animal or human food and in the last years new advances in protein hydrolysis and technological separations lead to products of high value that can be placed in the food-pharmaceutical industries interphase.

Most of the whey components have great value in human nutrition. Whey is the most important commercial lactose source. It is present in whey in percentages higher than 70% (on a dry basis) and permeates of ultrafiltered whey (PUF) shows even higher values.

Lactose favours the calcium and other minerals absorption in mammals and other oligosaccharides present in whey containing sialic acid promote the development of human brain [Park, 2009]. Whey is an important natural source of Ca^{+2} and other minerals (K, Na, P, Zn, Mg, Fe, etc.) some of them playing important roles in metabolism of the human being [Hernández-Ledesma et al., 2011]. The presence of these minerals usually causes technological problems when whey is processed at the industry (in most of the cases specific techniques are used to reduce mineral content in the final product) but they will be able to play important roles for human health in the next years.

However, more extensive research must be done at this point. Most of the water-soluble vitamins present in milk are in the whey fraction. Special interest has the B vitamin complex that is composed by different compounds with demonstrated bioactivity in metabolical rutes.

Concerning the protein fraction, the aminoacid composition of their soluble proteins is more valuable than others usually considered as reference (eggs proteins), and even more interesting than milk caseins. Considered as a whole, whey proteins have a number of technological properties (emulsion and foams stabilization, high water retention capacity, etc.) that are exploited in food industry using these proteins as additives in meat, baker and other food industries. From the point of view of human health, they seem to contribute to the regulation of body weight and improve the net muscle mass, among others benefits [Luhovyy et al., 2007; Phillips et al., 2009].

Most of the industrial products obtained from whey come from its protein fraction. Whey protein concentrates (WPC), whey protein isolates (WPI) with different levels of demineralization and lactose contents can be found in the market and are nowadays traditional ingredients in a number of adults and baby foods as well as they are present in special diets. In these protein products all proteins are concentrated maintaining the original proportions between them, that is, proteins are concentrated but not fractionated. Only in some cases (lactoferrin, lactoperoxidase, etc.) the proteins are separated from the rest of whey proteins and commercialised with high purity due to their high added value.

The first part of this chapter describes briefly main characteristics and health effects of major proteins present in whey and the actual state of whey upgrading from an industrial point of view. The second part is focused on the production of biopeptides and their main bio-functionalities that is considered one of the most interesting research lines for the next years.

2. CHEESE WHEY: COMPOSITION

World whey production increases at the same rate as cheese consumption (around 2% per year) [Smithers, 2008]. Around 80% of the total whey produced is rennet whey ("sweet whey") obtained by enzymatic attack of milk kappa-casein and the 20% remaining is acid whey (obtained in the manufacture of cottage cheese, caseins, etc.), obtained by acidification of milk (by adding acid or lactic bacteria cultures). Table I shows the composition of both types of whey.

As can be seen, main differences between them are related to the final pH of both liquids as well as the amount of salts (higher in acid whey) what affect the technologies used to reuse it (acid whey is difficult to dry in spray drying systems due to the sticky behaviour of concentrated whey). Protein fraction is similar in both types of whey except the presence of caseinomacropeptide (CMP or casein glycomacropeptide – GMP)(CMP is the soluble peptide obtained after the enzymatic action on the k-casein and then it is no present in acid whey). Lactic acid content in acid whey is due to the transformation of lactose by lactic bacteria.

Table I. Characteristics and composition of sweet and acid wheys [Goodall *et al.*, 2008]

	Sweet whey (Liquid)	Acid whey (Liquid)
pH	5.9 -6.3	4.3-4.6
Total solids (%)	6.4	6.2
Fat (%)	0.5	0.04
Lactose (%)	4.6	4.0
Lactic acid (%)	0.05	0.8
Minerals (%)	0.5	0.8
Total Nitrogen (%)	0.8	0.7
Aprox. Protein proportions (% on total proteins)*		
- β-Lg	40-55	
- α-La	11-23	
- IGs	8-11	
- CMP	10-15	
- BSA	4-12	
- Lactoferrin	1	
- Lactoperoxidase	1	
*CMP is only present in rennet whey		

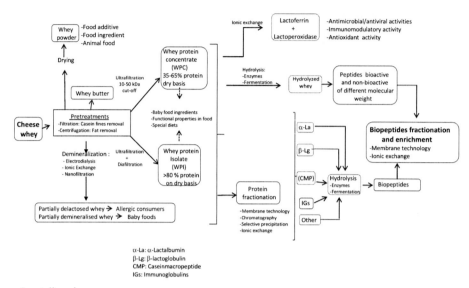

α-La: α-Lactalbumin
β-Lg: β-lactoglobulin
CMP: Caseinmacropeptide
IGs: Immunoglobulins

α-La: α-Lactalbumin.
β-Lg: β-lactoglobulin.
CMP: Caseinmacropeptide.
IGs: Immunoglobulins.

Figure 1. Scheme of whey processing. Protein upgrading.

There are a number of whey derivatives that are commercialised at an industrial scale. Figure 1 shows some of the most important whey transformations that lead to final industrial products. Around 50% of the whey produced is transformed into derivatives.

Whey powder is usually manufactured after evaporation and spray drying steps. The powder can be used as a complement in animal food or as an additive or ingredient in different human and baby foods (bakery, meat, confectionery, sauces, etc.). In some cases whey can be partially demineralised or delactosed in order to obtain products for specific diets. Common technologies to reduce minerals are nanofiltration, ion exchange and electro-dialysis, being former the more commonly used due to its lower cost and efficiency in the reduction of monovalent ions (reductions between 50 – 80 % in monovalent ions and between 3-20% for divalent ones) (Suárez et al., 2006; Minhalma et al., 2007).

Whey butter obtained after whey centrifugation is being considered in the last years as a source of phospholipids with interesting effects on human health affecting several cell functions, such as growth, molecular transport system, memory processing, stress response, etc. [Astaire et al., 2003; Fong et al., 2007; Rezende et al., 2010].

Whey protein concentrates (WPC) are well known products obtained from whey that are commercialised by many companies. These products are produced by means of membrane technologies (ultrafiltration with spiral wound or flat organic membranes between 10 and 50 kDa cut-off). WPC can be commercialised with different level of protein purity (between 35 and 65% based on total solids- WPC35-WPC65). Higher protein concentrations, named whey protein isolate (WPI) showing more than 80 % on total solids basis, can also be manufactured by a combination of ultrafiltration + diafiltration, and they are excellent starting materials to later hydrolysis or protein fractionation. WPC can also be used as ingredient in adult food and in baby foods if some demineralization processes have been made previously. These products are good as starting substrates to later protein fractionation and hydrolysis [Cheang and Zydney, 2004].

Technological and biofunctional properties of proteins can be upgrading by using these concentrated products. Theoretically these concentrates show certain biological activities due to their peptide composition (ACE-inhibitory, hypocholesterolemic, anticarcinogenic, etc.), but in most of the cases the intensity is too low due to that they are in the sequence of the parent proteins [Bounous, 2000; Foegeding *et al.,* 2002]. For this, if the objective is to enhance all these properties (especially in medical applications) it is compulsory to fractionate major proteins and try to obtain single protein streams as pure as possible. Some methods developed in the past as salting out, precipitation in presence of solvents and strong thermal techniques, have been proved to be impractical from an industrial point of view. The techniques used to get these objectives must be rapid, non-denaturing and they must guarantee a high yield product with maximum purity, non-chemical addition, they might be easily scaled-up and not too much expensive.

Unfortunately there is not an unique technique that fulfils these prerequisites. Among the most widely used techniques are chromatographic methods, membrane technologies, selective precipitations, ionic exchange, etc. [El-Sayed and Chase, 2011]. Chromatographic processes have the advantage of being less volume dependent because adsorbent capacity depends mostly on the mass of protein recovered and not on the volume of liquid processed, but production at industrial scale seems to be too much expensive. On the other hand, membrane techniques based on pressure driven methods (NF, UF, MF) produce reasonable yields but with low purities. Electrochemical processes (electrodialysis) have high electricity costs as main drawback. Selectivity precipitation shows some problems related to extreme pHs and difficulties to separate weak precipitates. As an alternative to single methods, coupling some of these techniques will be one of the major future challenges that protein fractionation industry must face [El-Sayed and Chase, 2011].

All proteins contained in whey have been studied in order to find biofunctional properties [Datta *et al.*, 2008; Goodall *et al.*, 2008; Saksena *et al.,* 2010; Camfield *et al.*, 2011; Hernández-Ledesma *et al.*, 2011]. The most interesting characteristics of main whey proteins are described below.

Lactoferrin and Lactoperoxidase

Lactoferrin (LF) is an 80 kDa iron-binding glycoprotein (673 amino acid residues) that belongs to the transferring family. In bovine milk, LF is found in small amounts varying from 0.02 to 0.20 $g.L^{-1}$ and the protein remains quantitatively in cheese whey. LF has multiple biological properties that include antimicrobial, anti-inflammatory, anticarcinogenic, immuno-modulatory, and bone growth factor properties and it is considered an important host defense molecule [Wakabayashi *et al.*, 2006]. There is considerable interest for its use as a natural bioactive ingredient in food and in health and nutritional products [Wakabayashi *et al.*, 2006; Branen and Davidson, 2009].

Lactoperoxidase (LP) is an enzyme present in milk and other external secretations that has antimicrobial, antiviral and immunomodulatory activities [Caccavo *et al.*, 2002; Mercier *et al.*, 2004; Shin *et al.*, 2005; Wakabayashi *et al.*, 2006]. LP is present in cheese whey in amounts around 0.002 $g.L^{-1}$ [Zydney, 1998].

LF and LP are actually obtained with high purity (>90%) at industrial scale using pretreated whey, WPC or WPI as starting raw material. Both proteins have a strong basic character with an isoelectric point (IEP) between 8.0 and 9.0 that contrasts with the acidic IEP of the major proteins in milk (caseins IEP:4.6 and the two main whey proteins β-lactoglobulin IEP: 5.13 and α-lactalbumin IEP: 4.2–4.5). That distinct charge property allows isolation of LF and LP from whey by cation-exchange chromatography. However, this process has some limitations at industrial scale such as its high cost and relatively low throughputs. Membrane filtration could represent an interesting alternative to chromatography for LF and LP production by designing an accurate fractionation cascade. However, fouling and poor selectivity in protein separation have been associated with such membrane filtration processes. Different strategies have been investigated to overcome the limitations associated with LF and LP separation by membrane filtration including variation of the hydrodynamic parameters, modification of the physico-chemical environment, use of different membrane types and alteration of the membrane surface properties [Brisson et al., 2007; Fweja et al., 2010].

β-Lactoglobulin

This protein represents around 50% of the total protein content in whey. Its physicochemical properties have been published in many papers [Kamau et al., 2010]. It has a globular structure and shows a molecular weight of 18.3 kDa and 162 amino acid residues (in its monomer form. β-Lg can be showed as dimer, trimer, tetramer and octomer mainly depending on the pH). This protein shows excellent gel formation and foaming properties and it can be used in a number of food industries as technical additive [Tolkach and Kulozik, 2005]. Nutritional and functional properties of this protein are described as carrier of retinol and immunomodulatory and anti-carcinogenic activities [Chatterton et al., 2006; Sutton and Alston-Mills, 2006; Kamau et al., 2010], however it is not present in human milk and it has been described as one of the main allergen in infant nutrition [Lönnerdal and Lien, 2003]. This protein is rich in cysteine (Cys) that stimulates anticarcinogenic peptides [Mcintosh et al., 1995]. β-Lg can be obtained from whey or WPC by different technologies (ion-exchange, conventional filtration, ion-exchange membrane chromatography, selective precipitation and combined methods) [El-Sayed and Chase, 2011]. β-Lg concentrates are produced as complement in sport man diets. Some attempts have been made to reduce the content of this protein in infant formulae [Lucena et al., 2006].

α-Lactalbumin

This bovine protein is similar to the human milk protein. Its main function is related with its participation in the lactose synthesis. It is described that the complex α-La and oleic acid has antitumoral activities (against bladder tumors and skill papillomas in human) [Chatterton et al., 2006; Hallgren et al., 2008]. This protein shows a relatively thermal stability and low gel formation properties.

This protein is formed by 123 amino acids and shows to disulphide bonds. It has the ability of binding two Ca^{+2} that increase its stability. α-La represents around 20% of the total protein content in the whey and can be obtained from whey by different technologies: Chromatographic methods [Bordin *et al.*, 2001]; gel filtration [Neyestani *et al.*, 2003]; selective and reversible precipitation [Bramaud *et al.*, 1997; Lucena *et al.*, 2007; Fernández *et al.*, 2011]; enzymimatic hydrolysis [Konrad and Kleinschmidt, 2008]. Among them, the reversible precipitation process is one of the most promising methods provided proper conditions are maintained. In the last years selective hydrolysis processes have been studied to separate β-Lg and α-La based on the higher resistance of the last one to enzymatic attack. After the hydrolysis step, membrane filtration retains α-la (less hydrolyzed) and most of the peptides from β-Lg and the rest of proteins permeate thorough the membrane [Kamau *et al.*, 2010].

Caseinomacropeptide (CMP)

CMP concentration in whey varies between 0.55 and 0.70 g.L^{-1}. This peptide is only present in rennet whey and it is released by chymosin cleavage of k-casein during cheese manufacture. CMP has been extensively studied due to its properties as prebiotic and anticariogenic activity. The absence of phenylalanine in its composition makes CMP adequate to phenylketonuria patient diets as well as for patients with hephatic diseases due to its high concentration in valine and isoleucine. Other important properties are described in the literature [Abd el Salam *et al.*, 1996; Setarehnejad *et al.*, 2010]. When whey is used as raw material for baby food manufacture CMP is a less desirable component due to its high content in threonin (hyperthreoninemia is described in infants) [Rigo *et al.*, 2001].

CMP isolation can be made by ultrafiltration processes due to the ability of this peptide of forming polymers higher than 50 kDa at neutral pH and its tendency to dissociate at acidic conditions [Kawasaki *et al.*, 1996]. Other fractionation processes are based on the aggregation of proteins at 90°C for 1 hour, except CMP that can be concentrated by ultrafiltration membranes (MWCO 10 kDa) at pH around 7 [Martin-Diana and Fontecha, 2002].

Other Proteins

The rest of whey proteins are less studied. Bovine sero-albumin bovine (BSA) participates in synthesis of lipids [Choi *et al.*, 2002] and has antioxidant properties [Hernández-Ledesma *et al.*, 2011], but industrial methods to isolate it have not been developed until now. Proteose-peptone fraction is a very complex heat-stable protein mixture containing phosphoglycoproteins (lactorphin with immunomodulatory properties) [Campagna *et al.*, 2004; Sugahara *et al.*, 2005].

Immunoglobulins (IGs) are globular proteins present in cheese whey in concentrations between 0.5 and 0.7 g.L^{-1}. Cow IGs are an heterogeneous fraction with important immunogenic properties against animal pathogens. Some attempts have been made to use cow IGs against human diseases (rotavirus, *Campylobacter jejuni, Salmonella, Helycobacter pylori*, etc.) [Freedman *et al.*, 1998]. However, all methods need a previous cow's injection with the pathogen to produce milk with activity. Additionally, cow colostrum (which IGs concentration is more than one hundred times the concentration in milk), seems to be the best raw material to investigate possible applications of these proteins on human diseases [Sarker *et al*., 1998].

3. BIOACTIVE PEPTIDES FROM CHEESE WHEY

Bioactive peptides have been defined as specific protein fragments that have a positive impact on body functions and may ultimately influence health [Kitts and Weiler, 2003]. In recent years it has been recognized that dietary proteins, especially milk proteins, provide a rich source of biologically active peptides. These peptides are inactive within the sequence of the protein but they can be released through proteolysis by enzymes, be it via digestive enzymes or by means of enzymes derived from microorganisms or plants. The activity of these valuable peptides is based on their inherent amino acid composition and sequence, being some of them multifunctional, and their size may vary from two to twenty amino acid residues. Bioactive peptides were first mentioned by Mellander in 1950 [Mellander, 1950], when he suggested that casein-derived phosphorylated peptides enhanced vitamin D-independent bone calcification in rachitic infants. The knowledge of bioactive peptides has steadily increased since 1979 and, at present, numerous peptides exhibiting biofunctionality have been reported.

The investigation strategies concerning the production of bioactive peptides include the following steps:

1. Development of an assay system to determine biological activity.
2. Design the way to hydrolyze the proteins by means of different kind of enzymes or fermentation processes.
3. Peptides fractionation or isolation according to some of their physico-chemical properties (size, charge, reactivity, hydrophobicity, etc.).
4. Analysis of the structures and the verification of activity (*"in vitro"*, *""in vivo""* and human clinical tests).

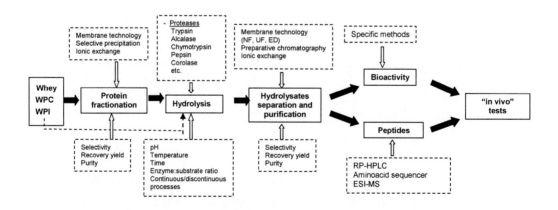

Figure 2. Steps in the production of biopeptides from whey and whey derivatives.

Table IIa. Bioactive peptides derived from α-La

Amino acid sequence	Bioactivity	Pharmacological properties [b]GPI inhibition	Production	"in vivo" studies	References
YGLF [α-La f(50-53)]: α-lactorphin	Opioid		α-La + pepsin	Rats: reduction of blood pressure [Nurminen, 2000]	Antila, 1991; Pihlanto-Leppälä, 1997
	AHT[a] (ACE-inhibition)	[c]IC$_{50}$ = 733 μM			
YGL [α-La f(50-52)]	AHT (ACE-inhibition)	IC$_{50}$ = 409 μM	α-La + pepsin + trypsin and chymotrypsin		Pihlanto-Leppälä, 2000
VGINYWLAHK [α-La f(99-108)]	AHT (ACE-inhibition)	IC$_{50}$ = 327 μM	α-La + trypsin		Pihlanto-Leppälä, 2000
WLAHK [α-La f(104-108)]	AHT (ACE-inhibition)	IC$_{50}$ = 77 μM	α-La + trypsin		Pihlanto-Leppälä, 2000
LAHKAL [α-La f(105-110)]	AHT (ACE-inhibition)	IC$_{50}$ = 621 μM	Fermentation of whey + pepsin and trypsin		Pihlanto-Leppälä, 1998
YG [α-La f(50-51)]	AHT (ACE-inhibition)	IC$_{50}$ = 1522 μM	α-La + trypsin		Mullally, 1996
	Limphocyte proliferation		Synthetic peptide		Kayser, 1996
YGG [α-La f(18-20)]	Limphocyte proliferation		Synthetic peptide		Kayser, 1996
EQLTK [α-La f(1-5)]	Antimicrobial	Against G+[e]	α-La + trypsin		Pellegrini, 1999
GYGGVSLPEWVCTTF-ALCSEK [α-La f(17-31)S-Sf(109-104)]	Antimicrobial	Against G+	α-La + trypsin		Pellegrini, 1999

Table IIa. (Continued)

Amino acid sequence	Bioactivity	Pharmacological properties	Production	"*in vivo*" studies	References
VSLPEW [α-La f(21-26)]	Antioxidative	RAS[d]	α-La + thermolysin		Sadat, 2011
YDTQA [α-La f(36-40)]	Antioxidative	RAS	α-La + thermolysin		Sadat, 2011
IWCKDDQNPHSSNI [α-La f(59-72)]	Antioxidative	RAS	α-La + thermolysin		Sadat, 2011
INY [α-La f(101-103)]	Antioxidative	RAS	α-La + thermolysin		Sadat, 2011
INYW [α-La f(101-104)]	Antioxidative	RAS	α-La + thermolysin		Sadat, 2011
LDQW [α-La f(115-118)]	Antioxidative	RAS	α-La + thermolysin		Sadat, 2011
KGYGGVSLPEW [α-La f(16-26)]	AHT (ACE-inhibition)	$IC_{50} = 0.8$ μg/mL	whey + proteases from *Cynara cardunculus*		Tavares, 2011
DKVGINYW [α-La f(97-104)]	AHT (ACE-inhibition)	$IC_{50} = 25.2$ μg/mL	whey + proteases from *Cynara cardunculus*		Tavares, 2011
RELKDLK [α-La f(10-16)]	Limphocyte proliferation		Synthetic peptide		Jacquot, 2010

[a] AHT: antihypertensive effect.

[b] GPI : Effect on the contractions of guinea pig ileum "*in vitro*".

[c] IC_{50} : concentration of an ACE-inhibitor needed to inhibit 50% of the ACE activity.

[d] RAS: Radical Scavenging activity.

[e] G+: Gram-positive bacteria; G-: Gram-negative bacteria.

Table IIb. Bioactive peptides derived from β-Lg

Amino acid sequence	Bioactivity	Pharmacological properties	Production	"in vivo" studies	References
YLLF [β-Lg f(102-105)]: β-lactorphin	Opioid	GPI stimulation	β-Lg + pepsin + trypsin or trypsin + chymotrypsin	Rats and mice: AHT and opioid effects [Nurminen, 2000; Ijäs, 2004]	Antila, 1991; Pihlanto-Leppälä, 1997
	AHT (ACE-inhibition)	IC_{50c} = 172 μM			
HIRL [β-Lg f(146-149)]: β-Lactotensin	AHT (ACE-inhibition)		β-Lg + chymotrypsin	Rats: hypocholesterolemic activity [Yamauchi, 2003]	Antila, 1991; Pihlanto-Leppälä 1997 and Paakkari, 1994; Yamauchi, 2003
	Hypocholesterolemic				
	Opioid	GPI stimulation			
LAMA [β-Lg f(22-25)]	AHT (ACE-inhibition)	IC_{50} = 556 μM	β-Lg + trypsin		Pihlanto-Leppälä, 2000
LDAQSAPLR [β-Lg f(32-40)]	AHT (ACE-inhibition)	IC_{50} = 635 μM	β-Lg + trypsin		Pihlanto-Leppälä, 2000
VFK [β-Lg f(81-83)]	AHT (ACE-inhibition)	IC_{50} = 1029 μM	β-Lg + trypsin		Pihlanto-Leppälä, 2000
ALPMHIR [β-Lg f(142-148)]	AHT (ACE-inhibition)	IC_{50} = 43 μM	β-Lg + trypsin		Mullally, 1997
	Limphocyte proliferation		Synthetic peptide		Jacquot, 2010
VLDTDYK [β-Lg f(94-100)]	AHT (ACE-inhibition)	IC_{50} = 946 μM	β-Lg + pepsin + trypsin and chymotrypsin		Pihlanto-Leppälä, 2000
ALPMH [β-Lg f(142-146)]: Lactosin B	AHT (ACE-inhibition)	IC_{50} = 521 μM	β-Lg + pepsin + trypsin and chymotrypsin		Pihlanto-Leppälä, 2000
GLDIQK [β-Lg f(9-14)]	AHT (ACE-inhibition)	IC_{50} = 580 μM	Fermentation of whey + pepsin and trypsin		Pihlanto-Leppälä, 1998
VAGTWY [β-Lg f(15-20)]	AHT (ACE-inhibition)	IC_{50} = 1682 μM	Fermentation of whey + pepsin and trypsin		Pihlanto-Leppälä, 1998; Pellegrini, 1999; Jacquot, 2010
	Antimicrobial	Against G+			
	Limphocyte proliferation				
IPA [β-Lg f(78-80)]: Lactosin A	AHT (ACE-inhibition)	IC_{50} = 141 μM	whey + proteinase K	Rats: reduction of blood pressure [Abubakar, 1998]	Abubakar, 1998)

Table IIb. (Continued)

Amino acid sequence	Bioactivity	Pharmacological properties	Production	"*in vivo*" studies	References
YL [β-Lg f(102-103)]	AHT (ACE-inhibition)	IC_{50} = 122 μM	Synthetic peptide		Mullally, 1996
LF [β-Lg f(104-105)]	AHT (ACE-inhibition)	IC_{50} = 349 μM	Synthetic peptide		Mullally, 1996
SAPLRVY [β-Lg f(36-42)]	AHT (ACE-inhibition)	IC_{50} = 8 μM	whey + Protease N Amano		Ortiz-Chao, 2009
ALPM [β-Lg f(142-145)]	AHT	Not Measured		Rats: reduction of blood pressure [Murakami, 2004]	Murakami, 2004
AASDISLLDAQSAPLR [β-Lg f(25-40)]	Antimicrobial	Against G+	β-Lg + trypsin		Pellegrini, 1999
IPAVFK [β-Lg f(78-83)]	Antimicrobial	Against G+	β-Lg + trypsin		Pellegrini, 1999
IIAEK [β-Lg f(71-75)]: Lactostatin	Hypocholesterolemic AHT (ACE-inhibition)		β-Lg + Trypsin	Rats: hypocholesterolemic activity [Nagaoka, 2001]	Nagaoka, 2001; Janssen, 2006
WYSLAMAASDI [β-Lg f(19-29)]	Antioxidative	RAS	β-Lg + Corolase PP		Hernández-Ledesma, 2005
MHIRL [β-Lg f(145-149)]	Antioxidative	RAS	β-Lg + Corolase PP		Hernández-Ledesma, 2005
YVEEL [β-l-g f(42-46)]	Antioxidative	RAS	β-Lg + Corolase PP		Hernández-Ledesma, 2005
DAQSAPLRVY [β-Lg f(33-42)]	AHT (ACE-inhibition)	IC_{50} = 13 μg/mL	whey + proteases from *Cynara cardunculus*		Tavares, 2011
RLSFNP [β-Lg f(148-152)]	AHT (ACE-inhibition)	IC_{50} = 177.4 μm	Milk fermented by *Lactobacillus helveticus* LB10		Pan, 2010
EILLQK [β-Lg f(55-60)]	Limphocyte proliferation		Synthetic peptide		Jacquot, 2010
IDALNENK [β-Lg f(84-91)]	Limphocyte proliferation		Synthetic peptide		Jacquot, 2010
VLVLDTDYKKYLLF [β-Lg f(92-105)]	Limphocyte proliferation		Synthetic peptide		Jacquot, 2010
ALKALPMHIR [β-Lg f(139-148)]	Limphocyte proliferation		Synthetic peptide		Jacquot, 2010

Table IIc. Bioactive peptides derived from other whey proteins

Source protein	Amino acid sequence	Bioactivity	Pharmacological properties	Production	in vivo studies	References
BSA	AKFAWAVAR [BSA f(208-216)]: Albutensin A	Opioid	GPI Contraction	BSA + trypsin	Mice: digestive system effects [Ohinata, 2002]	Yamauchi, 1992
		Digestive system effects	Delay gastric emptying, elevates blood glucose levels			
	YGFGNA [BSA f(399-404)]: Serophin	Opioid				Tani et al, 1993; Meisel and Schlimme, 1996
GMP		Digestive function regulator		Present in sweet whey	Humans: satiety control [Lam et al, 2009]	Yvon et al, 1994; Beucher et al, 1994; Brody et al, 2000; Malkoski et al, 2001
		Gastric digestion supression				
		Antimicrobial				
		Dental caries prevention				
		Satiety promotion				
	MAIPPKKNQDK [κ-CN f(106-116)]	Antithrombotic activity	Inhibits platelets aggregation		[Maubois et al, 1991]	Jolles et al, 1986
LF	FKCRRWQWRMKKLGAPSICVRRAF [LF f(17-41)]	Antimicrobial	Against G-, G+, virus, yeast			Bellamy et al, 1992; Hoek et al, 1997; Yoo et al, 1998; Wakabajashi et al, 2003; Samuelson et al, 2004
		Immunomodulatory properties		LF + pepsin or chymosin		
		Anti-inflamatory properties				
Source protein	Amino acid sequence	Bioactivity	Pharmacological properties	Production	in vivo studies	References
	APRKNVRWCTISQPEW-FKCRRWQWRMKKLGAPSITCVRRAFALE CIRA [LF f(1-16)S-S(17-48)]	Antimicrobial	Against *Escherichia coli*	LF + chymosin		Hoek et al, 1997

Table IIc. (Continued)

Source protein	Amino acid sequence	Bioactivity	Pharmacological properties	Production	in vivo studies	References
	APRKNVRWCTISQPEW-CIRA [LF f(1-16)S-S(45-48)]	Antimicrobial	Against *Micrococcus flavus*	LF + pepsin		Recio and Visser, 1999
	APRKNVRWCTI-FKCRRWQWRMKKLGAPSITCVRRAFALECIR [LF f(1-11)S-S(17-47)]	Antimicrobial	Against *Micrococcus flavus*	LF + pepsin		Recio and Visser, 1999
	FKCRRWQWRMKKLGAPSITCV [LF f(17-30)]	Antimicrobial	Against oral pathogenic bacteria	Synthetic peptide		Groenink et al, 1999
	SKCYQWQRRMRKLGAPSITCVRRTS [LF^d f(17-41)]	Antimicrobial	Against *Escherichia coli*	Synthetic peptide		Vorland et al, 1999
	WKLLSKAQEKFGKNKRS [LF f(268-284)]	Antimicrobial	Against *E. coli, Candida albicans Bacillus subtilis and Pseudomonas aeruginosa*	Synthetic peptide		van der Kraan et al, 2004
	DLIWKLLSKAQEKFGKNKRS [LF f(263-284)]	Antimicrobial	Against *E. coli, Candida albicans Bacillus subtilis and Pseudomonas aeruginosa*	Synthetic peptide		van der Kraan et al, 2005
	LIWKL	AHT (ACE-inhibition)	IC_{50} = 0.47 µM	LF + pepsin	Rats: reduction of blood pressure	Ruiz-Giménez et al, 2012
	RPYL	AHT (ACE-inhibition)	IC_{50} = 56.5 µM	LF + pepsin	Study with rats: reduction of blood pressure	Ruiz-Giménez et al, 2012
	LNNSRAP	AHT (ACE-inhibition)	IC_{50} = 105.3 µM	LF + pepsin	Study with rats: reduction of blood pressure	Ruiz-Giménez et al, 2012
Proteose Peptone Fraction	Proteose-peptone component 3 (PP3)	Lipolysis inhibitor				Girardet et al, 1993
	C-terminal peptide of bovine PP3 f(113-135)	Antimicrobial	Against G- and G+ bacteria	Synthetic peptide		Campagna et al, 2004

In spite of that many studies have been made on the bioactivity of peptides from caseins [Meisel, 2004a; Phelan *et al.*, 2009], it is well-known that whey proteins possess important nutritional and biological properties, particularly with regard to promotion of health and prevention of diseases [Madureira *et al.*, 2007]. They have and exceptional biological value and are a rich and balance source of sulphur amino acids (critical role as anti-oxidants) and essential amino acids, especially in the branched chain amino acids leucine, isoleucine and valine (metabolic regulators, weight control). Favorable combination of various biochemical and physiological features makes that whey peptides have the potential to play important roles in several areas of interest, namely as part of preventive and therapeutic health approaches [Meisel, 1997; Ko and Kwank, 2009]. Controlled hydrolysis of all whey proteins, mainly β-Lg and α-La, leads to the production of bioactive peptides. Due to the relative difficulty in obtaining peptides by microbial fermentation, enzymatic hydrolysis has been the most common route to produce bioactive peptides from whey proteins and pancreatic enzymes, like trypsin, have been associated with efforts towards production, as well as characterization and identification of many peptides. After the hydrolysis step, peptides must be purified by means of different methods.

Some of these bioactive peptides have shown their functionality *"in vitro"* but their potential as effective health ingredients remains to be demonstrated in most of the cases due to the lack of clinical evidences and the limitation of some *""in vivo""* models.

Table II summarizes bioactive peptides derived from whey proteins that will be commented next.

3.1. Functionality of Whey Protein Peptides

Whey proteins provide a rich source of peptides, which are latent until released and activated by enzyme proteolysis [Hui, 2007; Korhonen, 2009]. The potential bioactivities of the peptides released from these proteins are currently a subject of intensive research world-wide. The bioactivities most studied in the last years are:

1. Effects on the cardiovascular system (antihypertensive properties)
2. Hypocholesterolemic properties
3. Opioid and anti-opioid properties
4. Effects on the gastrointestinal system
5. Anticariogenic properties
6. Immunomodulation effects
7. Antibacteria properties
8. Antialergenic properties

The functions of peptides are being predominantly investigated in tissue culture systems and animal models. Whey peptides have so far been detected *"in vivo"* in blood or brain after ingestion of whole whey or whey proteins. These peptides can trigger physiological effects in the human body: on the nervous system via their opiate and ileum-contracting activities; on the cardiovascular system via their antithrombotic and antihypertensive activities; on the immune system via their antimicrobial and antiviral activities; and on the nutrition system via their digestibility and hypocholesterolemic effects. The physiological activity is measured by the direct fuctional effect after oral administration of whey, ingestion of synthetic peptides and consume of food additives or pharmacologically with specific sequences [Guo *et al.*, 2004; Townsend *et al.*, 2004; Li *et al.*, 2007; Quirós *et al.*, 2007]. Data prove the safety of fermented products by *Lactobacillus casei* strain *Shirota* (LcS) in healthy subjects and patients suffering from various diseases [Matsumoto *et al.*, 2005]. Also, the functionality of the peptides has been studied through simulations of gastrointestinal digestion of fermented products to obtain information about their route through the organism, further degradation due to digestive enzyme attack and the duration of the functional activity of the peptide [Didelot *et al.*, 2006; Hernández-Ledesma *et al.*, 2007; Wang *et al.*, 2007a, b].

Currently *"in vitro"* and *"in vivo"* data on potential of whey peptides are relatively abundant. However clinical evidences are necessary to confirm their functionality [Saint-Sauveur *et al.*, 2008].

3.1.1. Effects on the Cardiovascular System

The inhibition of the angiotensin-converting enzyme (ACE) by means of some whey peptides can exert an antihypertensive effect and the peptides that show this activity are usually called lactokinins [Wang *et al.*, 2007b]. At present, this is the most studied biological activity of whey derived peptides.

ACE is part of the renin-angiotensin system (RAS) and it has an important role in the regulation of blood pressure by converting angiotensin-I to a potent vasoconstrictor, angiotensin-II, which induces the release of aldosterone and therefore increases the sodium concentration and further blood pressure. By inhibiting ACE or by other still poorly known mechanisms, milk-derived peptides are able to low blood pressure in animal and humans [Jäkälä and Vapäätalo, 2010] and are believed to prevent cardiovascular diseases. Most of the ACE-inhibitory peptides derived from whey proteins are released by means of trypsin, being one of the most potent of them the heptapeptide ALPMHIR (IC_{50} = 43 µM) [Mullally *et al.*, 1997]. However, the use of a new food-grade proteolytic preparation, Protease N Amano, has resulted in the release of a novel peptide SAPLRVY which IC_{50} value is considerably lower (IC_{50} = 8 µM) [Ortiz-Chao *et al.*, 2009]. Nowadays, the main challenge in the production of these bioactive peptides is finding the suitable enzyme and hydrolysis conditions that enhance bioactivity and yield in their production.

Apart from ACE-inhibition, whey peptides may exert antihypertensive effects through other mechanisms such as inhibition of the release of endothelin-1 by endothelial cells [Maes *et al.*, 2004], stimulation of bradykinin activity [Perpetuo *et al.*, 2003], enhancement of endothelium-derived nitric oxide production [Sipola *et al.*, 2002] and enhancement of the vasodilatory action of binding to opiate receptors [Nurminen *et al.*, 2000].

Although there is a lot of information on the production and characterization of ACE-inhibitory peptides, their structure-activity relationship is not completely known. However, some general features have been found:

- ACE-inhibitory peptides usually contain between 2 and 12 amino acids residues, although active peptides with up to 27 amino acids have been identified. Amino acid sequences of peptides and the size of the peptides are associated to their biological activity or functional effect [Muro *et al.*, 2011].

– The binding to ACE is strongly influenced by the C-terminal sequence. The presence
of hydrophobic amino acids, e.g. proline, at each of the three C-terminal positions
and the presence of a positive charge of lisine and arginine as the C-terminal residue
may contribute to the inhibitory potency.

Amino acid sequences and the size of the peptides are associated to their biological
activity or functional effect [Muro *et al.*, 2011]. In general, it is recognized that short peptides
(<3 kDa) offer consistently higher ACE inhibitory activity [Hartmann and Meisel, 2007].
Other researchers [Tsai *et al.*, 2008; Miguel *et al.*, 2009] indicated that the greatest level of
ACE activity has been found in whey peptides up to 6 kDa. Sequences of short-chain with
proline residues (Pro) are also identified as peptides with ACE inhibitory activity having
hydrophobic amino acids such as tryptophan (Trp), tyrosine (Tyr) or phenylalanine (Phe), in
at least one of the three C-terminal positions. For example, the sequence Pro-Glu-Trp has
been found in four powerful ACE-inhibitory peptides derived from α-La hydrolysis by
thermolysin [Vinderola *et al.*, 2003; Foltz *et. al*, 2007; Otte *et al.*, 2007a, b]. Murakami *et al.*
(2004) found that under hydrolysis conditions of β-Lg (60 to 80 °C) is possible to obtain a
tetra-peptide with amino acid residues Ala-Leu-Pro-Met f(142-145) with hypotensive activity.
The effect is attributed to proline residue in the tetra-peptide. Additionally, it has been proved
that the power of inhibition can be increased with the presence in this terminal position of the
positive charges of Lys (group e-amine) and Arg (guanidine group) [Hernández-Ledesma *et
al.*, 2008]. Whey proteolysis by means of *Lactobacillus helveticus* extract release two
recognized ACE-inhibitory tripeptides: Val-Pro-Pro and Ile-Pro-Pro [Sipola *et al.*, 2001,
2002]. Recently the amino acid sequence Leu-Leu (LL) has been proved to show high ACE-
inhibitory characteristics. The molecular mechanisms, position, type, and energy of the
LL/ACE interaction were investigated by using flexible molecule docking technology
[Yamaguchi *et al.*, 2009; Pan *et al.*, 2012].

ACE inhibitory peptides are often produced by hydrolysis of β-lactorphins, that are
peptides present in the primary amino acid sequence of bovine β-LG and they can be released
by trypsin. Novel ACE inhibition has also been detected in synthetic peptides that
corresponded to sequences within both β-LG and α-LA [Mullally *et al.*, 1996; Li and Mine,
2004].

Peptide Quantitative Structure-Activity Relationship (QSAR) modeling has been used for
predicting milk peptides structures with high ACE-inhibitory activities. For peptides up to six
amino acids, a relationship was found between this activity and some of the peptides
characteristics (hydrophobicity and a positively charged amino acid at the C-terminal
position). No relationship was found between the N-terminal structure and the ACE-
inhibitory activity [Pripp *et al.*, 2004].

In vitro, ACE inhibitory activity is measured through the absorbance of hippuric acid
(HA) after the reaction of hydrolysates samples on hipuril-histidil-leucine (HHL). A variety
of methods (e.g., spectrophotometry and fluorometry) by which ACE activity can be detected
and analyzed are published [Cushman and Cheung, 1971; Gómez-Ruiz *et al.*, 2002; Wu and
Ding, 2002]. High-performance liquid chromatography (HPLC) is widely used because of the
effective separation of the substrate and product from the ACE reaction mixture to ensure
accurate measurements. HPLC requires the use of a reverse phase C18 column and large
amounts of organic solvents (acetonitrile or methanol). Capillary Electrophoresis (EC) is also
used for ACE assays. The most common electrophoresis buffer assays used in EC system is

sodium borate buffer, due to the dual role the latter plays as the basal solution for the ACE assay mixture [Zhang et al., 2000]. Electrophoretic experiments are carried out on a high voltage power supply. With HHL as the substrate, the enzymatic product (HA)is separated and quantified using capillary zone electrophoresis (CZE). CZE is performed with a 65 cm fused-silica capillary (55 cm effective length, 75 μm I.D.), using a 10 or 20 mM solution (pH 6.0) as the running buffer with an applied voltage of 20 kV at room temperature. Samples are applied in a 2 second electrokinetic injection and data are collected and peak migration time and area are analyzed [Chiang et al., 2005]. This method can be applied directly to analyze an ACE reaction mixture without organic extraction prior to injection.

In all methods, the quantity of HA produced by ACE is measured spectrophotometrically at 228 nm using a UV Visible spectrophotometer. The ACE inhibiting activity is calculated and expressed in terms of IC_{50}, defined as the protein concentration required in the sample to inhibit 50% of the ACE [Mao et al., 2007]. % ACE inhibition can be calculated with HA liberated by ACE and measured by RP-HPLC [Hyun and Shin, 2000]. ACE inhibitory activity is calculated according to equation |1|. Percentage of ACE inhibition is expressed per 0.1 mg of protein in the fractions.

$$\% \text{ ACE inhibitory activity} = \frac{HA_{control} - HA_{sample}}{HA_{control}} . 100 \tag{1}$$

The determination of ACE is very important since it constitutes a frequent test to evaluate antihypertensive drugs, by inhibition of angiotensin [Aleixandre et al., 2008]. However, the IC_{50} value is not always directly related to the "in vivo" hypotensive effect, because some peptides can be susceptible to degradation or modification in the gut, the vascular system and the liver. By contrast, hypotensive activity of a long-chain candidate peptide can be caused by peptide fragments generated by gastrointestinal enzymes [Meisel et al., 2006]. Active peptides must be absorbed in an intact form from the intestine after oral administration and further be resistant to degradation by plasma peptidases in order to reach the target sites. This is not always possible and, for example, peptide ALPMHIR is not sufficiently stable to gastrointestinal and serum proteinases [Walsh et al., 2004]. However, proline-containing peptides are generally resistant to degradation by digestive enzymes [Masuda et al., 1996]. On the other hand, only a few "in vivo" studies encompassing whey protein hydrolysates are available to date. In particular, peptides IPA and ALPM derived from β-Lg and YGLF derived from α-La were shown to reduce blood pressure "in vivo" [Abubakar et al., 1998; Nurminen et al., 2000; Murakami et al., 2004]. Further studies are still required for a better understanding of the blood pressure reducing mechanisms of whey peptides and well controlled clinical human studies are needed to demonstrate the long-term physiological effects delivered by consuming such peptides.

Different "in vivo" studies on the antihypertensive effect of whey peptides show controversial results [Chen et al., 2003; Ijas et al., 2004; Muro et al., 2011]. Hypotensive action is measured by lowering effect acute blood pressure after oral administration of whey, peptides, ingestion of whey or consume of dairy products. General therapeutic applications of whey proteins have been reviewed by Marshall (2004) and Saito (2008). Administration of pure peptides has produced a strong antihypertensive effect in spontaneously hypertensive rats (SHR) after a single-dose, but it has been found that IC_{50} values are even lower depending on the substrate concentration used in the *"in vitro"* experiments [Lehtinen *et al.*, 2010]. Tretrapeptides such as α-Lactorphin (Tyr-Gly-Leu-Phe), β-lactorphin (Tyr-Leu-Leu-Phe) and β-lactosin (Ala-Leu-Pro-Met) showed strong antihypertensive effect in SHR [Sipola *et al.*, 2002]. Also proteinase K-digested whey was shown to decrease blood pressure in SHR after single-dose administration [Jauhiainen and Korpela, 2007b]. From the digest, the peptide showing the strongest antihypertensive activity was found to be tripeptide Ile-Pro-Ala, originating from β-lactoglobulin.

Different methods to evaluate endothelial function have been used in clinical studies. Ambulatory arterial stiffness index (AASI) can be calculated from 24-hour blood pressure recordings, and it has been shown to be an independent predictor of cardiovascular mortality [Dolan *et al.*, 2006]. Another predictor of cardiovascular outcomes is aortic augmentation index (AAI), for which pulse waveform analysis is needed [Chirinos *et al.*, 2005]. In the study of Jauhiainen *et al.* (2007a), a significant improvement in AASI was observed after a 10-week treatment with *L. helveticus* fermented milk. In another study, AAI was decreased after 6 months' treatment with the same product.

On the other hand, various effects of tri-peptides (Ile-Pro-Pro) and (Val-Pro-Pro) in hypertensive subjects have been published [Xu *et al.*, 2008; de Leeuw *et al.*, 2009]. Significant decrease of systolic blood pressure (SBP) and diastolic blood pressure (DBP) were found in the meta-analysis. In other clinical study, hydrolyzed whey protein supplement decreased blood pressure of prehypertensive or stage I hypertensive subjects by 8.0 mmHg of systolic and 5.5 mmHg of diastolic blood pressure after 6 weeks of treatment [Pins and Keenan, 2006]. In contrast, milk drink supplemented with whey powder was not found to reduce blood pressure in mildly hypertensive subjects after 12 weeks' consumption [Lee *et al.*, 2007]. Thus, more intervention studies are needed to confirm the possible clinical benefits of the whey-derived peptides. Nevertheless, it´s mentioned that the results in human studies on antihypertensive peptides are usually quite small between the active and placebo treatment, so the study population should be enormously large to firmly prove the efficacy [Jäkälä and Vapäätalo, 2010]. Alternative studies related to antihypertensive effect by consumption of dairy products have demonstrated a relationship between the intake of milk products and reduction in blood pressure. For example, the first National Health and Nutrition Examination Survey (NHANES I) showed that intake of dairy low-fat products, has consistently been associated with lower blood pressure levels and reduced risk of hyper-tension. A nine years' follow-up study of 6,912 white, non hypertensive men and women showed that subjects consuming three or more servings of low-fat milk per day had lower increase of blood pressure compared to those consuming less than one serving per week [Alonso *et al.*, 2009].

Few studies did not find any significant effect either on SBP or DBP by treatment with whey peptide-containing products [van der Zander *et al.*, 2008; van Mierlo *et al.*, 2009].

Controversial human data on hypertensive peptides are discussed in a recent study [Jäkälä and Vapäätalo, 2010] where it´s presented that the following points affect the results found on antihypertensive peptides in human trials: administration of different products are not directly comparable, especially when the effects on a biological variable are small; the effective dose of lactotripeptides/day also affects the results; the concentrations of the peptides vary, especially if a regular product control during the long-term trial has not been conducted; the action of peptides can vary, because milk fermentation is produced by different species or strains; the reports on clinical trials have concentrated mainly on the changes in blood pressure and vascular effects, however clinical chemistry as serum, fecal and urinary, could predict potential benefits relating to a target function in the body. The influence of subject background is discussed also in the review of Boelsma and Kloek (2009).

Another functionality related with the cardiovascular system is the antithrombotic activity showed for various peptides derived from the soluble C-terminal fragment of bovine κ-casein, CMP. The main antithrombotic peptide derived from CMP, MAIPPKKNQDK, is termed casoplatelin and this peptide inhibits both the aggregation of ADP-activated platelets as well as the binding of human fibrinogen γ-chain to its receptor region on the platelet surface. Smaller fragments of this peptide can also affect platelet function although they have much lower inhibitory activity that the complete fragment [Jollés *et al.*, 1986]. Three amino acid residues (Ile, Lys and Asn) of the CMP derived peptide seem to be important for its activity because they are homologous in position to the γ-chain sequence of human fibrinogen. It is important to mention that the undecapeptide has shown antithrombotic activity *"in vivo"* and could potentially be used to treat or prevent thrombosis [Maubois *et al.*, 1991].

Regarding hypocholesterolemic effects numerous studies have shown that whey proteins, in contrast to milk casein, decreases serum cholesterol similar to soy protein. Peptide IIAEK derived from bovine β-Lg, also termed lastostatin, has shown this kind of functionality in both *"in vitro"* and *"in vivo"* studies [Nagaoka *et al.*, 2001]. This effect is supposed to be at least in part due to a decrease of micellar solubility of cholesterol which leads to lower intestinal cholesterol absorption but further results imply that the C-terminal side of lastostatin, in particular the glutamyl-lysine sequence, is crucial for the transcription of a human cholesterol-metabolizing enzyme.

3.1.2. Antioxidant Properties

Dietary consumption of antioxidants appears to provide extra benefits to the endogenous antioxidant defense strategies in the fight against oxidative stress. In addition to the well-know dietary antioxidants like vitamin C, vitamin E, polyphenols and carotenoids, recent studies have shown that peptides with antioxidant properties can be released from food sources like whey proteins. Various peptides derived from α-La and β-Lg hydrolyzed by means of thermolysin and Corolase PP respectively have demonstrated radical scavenging activity [Hernández-Ledesma *et al.*, 2005; Sadat *et al.*, 2011]. Whey, hydrolysate proteins and free peptides have ability to scavenge free peroxyl radicals as well as to chelate transition metals such as calcium, iron, copper, and zinc. These properties of whey peptides could be used as antioxidants to prevent oxidative damage in muscle foods [Lindmark-Mansson and Akesson, 2000; Peña-Ramos and Xiong, 2003]. The ability of peptides to inhibit deleterious changes caused by lipid oxidation appears to be related to certain amino acid residues in the peptides, such as tyrosine, methionine, histidine, lysine, and tryptophan, which are capable of chelating pro-oxidative metal ions [Bayram *et al.*, 2008], capture free radicals and/or extinguish the reactive oxygen species [Murakami *et al.*, 2004]. Amino acid composition, sequence, and configuration of peptides affect their antioxidant activity [Muro *et al.*, 2011]. Other researchers have published that antioxidant activity of whey-derived peptides and whey itself is linked to the presence of cysteine-rich proteins which promote the synthesis of glutathione, a potent intracellular antioxidant [Meisel, 2005]. Also, high amounts of histidine and some hydrophobic amino acids are related to the antioxidant potency [Peña-Ramos *et al.*, 2004].

Antioxidant properties have been identified in whey peptides with typical structures (4 to 20 kDa) and between 5 to 11 aminoacids. Peng *et al.* (2009) obtained four fractions with different molecular weights by enzymatic treatment of whey protein isolate (WPI) using Alcalase. The peptide fraction in the range from 0.1 to 2.8 kDa showed a free radical lowering effect significantly higher than the other fractions with larger peptides. The presence of cysteine in the peptides promotes the synthesis of glutathione, a potent intracellular antioxidant [Erdman *et al.*, 2008]. Characteristic sequences (SerP-SerP-SerP-Glu-Glu), are effective cation chelators that form complexes with calcium, iron and zinc.

Antioxidative activity is not only related with the prevention of cardiovascular disease. Peptides that own this characteristic also contribute to the endogenous antioxidant capacity of foods and their use as preservatives is already revised in various studies [Elias *et al.*, 2008]. Furthermore, as cancer could be a consequence of oxidative DNA-damage, the application of antioxidative peptides to prevent and control this illness is being studied [Phelan *et al.*, 2010]. Oxidative stress, increase the production of reactive oxygen species (ROS) which in combination with outstripping endogenous antioxidant defense mechanisms, is a significant causative factor for the initiation or progression of several vascular diseases. ROS can cause extensive damage to biological macromolecules like DNA, proteins and lipids. Free radicals modify DNA, proteins and other small cellular molecules Antioxidants may decrease the oxidative damage and its harmful effects [Collins *et al.*, 2005].

A variety of *"in vitro"* techniques have been developed for the detection of antioxidants on the basis of different antioxidative mechanisms under variable conditions reflecting the multifunctional properties of antioxidants in both physiological and food-related antioxidation processes. Antioxidant activity has been measured by means of three functions from peptides: antioxidant capacity, reduction capacity and metal chelating activity [Kim *et al.*, 2007a]. Antioxidant capacity can be determined through peroxyl radical of peptide using oxygen radical absorbance capacity (ORAC) assay based on quenching of fluorescence from the protein β-phycoerythrin by radicals utilizing the method of Cao *et al.* (1997). Final results are calculated based on the difference in the area under the fluorescence decay curve between the blank and each sample. Reduction capacity of peptide is determined through its capacity to reduce a metal such as Cu^{2+} to Cu^{1+} according to the method of Aruoma *et al.* (1998) or by the FRAP test, which consist in reduction of Fe^{+3} to Fe^{+2} [Benzie and Strain, 1999]. Metal chelating activity is determined by the method of Decker and Welch (1990) using ferric ions. The metal chelating activity of the test sample is calculated using the formula |2| below:

$$\text{Metal chelating activity \%} = \frac{A_0 - A_1}{A_0} x100 \qquad (2)$$

where A_0 is the absorbance of the control, and A_1 is the absorbance of the sample.

Antioxidant capacity of peptides is evaluated using the FRAP test, which consists in reduction Fe^{+3} to Fe^{+2} [Benzie and Strain, 1999].

Other method used to determine antioxidant activity of peptides is based on the evaluation of the ability to inhibit or halt lipid oxidation in model systems. Test measures changes in the concentration of oxidized compounds, on depletion of oxygen or on formation of oxidation products. Quantification of the loss of reactants (oxygen, unsaturated fatty acids), formation of free radicals, and formation of oxidation products may be the most appropriate markers depending on the stage of oxidation [Pihlanto-Leppälä 2006]. The depletion of oxygen and the electron spin resonance (ESR) spectroscopy detection of radical, either directly or indirectly by spin trapping, can be used to follow the initial steps during oxidation [Andersen and Skibsted, 2006].

On the other hand, different *"in vivo"* trials have been conducted to assay the effect of antioxidant supplements of whey in clinical test and animal models.

In addition, antioxidant capacity from peptide is assayed with synthetic peptides by the structure-function relationship between the amino acid sequences [Rival *et al.*, 2001]. In this test is shown that peptides inhibit enzymatic and nonenzymatic lipid peroxidation, most likely by being a preferred target over fatty acid free radicals. Indirect evidence suggested that proteins/peptides can be oxidized during the process, according to a site- or sequence-specific mechanism. The extracellular release of superoxide or intracellular ROS and superoxide production, is measured by a plate reader assay with cells in situ or by cytometric flow analysis. Biomarkers, such as 8-hydroxy-20-deoxyguanosine, of oxidative damage in cellular DNA have been developed by Collins (2002), Halliwell and Whiteman (2004), Hoelzl *et al.* (2005) and Philanto and Keenan (2006).

3.1.3. Effects on the Nervous System

The opioid peptides derived from whey proteins, as well as the derived from other food proteins, are called "atypical" opioid peptides because their N-terminal sequence is different from that of the "typical" endogenous opioid peptides like enkephalins, endorphins and dynorphins. The tyrosine residue at the N-terminal and the presence of another aromatic amino acid at the third or fourth position form an important structural motif that fits into the binding site of the opioid receptors. Lack of the tyrosine residues results in a total absence of bioactivity. Proline residue in the second position of their structure is crucial for the three-dimensional orientation of the tyrosine and phenylalanine side-chains. The individual receptor at which these peptides are joined is responsible for specific physiological effects [Pihlanto-Leppälä, 2001; Wang *et al.*, 2007a]. Agonistic activity is comparable to that of endogenous ligands, whereas antagonistic peptides exert inhibitory effects similar to naloxone, a potent opiate receptor antagonist applied as a drug (in the case of heroin overdose) [Meisel, 2005].

α-La and β-Lg contain opioid-like sequences in their primary structure called α- and β-lacorphins that have pharmacological characteristics similar to morphine and they can be used then as analgesics. These peptides could be released by means of digestive enzymes like pepsin, trypsin and chymotrypsin. Both peptides are μ-type receptor ligands so they affect emotional behavior and suppression of intestinal motility. Furthermore, it has been shown that digestion of β-Lg with chymotrypsin produces β-lactotensin, which pharmacological activity is similar to that of β-lactorphin. These peptides also have antihypertensive functions and some of them showed hypocholesterolemic activity after administration to mice [Yamauchi *et al.,* 2003]. Proteolysis of α-La with pepsin produces some oligopeptides (up to 10 aminoacids) with opioid properties as the tetrapeptide (Tyr-Gly-Leu-Phe) and fragment f102-105 from β-Lg [Kamau, *et al.,* 2010].

Tryptic digestion of BSA releases an opioid peptide, albutensin A [Tani *et al.*, 1993]. This peptide exhibits an ileum-contracting activity. It has been shown that the addition of this peptide on food intake in mice delays gastric emptying and elevates blood glucose too

[Ohinata *et al.*, 2002], so it may eventually be used in human diets to promote weight loss and prevent obesity.

Opioid antagonists peptides derived from LF digestion, also called lactoferroxins, seem to be capable of antagonizing the inhibition of gut motility induced by casomorphins.

In spite of this intensive research, only some of these peptides have been proved their effects upon oral or intragastric administration and most of the tests have been performed in animals, hence much work remains to do in human clinical tests [Teschemacher, 2003].

3.1.4. Effects on the Gastrointestinal System

An improvement in whey proteins digestibility may easily be achieved via non-specific hydrolysis and this is beneficial for patients who suffer from digestion disorders such as cystic fibrosis, short bowel syndrome or pancreatitis [Hernández-Ledesma *et al.*, 2004]. Furthermore, whey protein hydrolysates could play important functions in the intestinal tract.

One of the most important peptides involved in these processes is GMP and a lot of studies have attempted to establish the potential role of this peptide and its non-glycosylated form (CMP) in regulation of intestinal functions. CMP has been reported to inhibit gastric secretions, slows down stomach contractions and stimulates the release of cholecystokinin, the satiety hormone involved in controlling food intake [Beucher *et al.*, 1994]. However, its clinical efficacy remains to be established.

Besides satiating effect of GMP and CMP, peptides with opioid-like activities affect food intake by the delay of gastric emptying and intestinal transit [Meisel, 1997].

GMP seems to contribute to anticariogenic effect by inhibiting the adhesion and growth of plague-forming bacteria in oral mucosa [Brody, 2000] and it has been used as ingredient in some dental care products. This κ-casein derived peptide may have a beneficial role in modulating the gut microflora due to its carbohydrate content [Manso and López-Fandiño, 2004] but its main nutritional role derives from its use as an ingredient in diets designed for people suffering from phenylketonuria who are unable to metabolize phenylalanine [Marshall, 1991].

3.1.5. Immune Modulation Peptides

Whey contains a number of immunomodulatory peptides that are naturally present or that are part of the primary sequence of whey proteins. The development of whey protein-based immunomodulating peptides is currently limited by the lack of their characterization and identification from bioactive hydrolysates and by the absence of clinical data on the physiological effects of these peptides. In fact, most studies on the immunomodulating effects of peptides have targeted the specific immune system by evaluating lymphocyte activation and proliferation, cytokine secretion and antibody production. Very few studies have addressed the impact of these components on the innate immune system [Gill *et al.*, 2000; Gautier *et al.*, 2006].

Little research on peptides derivates from β-Lg and α-La, lactoferrin, (LF), milk growth factors and immunoglobulin G (IgG) have also been reported to modulate lymphocyte proliferation *"in vitro"*. Tests are based on stimulation of superoxide anions such as ROS, which trigger non-specific immune defense systems [Kitts and Weiler, 2003]. Other *"in vitro"* test consists in stimulation of phagocytosis of sheep red blood cells (SRBC) by murine peritoneal macrophages. Particularly LF is a potent modulator of inflammatory and immune responses, revealing host-protective effects not only against microbial infections but also in inflammatory disorders such as allergies, arthritis, and cancer [Mcintosh *et al.*, 1995]. Crouch *et al.,* (1992) isolated lactoferricin B peptide, obtained by hydrolysis of LF with pepsin; this peptide promotes phagocytic activity of human neutrophils via dual mechanisms that may involve direct binding to the neutrophil and opsonin-like activity. GMP has been discovered as a potent immunoenhancer even at low concentrations. This peptide enhances the pro-liferation and phagocytic activities of U937 cells [Li and Mine, 2004]. Also, this peptide seems to play positive effects on patients with inflammatory bowel disease, but the mechanisms remains unknown [Kamau *et al.*, 2010].

"In vitro" studies have demonstrated the potential of some whey components to modulate antibody production. For example, purified β-Lg enhances the production of IgM in cultures of murine spleen cells, but this effect can be abolished by trypsin hydrolysis of the protein.

Additionally, studies *"in vivo"* have shown that whey protein hydrolysates have an impact on the humoral immune system. The immune response has been evaluated in mice using the plaque forming cell (PFC) assay after systemic challenge with immune stimuli (SRBC). A study showing the effect of immunomodulatoy peptides by administration of LF to 95 elderly subjects before and after influenza vaccination in a double blind placebo controlled study. Before vaccination, the percentage of granulocytes of the total leukocytes was significantly higher in the lactoferrin group than in the placebo group. A similar effect was found for the monocytes 7 days after vaccination. The phagocytosis activity of the granulocytes was significantly enhanced in the lactoferrin group 1 day after vaccination. A small dipeptide, corresponding to the N-terminal end of bovine α-La (dipeptide) significantly increased proliferation of human peripheral blood lymphocytes. Bioactive peptides in yogurt preparations actually decreased cell proliferation. This report may explain, in part, why consumption of yogurt has been associated with a reduced incidence of colon cancer. Kayser and Meisel (1996) have described both stimulatory and suppressive immune responses of human lymphocytes to whey derived peptides.

An *"in vivo"* study of hydrolyzed whey proteins was used to evaluate inhibitory effects on the development of colon aberrant crypt foci (ACF) and intestinal tumors in azoxymethane (AOM). Pregnant Sprague-Dawley rats and their progeny were fed AIN-93G diets containing whey as the sole protein source. Colons and small intestines from the male progeny were obtained at 6, 12, 20 and 23 weeks after AOM treatment. At 6 and 23 weeks, post-AOM, WPH-fed rats had fewer ACF than did CAS-fed rats. Intestinal tumors were most frequent at 23 weeks, post-AOM. At this time point, differences in colon tumor incidence with diet were not observed; however, whey-fed rats had fewer tumors in the small intestine (7.6% vs. 26% incidence) [Xiaoa *et al.*, 2006].

Yamauchi *et al.* (2006) reported that bovine LF reduces the number of infiltrating leukocytes during influenza virus infection (pneumonia) and suppresses the hyperreaction of the host. LF decreases the recruitment of eosinophils, reduces pollen antigen-induced allergic airway inflammation and it displays immunological properties influencing both innate and acquired immunities. Especially, oral administration of bovine LF seems to influence mucosal and systemic immune responses in mice [Sfeir *et al.*, 2004].

Immunomodulatory peptides are also reported to influence cytokine production in cell culture experiments which are involved in immune and inflammatory actions of the body. Cross and Hill (1999) reported that a modified peptide rich in GMP suppresses the secretion of IL-4 and IFN-g in a ConA-induced murine splenic lymphocyte culture and that the effect is partly abolished following enzymatic digestion of the extract with pepsin and pancreatin. GMP also induces the production of IL-1 family cytokines in murine macrophages and a macrophage cell line. The immunoenhancer property of this peptide at very low concentration seems to be due to the presence of terminal sialic acid and specific peptides at the end of its chain [Li and Mine, 2004]. Chodaczek *et al.* (2006) demonstrated that a complex of LF with monophosphoryl lipid A is an efficient adjuvant of the humoral and cellular immune responses. Its stimulating effect on the immune system concerns mainly the maturation and differentiation of T lymphocytes, the Th1/Th2 cytokine balance and the activation of phagocytes.

In general, the mechanisms by which these milk-derived peptides exert either their immunopotentiating effects or influence proliferative responses are not currently known; however, is possible that the peptides exert an inhibitory effect on the proliferation of human lamina propria lymphocytes *"in vitro"* via the opiate receptor [Elitsur and Luk, 1991]. This antiproliferative response was reversed by the opiate receptor antagonist, naloxone. Ohnuki and Otani (2007) reported that bovin IgG stimulates antibody responses in mouse spleen cell culture, whereas oral ingestion of bovine milk IgG suppresses the response in mice. It is unclear why bovine milk IgG has different effects on antibody responses *"in vitro"* and *"in vivo"*. Immunocompetent cells such as dendritic cells and macrophages possess several types of IgG receptors (Fc γ R) on their surface. Therefore, the different effects of bovine milk IgG on antibody responses may be due to the difference in Fc γ R for milk IgG on immunocompetent cells. The immunomodulating potential of peptide fractions isolated from β-Lg enzymatic hydrolysates has also been demonstrated [Prioult *et al.*, 2004, Jacquot *et al.*, 2010].

In addition, immunomodulatory peptides are naturally present or are part of the primary sequence of whey proteins. Particularly peptides derived from the N-terminal α-La from bovine milk significantly increase the proliferation of human peripheral blood lymphocytes. Short-chain peptides (<5kDa) obtained from the enzymatic hydrolysis of whey proteins, were identified as stimulators the proliferation of immune system cells [Mercier *et al.*, 2004].

It has been shown that acidic and neutral peptides released from WPI digestion by means of a trypsin:chymotrypsin mixture stimulate splenocyte proliferation and cytokine secretion [Saint-Sauveur *et al.*, 2008]. The basic fraction of the aforementioned hydrolysate induces a sustained serum IgA secretion in mice infected with *Escherichia coli* while all the peptide fractions strongly stimulated total IgA production in non-infected mice [Saint-Sauveur *et al.*, 2009].

Major discrepancies in the effect of some peptides on lymphocyte proliferation have been reported while the more limited literature on antibody production is less controversial. The effects of whey peptides on hypersensitivity, induction of oral tolerance and response to infections and diseases are currently topics for important researches.

To sum up, there is growing evidence that whey peptides may have some physiological activities on specific components of the immune response: lymphocyte activation and proliferation, antibody function and cytokine expression. However, a number of contradictory results have to be acknowledged maybe due to the use of different methodologies, raw materials and models.

3.1.6. Antimicrobial Effects

Proteolysis of α-La and β-Lg by means of digestive enzymes releases several antibacterial peptides that possess strong activity against Gram-positive bacteria [Pellegrini et al., 1999, 2000, Pellegrini, 2003].

GMP, as well as some of its derived peptides released by digestion with pepsin have also shown antibacterial effects [Kawasaki et al., 1992; Clare and Swaisgood, 2003; Campagna et al., 2004; El-Zahar et al., 2004].

Short-medium chain length bioactive peptides (10-50 amino acids) with cationic and hydrophobic properties have been known to be potent host-defense substances offering antimicrobial activity against a wide spectrum of pathogenic microorganisms such as Gram-negative and Gram-positive bacteria, fungi, viruses and parasites [Hancock and Sahal, 2006].

One of the most studied peptide derived from whey is lactoferricin. This peptide is released from LF by enzymatic digestion with pepsin or chymosin. It has shown not only bactericidal activity but also antiviral, antifungal, antiprotozoal, immunomodulating and anti-inflammatory properties [Wakabayashi et al., 2003; Gauthier et al., 2006].

The role of lactoferricin in tumor growth and metastasis has also been investigated [Yoo et al., 1998]. Other potent antimicrobial peptides generated by degradation of LF with pepsin (lactoferricin B and lactoferrampine) have been effective against bacteria Gram positive, Gram negative, Bacillus subtilis, Escherichia coli and Pseudomonas aeruginosa [Clare and Swaisgood, 2000; López-Expósito et al., 2006a, López-Expósito and Recio, 2006b].

The results show that the phosphorylation is essential for the antimicrobial activity. Some other studies have also demonstrated an antiprotozoal activity from LF [Omata et al. 2001] which has been treated in a review paper [Orsi, 2004], where it´s shown that LF is a multifunctional iron glycoprotein which is known to exert a broad-spectrum primary defense activity against bacteria, fungi, protozoa and viruses. Inhibiting influenza virus hemagglutination, inhibiting the binding of cholera toxin (CT) and E.coli enterotoxins and various oral pathogens as Streptococcus mutans were also studied by Malkoski et al. (2001) using whey peptides.

Other peptides from oligopeptides of whey, as kappacina, fragment f (138-158) of GMP characterized by having a phosphorylated residue serine (Ser) and accumulate on the cell membrane anion forming a pore, making it a powerful antibacterial peptide against Gram-positive (Streptococcu mutans) and Gram-negative (P. gingivalis and E. coli) [Rizzello et al., 2005].

Antimicrobial activity is also attributed to β-Lg and α-La. Digestion of these proteins produced some antimicrobial peptides. The activity was identified "in vitro", acting against different Gram-positive and Gram-negative bacteria (Escherichia, Helicobacter, Listeria, Salmonella and Staphylococcus), yeasts and filamentous fungi [Fitzgerald and Murray, 2006].

The hydrolysis of whey proteins is especially important in the prevention of allergic diseases like, for example, in the design of hypoallergenic infant formulas [Exl, 2001].

Other effects as apoptosis of several types of cells and mineral binding properties have been described in several papers [Zhang et al., 2002; López-Expósito and Recio, 2008; Kim et al., 2007b; Kamau et al., 2010].

Table III shows the main human clinical studies of some commercial bioactive peptides.

Table III. Effects of whey proteins and whey hydrolyzed in human clinical studies

Whey components/peptides Human clinical study		Uses or commercial products	Reference
Whey proteins and whey hydrolysates	*Insulinotropic effects and reduces the postprandial glycemia in healthy subjects, and Type 2 diabetic patients * Decreases blood pressure of prehypertensive or stage I	"BioZate" 1; To low blood pressure and cholesterol	Kennedy, 1995 Rosaneli, 2002 Frid, 2005 ;Pins, 2006 Lee, 2007 ; Xu, 2008 de Leeuw, 2009
α-La and its hydrolysates	*Stress relief and reduced depressive mood *Improves cognitive functions in stress - vulnerable subjects by increased brain tryptophan and serotonin activity *Increases plasma tryptophan levels and its ratio to neutral amino acids *Inhibits the growth of skin papillomas in humans when topically applied	Ingredient for infant formulae "Vivinal alpha"	Markus, 2000, 2002, 2005 Gustafsson, 2004, 2005 Scrutton, 2007
3-hydroxyphthaloyl-β-Lg	Inhibits the human immunodeficiency virus type 1. Inhibits herpes simplex virus types 1	Not known	Oevermann, 2003
LF-enriched whey protein hydrolyzed and LF-bovine colostrum or probiotic bacteria	* Increases the number of bifidobacteria in fecal flora and the serum ferritin level *Decreases *Enterobacteriaceae, Streptococcus* and *Clostridium* * Decreases the incidence of bacteremia and severity of infection in neutropenic patients * Alleviates symptoms of hepatitis C virus infection and reduces small intestine permeability in drug - induced intestinal injury * Beneficial in stress - related neurodegenerative disorders and treatment of certain cancer types. * Induces apoptosis in human leukemia and carcinoma cell lines	Yogurt, baby foods and infant formulas. Oral care products: Toothpastes, mouth rinses, moisturizing gels and chewing gums. Oral products: "Modulen" and "Agennix"; treatment of cancer, asthma, wounds, and ulcers. "Talactoferrin product"; treatment of renal cell carcinoma, improve the healing of diabetic neuropathic ulcers in a phase I/II "Lactopharma"; decreases debilitating side effect of cancer chemotherapy and radiotherapy "Microlactin"; to alleviate the symptoms and dysfunction associated with osteoarthritis	Kayser, 1996 Iwasa, 2002 Ajello, 2002 Tamura, 2004 Mader, 2005 Zimecki, 2005 Hayes, 2006 Zimecki, 2007 Petitclerc, 2007 McBride, 2007 Lyons, 2007
GMP	*Alleviate hepatic diseases *Brain development and improvement of learning ability *Regulation of intestinal functions * Stimulate the release of cholecystokinin (CKK), the satiety hormone involved in controlling food intake and digestion in the duodenum * Promote the growth of bifidobacteria,	Fermented milk product "Calpis" or "Ameal S" and the Finnish fermented milk product "Evolus"	Wang, 2007b Manso, 2004

3.2. Production and Purification of Bioactive Peptides

Traditional therapeutic peptides were manufactured by transgenic, recombinant or synthetic methods but these approaches are known to be very expensive and thus are prohibitive for large-scale productions. Nowadays, the increasingly extensive knowledge about bioactive peptides encrypted in food proteins has open up the doors of new production processes starting from a relatively cheap raw material, especially in the case of whey and its industrial derivatives. This could result in a reduction in production costs with the added advantage of an efficient waste disposal.

Bioactive peptides can be incorporated in the form of ingredients into functional foods, novel foods and nutraceuticals, dietary supplements and even pharmaceuticals with the purpose of delivering specific health effects. In addition, bioactive peptides offer an interesting opportunity for personalized nutrition.

Some evidences suggest that bioactive peptides are produced naturally from dietary proteins during the gastrointestinal transit but that way they can´t be controlled and the amount of peptides released may be insufficient to generate a physiological response in adult humans. Suitable large-scale technologies for the production of bioactive peptides are needed. However, this is yet a non-resolved problem.

3.2.1. Protein Hydrolysis

Bioactive peptides released from food proteins are usually produced through *"in vitro"* enzymatic hydrolysis or *"in situ"* microbial fermentation but the first method is preferred due to the lack of residual organic solvents or toxic chemicals in the final products. Microbial fermentation products usually present a lack of uniformity and the risk of presence of inhibiting-fermentation compounds [Kamau *et al.*, 2010]. In fact, few studies have closely examined the microbial fermentation of whey proteins. ACE-inhibitory, immunomodulatory, antioxidative and antimicrobial peptides have been identified after microbial fermentation of milk but almost all of them result from casein hydrolysis [Korhonen and Pihlanto-Leppälä, 2006]. The resistance of whey proteins to breakdown by bacterial peptidases has also been a controversial topic of discussion [Madureira *et al.*, 2010].

The systematic use of parameters to describe hydrolysis reactions facilitates experimental work in protein hydrolysis. There are four parameters that define initial conditions for a given system enzyme-substrate (substrate concentration, enzyme/substrate ratio, pH and temperature) and other four that describe the reaction and the composition of the hydrolysate (degree of hydrolysis, protein solubilization index, average chain length of the soluble phase and percentage of trichloroacetic acid soluble peptides).

pH and temperature are the most important parameters to control in the case of enzyme reactions because they strongly affect the activity of these biocatalysts. Each enzyme works best at a certain pH and temperature, its activity decreases at values above and below that point. For example, the protease pepsin works best at pH 1-2 (found in the stomach) while the protease trypsin is inactive at this pH but it is very active at pH 8 (found in the small intestine as the bicarbonate of the pancreatic fluid neutralizes the arriving stomach contents). Furthermore, changes in pH alter the state of ionization of charged amino acids that may play a crucial role in substrate binding and/or the catalytic action itself. On the other hand, temperature increases the rate of enzymatic hydrolysis as with all chemical reactions. However, enzymes are biological molecules and they become denatured at high temperatures, causing them to lose their catalytic activity. Strong research efforts have been made in the last years to get active enzymes at high temperatures.

In protein hydrolysis the degree of hydrolysis (DH), defined as the percentage of cleaved peptide bonds, is the key parameter for monitoring the reaction. Several methods for monitoring the DH during protein hydrolysis have been described in the literature: pH-stat, osmometry, soluble nitrogen content, the o-phthaldialdehyde (OPA) method and the trinitro-benzene-sulfonic acid (TNBS) method [Nielsen *et al.*, 2001]. Among them, the most used technique is the pH-stat. This method evaluates the progress of hydrolysis by titrating the released amino groups with an alkaline solution. The amount of base used is proportional to the DH [Adler-Nissen, 1986]. Enzymes work at constant pH and temperature during the entire process, so that no buffering is needed. Furthermore, the method can be used to follow a hydrolysis reaction continuously, it is not laborious and does not include hazardous and unstable chemicals.

It has been shown that hydrolysis conditions influence enzymatic hydrolysis of proteins and peptide composition of hydrolysates depends on parameters like temperature, pH, concentration, buffer used and DH [Cheison *et al.*, 2010, 2011]. The study and control of these parameters is of vital importance to produce bioactive peptides in the desired extension. Response surface methodology, tool used in the design of experiments to obtain an optimal relationship between several explanatory variables and one or more response variables, has been used in recent studies to optimize hydrolysis conditions including enzyme-substrate ratio, pH and temperature with the purpose of obtaining the most powerful ACE-inhibitory peptides [Guo *et al.*, 2009].

The proteases used for the production of bioactive peptides derived from whey can be from plants, microorganisms and animals. The most commonly used enzymes of animal origin are trypsin, pepsin, and chymotrypsin. Microbial proteases widely used are those obtainable from the *Bacillus* spp. *Bifidobacterium* and proteases from the Lactic Acid Bacteria. Microbial proteases provide some advantages over proteases from other sources because it costs relatively less to cultivate microorganisms and most of these proteases are expressed on the cell membrane, making harvesting and purification relatively cheap and less laborious [Agyei and Danquah, 2011]. However, studies using digestive enzymes like trypsin or pepsin are more abundant in the case of whey proteins.

Trypsin specifically hydrolyses peptide bond with lysine of arginine residues on the carbonyl side. As others serin-proteases, it reaches its maximum catalytic activity at alkaline pH but its stability is limited by autolysis. This autolysis reaction is only important when handling the enzyme preparation before being added to the reaction mixture. The peptides resulting from trypsin hydrolysis of whey proteins, due to the high specificity of this enzyme, results in hydrolysate with excellent emulsifying properties [Chobert *et al.*, 1988]. ACE-inhibitory peptides are the most commonly produced by trypsin and they have been identified in tryptic hydrolysates of bovine β-Lg, α-La [Pihlanto-Leppälä *et al.*, 2000] and in bovine, ovine and caprine κ-casein [Manso and López-Fandiño, 2003]. Like trypsin, pure solution of pepsin is slowly degraded by autolysis reactions at pH values close to its optimum point. The enzyme is relatively stable to temperature and can be used up to 60°C. Pepsin can release peptides from LF having antimicrobial activity [Recio and Visser, 1999; Ruíz-Giménez *et al.*, 2012].

Batch reactors are commonly used at laboratory scale for enzymatic hydrolysis of proteins. The use of this kind of reactors is relatively simple and the main parameters which need to be controlled being the temperature and the pH. However, they present disadvantages when they are going to be used under industrial scale conditions: low productivity, high operating costs, loss of catalytic activity due to inactivation, great variability of the quality of the products, etc. [Rios *et al.*, 2004]. Continuous processes are preferred at industrial scale conditions.

Another common approach is the use of immobilized enzymes onto highly activated supports [Lamas *et al.*, 2001; Sousa *et al.*, 2004]. It allows enzymatic hydrolysis under mild and more controlled conditions. Additionally, immobilized enzymes can be recycled and the generation of secondary metabolites originating from autolysis of enzymes is avoided [Pedroche *et al.*, 2007]. Since there are loss of enzyme activity and constraints for diffusion into the support, the use of this technique is limited.

Use of enzymatic membrane reactors (EMR) for the production of bioactive peptides is gaining interest in the food industry because it´s a specific mode for running continuous processes in which enzymes are separated from end-products with the help of a selective membrane. That way it´s possible to obtain complete retention of the enzyme without de-activation problems commented for enzyme immobilization. Furthermore, EMR has been shown to improve the efficiency of enzyme-catalyzed bioconversion, to increase product yields and they can be easily scaled up [Perea and Ugalde, 1996; Martín-Orue *et al.*, 1999; Prata-Vidal *et al.*, 2001; Guadix *et al.*, 2006]. EMR operating in continuous mode has been applied for the production of bioactive peptides under lab-scale conditions: antithrombotic peptides derived from CMP [Bouhallab and Touzé, 1995]; emulsifying peptides from β-Lg [Gauthier and Pouliot, 1996]; opioid peptides from goat whey [Bordenave *et al.*, 1999]. The use of a multi-step recycling membrane reactor combined with and appropriate ultrafiltration membrane system has been used to separate marine-derived bioactive peptides [Kim and Wijesekara, 2010].

Because most of enzymes have molecular weight between 10 and 80 kDa, ultrafiltration membranes with cut-off between 1 and 100 kDa are frequently used to retain the enzyme.

It has also been reported that electrostatic or hydrophobic interactions between the biological molecules and the membrane surface could also influence the membrane process [Marshall *et al.*, 1993; Lapointe *et al.*, 2005]. Permeate flux decline due to membrane fouling and enzyme activity decay are the main inconveniences of EMR. It has been shown that the presence a pre-hydrolysis step before the continuous operation minimizes fouling troubles due to the decrease of the viscosity of the initial solution [Darkono *et al.*, 1989]. In the specific case of protein hydrolysis, membrane fouling may, to a certain extent, be due to interactions peptide-peptide and membrane-peptide, especially if a charged membrane is used. In many occasions fouling problems are pH-dependent and the study of these inter-actions is very important to avoid or minimize it [Lapointe *et al.*, 2005]. It´s worth men-tioning that enzymes are widely applied in the detergent industry to clean ultrafiltration membranes used in protein concentration [Argüello *et al.*, 2005] as well as in EMR. However, little information is available on their role in simultaneous membrane cleaning during substrate hydrolysis. It´s of industrial interest to choose an enzyme with may confer on the EMR an auxiliary function of cleaning, hence reducing the gel layer on order to maintain permeate flux stability. On the other hand, the enzyme activity decay seems to be related with effects of temperature and denaturation of catalyst by adsorption/deposit onto the membrane [Paolucci-Jeanjean *et al.*, 2001].

A membrane reactor operating in a cyclic batch mode is one of the latest developments regarding the selection of the operation conditions. This way of operation combines the advantages of both batch (easy operation and control) and membrane recycle reactor (enzyme reuse) [Prieto *et al.*, 2007].

By the use of EMR a first peptide fractionation is achieved. Ultrafiltration using cut-off membranes of low molecular mass have been found as a possibility for separating out small peptides from high molecular mass residues and remaining enzymes. If a more purified permeate is required, EMR can be coupled with other separation techniques/units.

3.2.2. Fractionation and Isolation of Bioactive Peptides

Once the peptides are produced they remain in a mixture together with enzymes that must be deactivated by means of different techniques (heating, pH modification or chemical addition). Fractionation of peptides is a step that must be performed later in order to enrich the products in bioactive peptides and to assay their individual activity.

The methods commonly used for peptide fractionation and enrichment include ultra-filtration and nanofiltration, ion exchange, gel filtration technologies and liquid chroma-tography.

Liquid chromatography is the most extended isolation technique at lab-scale [Murakami *et al.*, 2004; Tavares *et al.*, 2011]. In the same way, ion exchange chromatographic methods have been developed for the enrichment of casein phosphopeptides from casein hydrolysates. Most of these methods are effective under laboratory scale but they are prohibitive for large scale applications due to production costs. The high cost of purification techniques is a limiting factor to the commercialization of peptide-based products [Korhonen and Pihlanto-Leppälä, 2006]. It has been estimated that separation and purification stages in industrial biotechnology processes can account for up to 70% of the capital and operating costs [Brady *et al.*, 2008]. Investigation into methodologies for the isolation of bioactive peptides under optimized conditions to reduce time and cost are ongoing.

A process-scale method for the isolation of casein phosphopeptides using acid precipitation, diafiltration and anion-exchange chromatography has been developed [Ellegård *et al.*, 1999]. The method was able to generate a process output of 40 kg casein phosphor-peptides. Furthermore, a sequential chromatographic method involving gel filtration chroma-tography, ion-exchange chromatography and HPLC analysis has been used to isolate anti-oxidant peptides from porcine skin collagen [Li *et al.*, 2007].

Ion exchange membrane chromatography has emerged as a promising technique for the enrichment of peptide fractions from protein hydrolysates. In this kind of technique the protein of interest is concentrated within the chromatographic medium and hydrolyzed *"in situ"*. The resulting active peptides are retained on the ion exchanger while the other peptides are washed out and finally the fraction containing the active peptides is eluted. This metho-dology was used to isolate cationic antibacterial peptides from lactoferrin [Recio and Visser, 1999].

As mentioned before, it´s established that pressure-driven membrane-based processes, such as ultrafiltration and nanofiltration, can be used to fractionate peptide mixtures and amino acids [Martín-Orue *et al.*, 1998; Timmer *et al.*, 1998; Lapointe *et al.*, 2003; Lucena *et al.*, 2006; Prieto *et al.*, 2010]. Membrane techniques are useful to obtain a permeate product enriched in small peptides and variations in operating conditions, may favour the permeation of bioactive peptides [Pouliot *et al.*, 1999; Lapointe *et al.*, 2005]. Ultrafiltration cascades by using different membranes cut-off combined with diafiltration steps have been demonstrated quite effective in α-La recovery from WPC [Lightfoot, 2006].

Nanofiltration separations are especially attractive for the fractionation of peptides contained in enzymatic hydrolysates. As surface charges (negative or positive) of nanofiltration membranes are their main distinctive feature, they offer the possibility of separating solutes through a combination of size and charge effects. Some researchers [Pouliot et al., 1999] have studied the fractionation of whey protein hydrolysates using charged membranes with a molecular weight cut-off between 1 and 5 kDa. They have shown, by changing the pH and the ionic strength of the hydrolysate, that the peptide separation is mainly governed by charge effects. Moreover, they reported that the best separation between acidic peptides (low isoelectric point) and basic peptides (high isoelectric point) was obtained at basic pH so it's interesting to further investigate the alkaline pH zone in order to identify optimal conditions for acidic and basic peptides separation. The same authors demonstrated that two peptides, differing by only one amino acid, were transmitted differently through the membrane. In a subsequent study it was found that the same peptide can be transmitted when issued from different hydrolysates, reflecting the importance of surrounding peptides, and, hence, the possible occurrence of peptide-peptide interactions [Pouliot et al., 2000]. Additionally, there are peptides that can interact in the polarized layer during the filtration process and their transmission decreases with the time under specific conditions [Lapointe et al., 2005]. Due to the aforementioned peptide-peptide and peptide-membrane interactions, it is difficult to predict the selectivity of the separation when using nanofiltration membranes and the process needs to be tailored to suit the peptide range aimed at and to minimize fouling by choosing the pH and the membrane material correctly [Butylina et al., 2006].

Ultrafiltration and nanofiltration seem to be the most promising techniques for peptide fractionation because of their low cost and easy scale-up. However, the process needs to be tailored to suit the peptide range aimed at and to minimize fouling by choosing the pH and the membrane material correctly [Butylina et al., 2006].

Electro-membrane filtration is an alternative method for the isolation of strongly charged biomolecules. It combines conventional membrane filtration with electrophoresis, making it more selective than membrane filtration alone and less costly than chromatography. By the manipulation of parameters like the type of membrane, electrical field strength, salination of hydrolysate and hydrolysate concentration, the product transfer and separation rate can be improved [Bargeman et al., 2002; Vanhoute et al., 2010]. Lapointe et al. (2006) have been used this technique for the selective separation of cationic peptides from a Tryptic hydrolysate of β-Lg and special attention has been paid on peptide ALPMHIR (ahtihypertensive peptide). This peptide showed the highest transmission among all the peptides present in the hydrolysate during electrofiltration at basic pH.

The electro-membrane of electrodialysis process uses homopolar membranes (anionic or cationic) to allow the migration of ions mainly according to their charges. Ultrafiltration membranes can also be introduced in an electrodialysis stack, in addition to ion-exchange membranes, to improve electrodialysis applications and to concentrate specific molecules depending on their charge and size. In replacement of ion-exchange membrane, Galier and Roux-de Balmann (2004) investigated the use of porous membranes to separate poly (L-glutamic), α-La and bovine hemoglobin with good results. The use of electrodialysis with ultrafiltration membranes has been used to fractionate β-Lg hydrolysates during a batch recirculation process with the objective to separate acidic, basic and neutral peptides [Poulin *et al.*, 2006; Firdaous *et al.*, 2009]. This seems to be a very selective method of separation since amongst a total of approximately 40 peptides in the raw hydrolysate only 13 of them were recovered in the adjacent solutions. It has been shown that electrodialysis with ultrafiltration membranes would minimize the fouling of the ultrafiltration membrane. This promising technique could be applied to separate bioactive peptides and other charged molecules of interest from complex feedstocks in the food, pharmaceutical, fine chemistry and fermentation industries.

All the membrane techniques used to fractionate proteinaceous streams have fouling and polarization concentration as main drawbacks. Both of those effects reduce the permeate flow rate (increasing the installation size) and modify the membrane selectivity due to the effect of an additional "membrane" formed by the deposits on the membrane surface. Besides, proteins (especially hydrophobic proteins) usually show strong tendencies to be adsorbed on membrane surfaces. High lineal velocities, low protein concentration, low transmembrane pressures (lower that critical flux) and some mechanic techniques (as back-pulsing o back-flushing) can improve the efficiency of the membrane technology.

3.3. Analytical Techniques to Identify Biopeptides

Whey peptides produced by gastrointestinal digestion, in the fermentation process of milk and enzymatic hydrolysis, have different composition, and consequently different properties. Peptides usually contain 2-20 amino acid residues per molecule and their molecular structure and amino acid sequences are dependent of whey protein and enzyme used, as well as process conditions (temperature, pH, enzyme to substrate ratio and reaction time). Chemical measurements and analytical techniques are used to investigate correlations between these whey hydrolysate characteristics. Identification and quantification of peptides are based on description of their amino acid sequences, molecular mass, biological activity and functionally effects.

Electrophoresis (MCE), reverse-phase high-performance liquid chromatography (RP-HPLC) and mass spectrometry (ESI-MS) are the main analytical methods used to identify peptides resulting in a well-defined peak structure [Careri and Mangia, 2003; Muro *et al.*, 2011]. MCE method is often used for obtaining data from peptide fragments for sequence analysis. Peptides are electrophoretically separate by one-or two-dimensional polyacrylamide gel. The proteins-containing regions are detected by reversible staining and are cut out, and each protein is digested in situ by proteolytic enzymes. The resulting peptide fragments are separated by narrow-bore reverse-phase HPLC (according their polarity), collected, and sequenced by mass spectrometry methods (ESI-MS) and/or N-terminal sequencing. General tests of protein fractionation using gel electrophoresis (SDS-PAGE) have also been used to evaluate the protein profile after each step of hydrolysis [Gómez *et al.*, 2002; Tauzín *et al.*, 2002; Seppo *et al.*, 2003; Matar *et al.*, 2003; Meisel, 2001, Meisel and FitzGerald, 2004b; Fitzgerald *et al.*, 2004; Gobbetti *et al.*, 2004; Korhonen and Pihlanto-Lepäala, 2001; Yamamoto *et al.*, 2003]. Methods of Lowry *et al.* (1951) and the traditional Bradford method are used for measured proteins content in samples.

Monitorization of peptides formation throughout reverse phase RP-HPLC is described [Mota *et al.*, 2006]. Gradient elution of β-Lg and α-La hydrolysates was carried out with a mixture of two solvents (solvent A: 0.1% trifluoroacetic acid (TFA) in water and solvent B:

0.1% TFA in 80% aqueous acetonitrile, [v/v]). Peptides were eluted as follows: 0-1 min, 90% A; 1-10 min, 90–80% A; 10-15 min, 80-75% A; 15-20 min, 75-60% A; 20-30 min, 60-50% A; 30-33 min, 50-40% A; 33-36 min, 40-30% A; 36-39 min, 30-20% A; 39-41 min, 20-0% A. The flow-rate was 0.5 mL/min. The column was used at ambient temperature and detection at 215 nm. Total run time was 50 min. The chromatographic system was calibrated by the external standard method with solutions that contained bovine α-La in the range of 0.039-1.0 mg/mL and bovine β-Lg in the range of 0.0039-1.0 mg/mL. Major fractions are identified as peptides formation in HPLC profiles. Peptide recoveries and the absence of extraneous contaminants in the separation of the peptide fragment mixture allowed the generation of extensive internal sequence information. However the fractions usually contain multiple compounds that require further additional cycles of fractionation, concentration and assessment of bioactivity in order to identify the molecule responsible of the activity.

The molecular mass and amino acid sequences of peptides released by protease enzymes are studied by matrix-assisted laser desorption/ionization mass spectrometry (MALDI-MS) or electrospray (ESI-MS) techniques. The positive ions analysis function and 20 kV accelerating voltage are generally used. The adopted RP –HPLC, MALDI-MS and ESI-MS protocols provide molecular data of peptides and their concentrations. The methods are coupled to separate peptides and later fragment them by collision with an inert gas in the MS method.

The masses of the derived fragments are used to assay their composition according to their hydrophobicity, molecular size, and net charge. The results are compared with the theoretical values of the mass of fragments of protein sequences previously established. Similarly the potential of bioactive peptides is determined by comparison of the sequences previously reported [Mamone et al., 2009].

Standard electrospray ionization tandem mass spectrometry (ESI-MS/MS) for different detection methods is often used as a rapid preliminary verification of the identity of various molecular structures including ranging from 7 to 44 kDa with an accuracy of 0.01-0.03%. Intensity of characteristic picomol is showed in mass spectrums between m/z 0 to 1000 of each amino acid produced by digestion of whey proteins. ESI-MS/MS not only improves the speed but also the reliability of the structure determination when used in conjunction with other methods of peptides analysis. Charge states of peptides are identified by molecular mass determination via a charge deconvolution procedure. For example the hydrolysis of β-Lg by four enzymes (porcine trypsin (PT), Fusarium oxysporum trypsin (FOT), Bacillus licheniformis proteinase (BLP) and Bacillus subtilis proteinase, Neutrase®) was characterized by RP-HPLC, size exclusion high performance liquid chromatography, SE-HPLC, and by capillary electrophoresis (CE).

After 24 h of hydrolysis, all β-Lg was degraded by PT and BLP, but a large part of the protein was still intact after hydrolysis by FOT or Neutrase®. The hydrolysis catalysed by each enzyme resulted in different peptide profiles by RP-HPLC and CE. The main fraction of peptides was found to have MWs ranging from 1.0 to 3.0 kDa. Hydrolysates produced by PT or FOT were resolved into 18 peaks, while BLP hydrolysates were resolved into 25 peaks, corresponding well to the numbers of possible cleavage sites in β-Lg. Neutrase®, with a broad specificity, produced the largest number of peptides. However seven peptides from PT hydrolysis, eight from FOT hydrolysis and one from BLP hydrolysis were identified by mass spectrometry (MS) and Edman degradation [Madsen et al., 1997].

CONCLUSION

Cheese whey can be considered as a great protein source that is not completely exploited at industrial scale today. Whey, delactosed and desalting whey powders, whey protein concentrates and whey protein isolates are well known and all of them are being produced by whey processing companies and they are commonly used as functional ingredients in food and special diets. Other proteins such as lactoferrin, lactoperoxisade, β-lactoglobuline and α-lactoalbumin can be found in the market with different purity degrees. Improvement of different technologies is necessary to get higher purity and recovery rates and probably the use of combined technologies is compulsory to develop economical processes.

Whey hydrolysates are being investigated nowadays in order to produce bioactive peptides that could be added in form of novel foods or even produced as pharmaceuticals products to deliver specific health benefits. Researchers are continuing to discover new whey protein peptides bioactivities. Only some of the peptides that can be obtained by enzymatic hydrolysis have been studied, then and extra work must be done to identify possible activities of many others. Technologies to separate, purify and concentrate these biopeptides must be developed at industrial scale. Membrane technologies (ultrafiltration, nanofiltration, electrofiltration, electrodialysis, etc.) have potentialities to be scaled-up, however better separation efficiencies are necessary to produce higher purity. For this, combination of different technologies will be probably useful to get these objectives. The development of other novel techniques as nanoencapsulation and nanoemulsions can help to increase the stability of these peptides after their isolation.

With respect to the activity of biopeptides there is a strong need for further human clinical tests so that most of the analysis conclusions have been obtained after *"in vitro"* or *"in vivo"* tests with animals.

REFERENCES

Abd El-Salam, M. H.; El-Shibiny, S.; Buchheim, W. Characteristics and potential uses of the casein macropeptide. *Int. Dairy J.* 1996, *6*, 327-341.

Abubakar, A.; Saito, T.; Kitazawa, H.; Kawai, Y.; Itoh. T. Structural analysis of new antihypertensive peptides derived from cheese whey protein by proteinase K digestion. *J. Dairy Sci.* 1998, *81*, 3131–3138.

Adler-Nissen, J. *Enzymatic hydrolysis of food proteins*, London: Elsevier Applied Science Publishers, 1986.

Agyei, D. and Danquah, M.K. Industrial-scale manufacturing of pharmaceutical-grade bioactive peptides. *Biotechnol. Adv.* 2011, *29*, 272-277.

Ajello, M.; Greco, R.; Giansanti, F.; Massucci, M.T.; Antonini, G.; Valenti, P. Anti-invasive activity of bovine lactoferrin towards group A Streptococci. *J. Biochem. Cell Biol.* 2002, *80*, 119-124.

Aleixandre, A.; Miguel, M.; Muguerza, B. Péptidos hipertensivos derivados de proteínas de leche y huevo. *Nutr. Hosp.* 2008, *23*, 313-318.

Alonso, A.; Steffen, L.M.; Folsom, A.R. Dairy intake and changes in blood pressure over 9 years: The ARIC study. *Eur. J. Clin. Nutr.* 2009, *63*, 1272-1275.

Andersen, M.L. and Skibsted, L.H. *ESR spectroscopy for the study of oxidative processes in food and beverages.* In Webb, G. A. (ed.) *Modern Magnetic Resonance*, London, Kluwer Academic Publishers, 2006.

Antila, P.; Paakkari, I.; Järvinen, A.; Mattila, M.J.; Laukkanen, M.; Pihlanto-Leppälä, A.; Mäntsälä, P; Hellman, J. Opioid peptides derived from in-vitro proteolysis of bovine whey proteins. *Int. Dairy J.* 1991, *1*, 215-229.

Argüello, M.A.; Álvarez, S.; Riera, F.A.; Álvarez, R. Utilization of enzymatic detergents to clean inorganic membranes fouled by whey proteins. *Sep. Purif. Technol.* 2005, *41*, 147-154.

Aruoma, O.I.; Deiana, M.; Jenner, A.; Halliwell, B.; Kaur, H.; Banni, S. Effect of hydroxytyrosol found in extra virgin olive oil on oxidative DNA damage and on low-density lipoprotein oxidation. *J. Agr. Food Chem.* 1998, *46*, 5181-5187.

Astaire, J.C.; Ward, R.; German, J.B.; Jiménez-Flores, R. Concentration of polar MFGM lipids from buttermilk by microfiltration and supercritical fluid extraction. *J.Dairy Sci.* 2003, *86*, 2297-2307.

Bargeman, G.; Koops, G.H.; Houwing, J.; Breebaart, I.; van der Horst, H.C.; Wessling, M. The development of electro-membrane filtration for the isolation of bioactive peptides: the effect of membrane selection and operating parameters on the transport rate. *Desalination*, 2002, *149*, 369-274.

Bayram, T.; Pekmez, M.; Arda, N.; Yalcin, A. Antioxidant activity of whey protein fractions isolated by gel exclusion chromatography and protease treatment. *Talanta,* 2008, *75*, 705-709.

Bellamy, W.; Takase, M.; Wakabayashi, H.; Kawase, K.; Tomita, M. Antibacterial spectrum of lactoferricin B, a potent bactericidal peptide derived from the N-terminal region of bovine lactoferrin. *J. Appl. Bacteriol.* 1992, *73*, 472–479.

Benzie, F.F. and Strain J.J. The ferric reducing ability of plasma (FRAP) as a measure of antioxidant power: The FRAP assay. *Anal. Biochem.* 1999, *239*, 70-76.

Beucher, M.; Levenez, F.; Yvon, Y.; Corring, T. Effect of caseinomacropeptide (CMP) on cholecystokinin (CCK) release in rats. *Reprod. Nutr. Dev.* 1994, *34*, 613–614.

Boelsma, E. and Kloek, J. Lacto-tripeptides and antihypertensive effects: A critical review. *Brit. J. Nutr.* 2009, *101*, 776-786.

Bordenave, S.; Sannier, F.; Ricart, G.; Piot, J.M. Continuous hydrolysis of goat whey in an ultrafiltration reactor: Generation of alpha-lactorphin. *Prep. Biochem. Biotech.* 1999, *29*, 189–202.

Bordin, G., Cordeiro, F., de la Calle, B., Rodríguez, A.R. Identification and quantification of major bovine milk proteins by liquid chromatography. *J. Chromatogr. A*, 2001, *928*, 63-76.

Bouhallab, S. and Touzé , C. Continuous hydrolysis of caseinomacropeptide in a membrane reactor: Kinetic study and gram-scale production of antithrombotic peptides. *Lait.* 1995, *75*, 251–258.

Bounous, G. Whey protein concentrate (WPC) and glutathione modulation in cancer treatment. *Anticancer Res.* 2000, *20*, 4785-4792.

Brady, R.; Woonton, B.; Gee, M.I.; O′Connor, A.J. Hieralchical mesoporous silica materials for separation of functional food ingredients – a review. *Innovat. Food Sci. Emerg. Tech.* 2008, *9*, 243-248.

Bramaud, C.; Aimar, P.; Daufin, G. Optimisation of a whey protein fractionation process based on the selective precipitation of α-lactalbumin. *Lait*, 1997, *77*, 411-423.

Branen, J. and Davidson, P.M. Activity of hydrolysed lactoferrin against food borne pathogenic bacteria in growth media: The effect of EDTA. *Lett. Appl. Microbiol.* 2009, *30*, 233-237.

Brisson, G.; Britten, M.; Pouliot, Y. Electrically-enhanced crossflow microfiltration for separation of lactoferrin from whey protein mixtures. *J. Membrane Sci.* 2007, *297*, 206-216.

Brody, E.P. Biological activities of bovine glycomacropeptide. *Br. J. Nutr.* 2000, *84*, 39–46.

Butylina, S.; Luque, S.; Nyström, M. Fractionation of whey-derived peptides using a combination of ultrafiltration and nanofiltration. *J. Membrane Sci.* 2006, *280*, 418-426.

Caccavo, D.; Pellegrino, N.M.; Altamura, M.; Rigon, A.; Amati, L.; Amoroso, A.; Jirillo, E.J. Antimicrobial and immunoregulatory functions of lactoferrin and its potential therapeutic application. *J. Endotoxin Res.* 2002, *8*, 403-417.

Camfield, D.A.; Owen, L.; Scholey, A.B.; Pipingas, A.; Stough, C. Dairy constituents and neurocognitive health in ageing. *British J. Nutr.* 2011, *106*, 159-174.

Campagna, S.; Mathot, A.G.; Fleury, Y.; Girardet, J.M.; Gaillard, J.L. Antibacterial activity of lactophoricin, a synthetic 23-residue peptide derived from the sequence of bovine milk component-3 of proteose-peptone. *J. Dairy Sci.* 2004, *87*, 1621–1626.

Cao, G.; Sofic, E.; Prior, R. Antioxidant and prooxidant behaviour of flavonoids: Structure-activity relationships. *Free Radical Bio.Med.* 1997, *22*, 749-760.

Careri, M. and Mangia, A. Analysis of food proteins and peptides by chromatography and mass spectrometry. *J.Chromatogr. A,* 2003, *1000*, 609-635.

Chatterton, E.W.; Smithers, G.; Roupas, P.; Brodkorb, A. Bioactivity of β-lactoglobolin and α-lactalbumin. Technological implications for processing. *Int. Dairy J.* 2006, *16*, 1229-1240.

Cheang, B. and Zydney, A.L. A two-stage ultrafiltration process for fractionation of whey protein isolate. *J. Membrane Sci.*, 2004, *231*, 159-167.

Cheison, S.C.; Schmitt, M.; Leeb, E.; Letzel, T.; Kulozik, U. Influence of temperature and degree of hydrolysis on the peptide composition of trypsin hydrolysates of β-lactoglobulin: Analysis by LC-ESI-TOF/MS. *Food Chem.* 2010, *121*, 457-467.

Cheison, S.C.; Leeb, E.; Letzel, T.; Kulozik, U. Influence of buffer type and concentration on the peptide composition of trypsin hydrolysates of β-lactoglobulin. *Food Chem.* 2011, *125*, 121-127.

Chen, T.L.; Lo, Y.C.; Hu, W.T.; Wu, M.C.; Chen, S.T.; Chang, H.M. Microencapsulation and Modification of Synthetic Peptides of Food Proteins Reduces the Blood Pressure of Spontaneously Hypertensive Rats. *J. Agric. Food Chem.* 2003, *51*, 1671-1675.

Chiang, M.Ch.; Yang, S.Ch.; Li, K.Y.; Tsaichiang, T.Ch. An Assay of Angiotensin-Converting Enzyme Activity Obtained Using Capillary Electrophoresis. *J.Food Drug Anal.* 2005, *13*, 267-272.

Chirinos, J.A.; Zambrano, J.P.; Chakko, S.; Veerani, A.; Schob, A.; Willens, H.J.; Perez, G.; Mendez, A.J. Aortic pressure augmentation predicts adverse cardiovascular events in patients with established coronary artery disease. *Hypertension.* 2005, *45*, 980-985.

Chobert J. M.; Bertrand H.C.; Nicolas M.G. Solubility and emulsifying properties of caseins and whey proteins modified enzymatically by trypsin. *J. Agric. Food. Chem.* 1988, *36*, 883–892.

Chodaczek, G.; Zimecki, M.; Lukasiewicz, J.; Lugowski, C. A complex of lactoferrin with monophosphoryl lipid A is an efficient adjuvant of the humoral and cellular immune response in mice. *Med. Microbiol. Immun.* 2006, *195*, 207–216.

Choi, J.K.; Curry, S.; Qin, D.H.; Bittman, R.; Hamilton, J.A. Interactions of very long-chain saturates fatty acids with serum albumin. *J. Lipid Res.* 2002, *43*, 1000-1010.

Clare, D.A. and Swaisgood, H.E. Bioactive milk peptides: A prospectus. *J. Dairy Sci.* 2000, *83*, 1187-1195.

Clare, D.A.; Catignani, G.L.; Swaisgood, H. E. Biodefense properties of milk: The role of antimicrobial proteins and peptides. *Curr. Pharm. Des.* 2003, *9*, 1239-1255.

Collins, A.; Gedik, C.; Vaughan, N.; Woods, S.; White, A.; Dubois, J.; Duez, P. (*and others*). Comparative analysis of baseline 8-oxo-7, 8-dihydroguanine in mammalian cell DNA, by different methods in different laboratories: An approach to consensus. *Carcinogenesis,* 2002, *23*, 2129-2133.

Collins, A. Antioxidant intervention as a route to cancer prevention. *Eur. J. Cancer,* 2005, *41*, 1923-1930.

Cross, M.L. and Gill, H.S. Modulation of immune function by a modified bovine whey protein concentrate. *Immunol. Cell Biol.* 1999, *77*, 345-350.

Crouch, S.P.; Slater, K.J.; Fletcher, J. Regulation of cytokine release from mononuclear cells by the iron-binding protein lactoferrin. *Blood*, 1992, *80*, 235-240.

Cushman, D.W. and Cheung, H.S. Spectrophotometric assay and properties of the angiotensin-converting enzyme of rabbit lung. *Biochem. Pharmacol.* 1971, *20*, 1637-1648.

Darnoko, D.; Cheryan, M.; Artz, W.E. Saccharification of cassava starch in an ultrafiltration reactor. *Enzyme Microb. Technol.* 1989, *11*, 154-159.

Datta, D.; Bhattacharjee, C.; Datta, S. Whey fractionation of proteins using membrane filtration: A review. *J. Inst. Eng .Chem. (India): Chem. Eng. Div.* 2008, *89,* 45-50.

de Leeuw, P.W.; van der Zander, K.; Kroon, A.A.; Rennenberg, R.M.; Koning, M.M. Dose dependent lowering of blood pressure by dairy peptides in mildly hypertensive subjects. *Blood Pressure,* 2009, *18*, 44-50.

Decker E.A. and Welch, B. Role of ferritine as a lipid oxidation catalyst in muscle food. *J. Agric. Food Chem.* 1990, *38*, 674-677.

Didelot, S.; Bordenave, J.S.; Rosenfeld, E.; Fruitier, A.I.; Piot, J.M.; Sannier, F. Preparation of angiotensin I-converting enzyme inhibitory hydrolysates from unsupplemented caprine whey fermentation by various cheese microflore. *Int. Dairy J.* 2006, *16*, 976-983.

Dolan, E.; Thijs, L.; Li, Y.; Atkins, N.; McCormack, P.; McClory, S.; O'Brien, E.; Staessen, J.A.; Stanton, A.V. Ambulatory arterial stiffness index as a predictor of cardiovascular mortality in the Dublin Outcome Study. *Hypertension,* 2006, *47*, 365-370.

Elias, R.J.; Kellerby, S.S.; Decker, E.A. Antioxidant activity of proteins and peptides. *Crit. Rev. Food Sci.* 2008, *48*, 430-441.

Elitsur, Y. and Luk, G.D. Beta-casomorphin (BCM) and human colonic lamina propria lymphocyte proliferation. *Clin. Exp. Immunol.* 1991, *123*, 1068-1070.

Ellegård, K.H.; Gammelgård-Larsen, C.; Sörensen, E.S.; Fedosov, S. Process scale chromatographic isolation, characterization and identification of tryptic bioactive casein phosphopeptides. *Int. Dairy J.* 1999, *9*, 639–652.

El-Sayed, M.M.H. and Chase, H.A. Trends in whey protein fractionation. *Biotechnol. Lett.* 2011, *33*, 1501-1511.

El-Zahar, K.; Sitohy, M.; Choiset, Y.; Metro, F.; Haertle, T.; Chobert, J.M. Antimicrobial activity of ovine whey protein and their peptic hydrolysates. *Milchwissenschaft,* 2004, *59*, 653- 656.

Erdmann, K.; Cheung, B.; Schroder, H. The possible roles of food derived bioactive peptides in reducing the risk of cardiovascular disease. *J. Nutr. Biochem.* 2008, *19*, 643-654.

Exl, B.M. A review of recent developments in the use of moderately hydrolyzed whey formulae in infant nutrition. *Nutr. Res.* 2001, *21*, 355-379.

Fernández, A.; Menéndez, V.; Riera, F.A.; Alvarez, R. Caseinomacropeptide behaviour in a whey protein fractionation process based on α-lactalbumin precipitation. *J. Dairy Res.* 2011, *78*, 196-2002.

Firdaous, L.; Dhulster, P.; Amiot, J.; Gaudreau, A.; Lecouturier, D.; Kapel, R. ; Lutin, F. ; Vézina, L-P. ; Bazinet, L. Concentration and selective separation of bioactive peptides from an alfalfa white protein hydrolysate by electrodialysis with ultrafiltration membranes. *J. Membrane Sci.* 2009, *329*, 60-67.

FitzGerald, R.J.; Murray, B.A.; Walsh, D.J. Hypotensive peptides from milk proteins. *J. Nutr.* 2004, *134*, 980S-988S.

FitzGerald, R.J. and Murray, B.A. Bioactive peptides and lactic fermentations. *Int. J. Dairy Technol.* 2006, *59*, 118-125.

Foegeding, E.A.; Davis, J.P.; Doucet, D.; McGuffey, M.K. Advances in modifying and understanding whey protein functionality. *Trends in Food Sci. and Technol.* 2002, *13*, 151-159.

Foltz, M.; Meynen, E.E.; Bianco, V.; van Platerink, C.; Koning, T.M.; Kloek, J. Angiotensin converting enzyme inhibitory peptides from a lactotripeptide-enriched milk beverage are absorbed intact into the circulation. *J. Nutr.* 2007, *137*, 953-958.

Fong, B.Y.; Norris, C.S.; Macgibbon, A.K.H. Protein and lipid composition of bovine milk-fat-globule membrane. *Int. Dairy J.* 2007, *17*, 275-288.

Freedman, D.J.; Tacket, C.O.; Delehanty, A.; Maneval, D.R.; Naturo, J.; Crabb, J.H. Milk immunoglobulin with specific activity against challenge with enterotoxigenic *Escheriquia Coli. J. Infect. Diseases*, 1998, *77*, 662-667.

Frid, A.H.; Nilsson, M.; Holst, J.J.; Bjorck, I.M. Effect of whey on blood glucose and insulin responses to composite breakfast and lunch meals in type 2 diabetic subjects. *Am. J. Clin. Nutr.* 2005, *82*, 69-75.

Fweja, L.W.T.; Lewis, M.J.; Graudison, A.S. Isolation of lactoperoxidase using different cation exchange resins by batch and column procedures. *J. Dairy Res.* 2010, *77*, 357-367.

Galier, S. and Roux-de Balmann, H. Study of biomolecules separation in an electrophoretic membrane contactor. *J. Membrane Sci.* 2004, *241*, 79-87.

Gauthier, S.F. and Pouliot, M. Use of ultrafiltration for the preparation of enzymatic hydrolysates from milk proteins. *IDF Bull.* 1996, *311*, 31–32.

Gauthier, S.F.; Pouliot, Y.; Saint-Sauveur, D. Immunomodulatory peptides obtained by the enzymatic hydrolysis of whey proteins. *Int. Dairy J.* 2006, *16*, 1315-1323.

Gill, H.S.; Doull, F.; Rutherfurd, K.J.; Cross, M.L. Immunoregulatory peptides in bovine milk. *Br. J. Nutr.* 2000, *84*, S111-S117.

Girardet, J.M.; Linden, G.; Loye, S.; Courthaudon, J.L.; Lorient, D. Study of a mechanism of lipolysis inhibition by bovine milk proteose peptone component-3. *J. Dairy Sci.* 1993, *76*, 2156–2163.

Gobbetti, M.; Minervini, F.; Rizzello, C.G. Angiotensin I converting-enzyme-inhibitory and antimicrobial bioactive peptides. *Int. J. Dairy Technol.* 2004, *57*, 172-188.

Gómez-Ruiz, J.A.; Ramos, M.; Recio, I. Angiotensin converting enzyme-inhibitory peptides in Manchego cheese manufactured with different starter cultures. *Int. Dairy J.* 2002, *12*, 697-706.

Goodall, S.; Grandison, A.S.; Jauregi, P.J.; Price, J. Selective separation of the major whey proteins using ion exchange membranes. *J. Dairy Sci.* 2008, *91*, 1-10.

Groenink, J.; Walgreen-Weterings, E.; van't Hof, W.; Veerman, E.C.; Amerongen, A.V.N. Cationic amphipathic peptides, derived from bovine and human lactoferrins, with antimicrobial activity against oral pathogens. *FEMS Microbiol. Lett.* 1999, *179*, 217–222.

Guadix, A.; Camacho, F.; Guadix, E.M. Production of whey protein hydrolysates with reduced allergenicity in a stable membrane reactor. *J. Food Eng.* 2006, *72*, 398-405.

Guo, Y.; Pan, D.; Tanokura, M. Antihypertensive peptides from skimmed milk hydrolysate digested by cell-free extract of Lactobacillus helveticus JCM1004. *Food Chem.* 2004, *91*, 123-129.

Guo, Y.; Pan, D.; Tanokura, M. Optimisation of hydrolysis conditions for the production of the angiotensin-I converting enzyme (ACE) inhibitory peptides from whey protein using response surface methodology. *Food Chem.* 2009, *114*, 328-333.

Gustafsson, L.; Leijonhufvud, I.; Aronsson, A.; Mossberg, A.K.; Svanborg, C. Treatment of skin papillomas with topical alpha-lactalbumin-oleic acid. *New Engl. J. Med.* 2004, *350*, 2663-2672.

Gustafsson, L.; Hallgren, O.; Mossberg, A.K.; Pettersson, J.; Fischer, W.; Aronsson, A.; Svanborg, C. HAMLET kills tumor cells by apoptosis: structure, cellular mechanisms, and therapy. *J. Nutr.* 2005, *135*, 1299-1303.

Hallgren, O.; Aits, S.; Brest, P.; Gustafsson, L.; Mossberg, A.K.; Wullt, B.; Svanborg, C. Apoptosis and tumor cell death in response of HAMLET (human alpha-lactalbumin made lethal to tumor cells). *Adv. Exp. Med. Biol.* 2008, *606*, 217-240.

Halliwell, B. and Whiteman, M. Measuring reactive species and oxidative damage *"in vivo"* and in cell culture: How should you do it and what do the results mean. *Brit. J. Pharm.* 2004, *142*, 231-255.

Hancock, R.E.W. and Sahl, H.G. Antimicrobial and host-defense peptides as new anti-infective therapeutic strategies. *Nat. Biotechnol.* 2006, *12*, 1551-1557.

Hartmann, R. and Meisel, H. Food-derived peptides with biological activity: From research to food applications. *Curr. Opin. Biotech.* 2007, *18*, 1-7.

Hayes, T.G.; Falchook, G.F.; Varadhachary, G.R.; Smith, D.P.; Davis, L.D.; Dhingra, H.M.; Hayes B.P.; Varadhachary, A. Phase I trial of oral talactoferrin alfa in refractory solid tumors. *Invest. New Drugs*, 2006, *24*, 233-240.

Hernández-Ledesma B.; Amigo L.; Ramos M.; Recio I. Angiotensin converting enzyme inhibitory activity in commercial fermented products. Formation of peptides under simulated gastrointestinal digestion. *J. Agr. Food Chem.* 2004, *52*, 1504-1510.

Hernández-Ledesma, B.; Dávalos, A.; Bartolomé, B.; Amigo, L. Preparation of antioxidant enzymatic hydrolysates from α-lactalbumin and β-lactoglobulin. Identification of active peptides by HPLC-MS/MS. *J. Agr. Food Chem.* 2005, *53*, 588-593.

Hernández-Ledesma, B.; Miguel, M.; Amigo, L.; Aleixandre, M.A.; Recio, I. Effect of simulated gastrointestinal digestion on the antihypertensive properties of lactoglobulin peptides. *Int. Dairy J.* 2007, *74*, 336-339.

Hernández-Ledesma, B.; Recio, I.; Amigo, L. β-Lactoglobulin as a source of bioactive peptides. *Amino acids*, 2008, *35*, 257-265.

Hernández-Ledesma, B.; Ramos, M.; Gómez-Ruiz, J.A. Bioactive components of ovine and caprine cheese whey. *Small Ruminant Res.* 2011, 101, 196-204.

Hoek, K.S.; Milne, J.M.; Grieve, P.A.; Dionysius, D.A.; Smith, R. Antibacterial activity of bovine lactoferrin-derived peptides. *Antimicrob. Agents Chemother.* 1997, *41*, 54–59.

Hoelzl, C.; Bichler, J.; Ferk, F.; Simic, T.; Nersesyan, A.; Elbling, L.; Ehrlich, V.; Chakraborty, A.; Knasmüller, S. Methods for the detection of antioxidants which prevent age related diseases: A critical review with particular emphasis on human intervention studies. *J. Physiol. Pharmacol.* 2005, *56*, 49-64.

Hui, Y.H. (ed.). *Handbook of food products manufacturing.* New York: John Wiley and Sons, 2007.

Hyun, C-K. and Shin, H-K. Utilization of bovine blood plasma proteins for the production of angiotensin I converting enzyme inhibitory peptides. *Process Biochem.* 2000, *36*, 65-71.

Ijas, H.; Collin, M.; Finckenberg, P.; Pihlanto-Leppälä, A.; Korhonen, H.; Korpela, P.; Vapaatalo, H. ; Nurminem, M.L. Antihypertensive opioid-like milk peptide α-lactorphin: Lack of effect on behavioural tests in mice. *Int. Dairy J.* 2004, *14*, 201–205.

Iwasa, M.; Kaito, M.; Ikoma, J.; Takeo, M.; Imoto, I.; Adachi, Y.; Yamauchi, K.; Koizumi, R.; Teraguchi, S. Lactoferrin inhibits hepatitis C virus viremia in chronic hepatitis C patients with high viral loads and HCV genotype 1b. *Am. J. Gastroenterol.* 2002, *97*, 766-767.

Jacquot, A.; Gauthier, S.F.; Drouin, R.; Boutin, Y. Proliferative effects of synthetic peptides from β-lactoglobulin and α-lactalbumin on murine splenocytes. *Int. Dairy J.* 2010, *20*, 514-521.

Jäkälä, P. and Vapäätalo, H. Antihypertensive Peptides from Milk Proteins. *Pharmaceuticals,* 2010, *3*, 251-272.

Janssen, J.G. and Schalk, J. Peptides having and ACE inhibiting effect. Patent US 2006, 2006/0216330 A1.

Jauhiainen, T.; Rönnback, M.; Vapaatalo, H.; Wuolle, K.; Kautiainen, H.; Korpela, R. *Lactobacillus helveticus* fermented milk reduces arterial stiffness in hypertensive subjects. *Int. Dairy J.* 2007a, *17*, 1209-1211.

Jauhiainen, T. and Korpela, R. Milk peptides and blood pressure. *J. Nutr.* 2007b, *137*, 825S-829S.

Jollés, P.; Lévy-Toledano, S.; Fiat, A.M.; Soria, C.; Gillessen, D.; Thomaidis, A.; Dunn, F.W.; Caen, J.B. Analogy between fibrinogen and casein. *Eur. J. Biochem.* 1986, *158*, 379-384.

Kamau, S.M.; Cheison, S.C.; Chen, W.; Liu, X-M.; Lu, R-R. Alpha-lactalbumin: Its production, technologies and bioactive peptides. *Comprehensive. Rev. in Food Sci. and Food Safety,* 2010, *9*, 197-212.

Kawasaki, Y.; Isoda, H.; Tanimoto, M.; Dosako, S.; Idota, T.; Ahiko, K. Inhibition by lactoferrin and casein glycomacropeptide of binding of cholera toxin to its receptor. *Biosci. Biotechnol. Biochem.* 1992, *56*, 195–198.

Kawasaki, Y.; Kawakami, M.; Tanimoto, M.; Dosako, S.; Tomizawa, A.; Kotake, M. pH-dependent molecular weight changes of k-casein glycomacropeptide and its preparation by ultrafiltration. *Milchwissenschaft*, 1996, *48*, 191-196.

Kayser, H. and Meisel, H. Stimulation of human peripheral blood lymphocytes by bioactive peptides derived from bovine milk proteins. *FEBS Lett.* 1996, *383*, 18–20.

Kennedy, R.S.; Konok, G.P.; Bounous, G.; Baruchel, S.; Lee, T.D. The use of a whey protein concentrate in the treatment of patients with metastatic carcinoma: a phase I-II clinical study. *Anticancer Res.* 1995, *15*, 2643-2649.

Kim, S.Y.; Je, J.Y.; Kim, S.K. Purification and characterization of antioxidant peptide from hoki (Johnius belengerii) frame protein by gastrointestinal digestion. *J. Nutr. Biochem.* 2007a, *18*, 31-38.

Kim, S.B.; Seo, I.S.; Khan, M.A.; Ki, K.S.; Lee, W.S.; Lee, H.J.; Shin, H.S.; Kim, H.S. Enzymatic hydrolysis of heated whey: Iron binding ability of peptides antigenic protein fractions. *J. Dairy Sc.,* 2007b, *90*, 4033-4042.

Kim, S.K. and Wijesekara, I. Development and biological activities of marine-derived bioactive peptides: a review. *J. Func. Foods,* 2010, *2*, 1-9.

Kitts. D.D. and Weiler, K. Bioactive proteins and peptides from food sources. Applications of bioprocesses used in isolation and recovery. *Curr. Pharm. Des.* 2003, *9*, 1309-1323.

Ko, S. and Kwank, H-S. *Bioactive components in whey products*. In Park, Y.W. (ed.). *Bioactive components in milk and dairy products*. IO, USA: Wiley-Blackwell, 2009.

Konrad, G. and Kleinschmidt, T. A new method for isolation of native α-lactalbumin from sweet whey. *Int. Dairy J.* 2008, *18*, 47-54.

Korhonen, H. and Pihlanto-Leppälä, A. Milk protein-derived bioactive peptides-novel opportunities for health promotion. *IDF Bull.,* 2001, *363*, 17-26.

Korhonen, H. and Pihlanto-Leppälä, A. Bioactive peptides: Production and functionality. *Int. Dairy J.* 2006, *16*, 945-960.

Korhonen, H. Milk-derived bioactive peptides: From science to applications. *J. Funct. Foods,* 2009, *1*, 177-187.

Lam, S.M.; Moughan, P.J.; Awati, A.; Morton, H.R. The influence of whey protein and glycomacropeptide on satiety in adult humans. *Physiol. Behav.* 2009, *96*, 162–168.

Lamas, E.M.; Barros, R.M.; Balcao, V.M.; Malcata, F.X. Hydrolysis of whey proteins by proteases extracted from *Cynara cardunculus* and immobilized onto highly activated supports. *Enzyme Microb. Tech.* 2001, *28*, 642-652.

Lapointe, J.F.; Gauthier, S.F.; Pouliot, Y. ; Bouchard, C. Effect of hydrodynamic conditions on fractionation of β-lactoglobulin tryptic peptides using nanofiltration membranes. *J. Membrane Sci.* 2003, *212*, 55-67.

Lapointe, J.F.; Gauthier, S.F.; Pouliot, Y.; Bouchard, C. Fouling of a nanofiltration membrane by a β-lactoglobulin tryptic hydrolysate: impact on the membrane sieving and electrostatic properties. *J. Membrane Sci.* 2005, *253*, 89-102.

Lapointe, J.F.; Gauthier, S.F.; Pouliot, Y.; Bouchard, C. Selective separation of cationic peptides from a tryptic hydrolysate of beta-lactoglobulin by electrofiltration. *Biotechnol. Bioeng.* 2006, *94*, 223-233.

Lee, Y.M.; Skurk, T.; Hennig, M.; Hauner, H. Effect of a milk drink supplemented with whey peptides on blood pressure in patients with mild hypertension. *Eur. J. Nutr.* 2007, *46*, 21-27.

Lehtinen, R.; Jauhiainen, T.; Kankuri, E.; Lindstedt, K.; Kovanen, P.T.; Kerojoki, O.; Korpela, R.; Vapaatalo, H. Effects of milk casein-derived tripeptides Ile-Pro-Pro, Val-Pro-Pro, and Leu-Pro-Pro on enzymes processing vasoactive precursors *"in vitro"*. *Arzneimittel Forsch.* 2010, *60*, 182-185.

Li, E.W.Y. and Mine, Y. Immunoenhancing effects of bovine glycomacropeptide and its derivatives on the proliferative response and phagocytic activities of human macrophagelike cells, U937. *J. Agric. Food Chem.* 2004, *52*, 2704-2708.

Li, B.; Chen, F.; Wang, X.; Ji, B.; Wu, Y. Isolation and identification of antioxidative peptides from porcine collagen hydrolysate by consecutive chromatography and electrospray-ionization-mass spectrometry. *Food. Chem.* 2007, *102*, 1135-1143.

Lightfoot, E.N. Membrane cascade-based separation. US patent, 2006, 7,141,171, B2.

Lindmark-Mansson, H. and Akesson, B. Antioxidative factors in milk. *Brit. J. Nutr.* 2000, *84*, S103-S110.

Lönnerdal, B. and Lien, E.L. Nutritional and physiologic significance of α-lactalbumin in infants. *Nutr. Rev.* 2003, *61*, 295-305.

López-Expósito, R.; Gómez, G.A.; Amigo, L.; Recio, I. Identification of antibacterial peptides from α_{s2}-casein. *Int. Dairy J.* 2006a, *16*, 1072-1080.

López-Expósito, R. and Recio, I. Antibacterial activity of peptides and folding variants from milk proteins. *Int. Dairy J.* 2006b, *16*, 1294-1305.

López-Expósito, R. and Recio, I. Protective effect of milk peptides: Antibacterial and antitumor properties. *Adv. Exp. Med. Biol.* 2008, *606*, 271-293.

Lowry, O.H.; Rosebrough, N.J.; Farr, A.L.; Randall, R.J. Protein measurement with the folin phenol reagent. *J. Biol. Chem.* 1951, *193*, 265-275.

Lucena, E.; Álvarez, S.; Menéndez, C.; Riera, F.A.; Álvarez, R. Beta-lactoglobulin removal from whey protein concentrates. Production of milk derivatives as a base for infant formulas. *Sep. Purif. Technol.* 2006, *52*, 310-316.

Lucena, E.; Álvarez, S.; Menéndez, C.; Riera, F.A.; Álvarez, R. α-Lactalbumin precipitation from commercial whey protein concentrates. *Sep. Purif. Technol.* 2007, *52*, 446-453.

Luhovyy, B.L.; Akhavan, T.; Anderson, G.H. Whey proteins in the regulation of body intake and satiety. *J. Am. Coll. Nutr.* 2007, *26*, 704S-712S.

Lyons, T.E.; Miller, M.S.; Serena, T.; Sheehan, P.; Lavery, L.; Kirsner, R.S.; Armstrong, D.G., Reese, A.; Yankee, E.W.; Veves, A. Talactoferrin alfa, a recombinant human lactoferrin promotes healing of diabetic neuropathic ulcers: a phase 1/2 clinical study. *Am. J. Surg. Pathol.* 2007, *193*, 49-54.

Mader, J.S.; Salsman, J.; Conrad, D.M.; Hoskin, D.W. Bovine lactoferricin selectively induces apoptosis in human leukemia and carcinoma cell lines. *Mol. Cancer Ther.* 2005, *4*, 612-624.

Madsen, J.S.; Ahmta, T.; Ottea, J.; Halkierb, T.; Qvista, K.V. Hydrolysis of β-lactoglobulin by four different proteinases monitored by capillary electrophoresis and high performance liquid chromatography. *Int. Dairy J.* 1997, *7*, 399-409.

Madureira, R.A.; Pereira, I.C.; Gómez, P.A.; Pintado, E.M.; Malcata, F.X. Bovine whey proteins-Overview on their main biological properties. *Food Res. Int.* 2007, *40*, 1197-1211.

Madureira, A.R.; Tavares, T.; Gomes, A.M.P.; Pintado, M.E.; Malcata, F.X. Physiological properties of bioactive peptides obtained from whey proteins. *J. Dairy Sci.* 2010, *93*, 437-455.

Maes, W.; van Camp J.; Vermeirssen, V.; Hemeryck, M.; Ketelslegers, J.; Schezerenmeire, J. Influence of the lactokinin Ala-Leu-Pro-Met-His-Ile-Arg (ALMPHIR) on the release of endothelin-1 by endothelial cells. *Regul. Peptides*, 2004, *118*, 105-109.

Malkoski, M.; Dashper, S.G.; O'Brien-Simpson, N.M.; Talbo, G.H.; Macris, M.; Cross, K.J.; Reynolds, E.C. Kappacin, a novel antibacterial peptide from bovine milk. *Antimicrob. Agents Chemotherapy.* 2001, *45*, 2309–2315.

Mamone, G.; Picariello, G.; Caira, S.; Addeo, F.; Ferranti, P. Analysis of food proteins and peptides by mass spectrometry-based techniques. *J. Chromatogr. A,* 2009, *1216*, 7130-7142.

Manso, M.A. and López-Fandiño, R. Angiotensin I converting enzyme-inhibitory activity of bovine, ovine and caprine kappa-casein macropeptides and their Tryptic hydrolysates. *J. Food Protect.* 2003, *66*, 1686-1692.

Manso, M.A. and López-Fandiño, R. k-Casein macropeptides from cheese whey: Physicochemical, biological, nutritional, and technological features for possible uses. *Food Rev. Int.* 2004, *20*, 329–355.

Mao, X.Y.; Ni, J.R.; Sun, L.W.; Hao, P.P.; Fan, L. Value-added utilization of yak milk casein for the production of angiotensin-I-converting enzyme inhibitory peptides. *Food Chem.* 2007, *103*, 1282-1287.

Markus, C.R.; Olivier, B.; Pamhuysen, G.E.; van der Gugten, J.; Alles, M.S.; Tuiten, A. The bovine protein α-lactalbumin increases the plasma ratio of tryptophan to the other large neutral amino acids, and in vulnerable subjects raises brain serotonin activity, reduces cortisol concentration and improves mood under stress. *Am. J. Clin. Nutr.* 2000, *71*, 1536-1544.

Markus, C.R.; Olivier, B.; Haan, E.H. Whey protein rich in α-lactalbumin increases the ratio of plasma tryptophan to the sum of the large neutral amino acids and improves cognitive performance in stress-vulnerable subjects. *Am. J. Clin. Nutr.* 2002, *75*, 1051-1056.

Markus, C.R.; Jonkman, L.M.; Lammers, J.H.; Deutz, N.E.; Messer, M.H.; Rigtering, N. Evening intake of alpha-lactalbumin increases plasma tryptophan availability and improves morning alertness and brain measures of attention. *Am. J. Clin. Nutr.* 2005, *81*, 1026-1033.

Marshall, A.D.; Munro, P.A.; Trägårdh, G. The effect of protein fouling in microfiltration and ultrafiltration on permeate flux, protein retention and selectivity: A literature review. *Desalination,* 1993, *91*, 65-108.

Marshall, S.C. Casein macropeptide from whey—A new product opportunity. *Food Res. Quart.* 1991, *51*, 86–89.

Marshall, K. Therapeutic applications of whey protein. *Alternat. Med. Rev.* 2004, *9*, 136-156.

Martin-Diana, A.B. and Fontecha, M.J.F.J. Isolation and characterisation of caseinomacropeptide from bovine, ovine and caprine cheese whey. *Eur. Food Res. Technol.* 2002, *214*, 282-286.

Martín-Orue, C.; Bouhallab, S.; Garem, A. Nanofiltration of amino acid and peptide solutions: mechanisms of separation. *J. Membrane Sci.* 1998, *142*, 225-233.

Martín-Orue, C.; Henry, G.; Bouhallab, S. Tryptic hydrolysis of k-caseinomacropeptide: Control of the enzymatic reaction in a continuous membrane reactor. *Enzyme Microb. Tech.* 1999, *24*, 173–180.

Masuda, O.; Nakamura, Y.; Takano, T. Antihypertensive peptides are present in aorta after oral administration of sour milk containing these peptides to spontaneously hypertensive rats. *J. Nutr.* 1996, *126*, 3063–3068.

Matar, C.; Valdez, J.C.; Medina, M.; Rachid, M.; Perdigón, G. Immunomodulating effects of milks fermented by *Lactobacillus helveticus* and its non-proteolytic variant. *J. Dairy Res.* 2003, *68*, 601-609.

Matsumoto, S.; Hara, T.; Hori, T.; Mitsuyama, K.; Nagaoka, M.; Tomiyasu, N.; Suzuki, A.; Sata, M. Probiotic *Lactobacillus*-induced improvement in murine chronic inflammatory bowel disease is associated with the down-regulation of proinflammatory cytokines in lamina propria mononuclear cells. *Clin. Exp. Immunol.* 2005, *140*, 417-426.

Maubois, J.L.; Leonil, J.; Trouvé, R.; Boullahab, S. Milk peptides with physiological activities: III Peptides with a cardiovascular effect: antithrombotic and antihypertensive activity. *Lait.* 1991, *71*, 249-255.

McBride, D. Talactoferrin alpha receives fast-track designation for the treatment of non-small cell lung cancer. *ONS Connect,* 2007, *22*,14.

Mcintosh, G.H.; Regester, G.D.; Lelue, R.K.; Royle, P.J.; Smithers G.W. Dairy proteins protect against dimethylhydrazine-induced intestinal cancers in rats. *J. Nutr.* 1995, *125*, 809-816.

Meisel, H. and Schlimme, E. Bioactive peptides derived from milk proteins: Ingredients for functional foods. *Kieler Milchw. Forsch.* 1996, *48*, 343–357.

Meisel, H. Biochemical properties of bioactive peptides derived from milk proteins: Potential nutraceuticals for food and pharmaceutical applications. *Livest. Prod. Sci.* 1997, *50*, 125-138.

Meisel, H. Bioactive peptides from milk proteins: A perspective for consumers and producers. *Aust. J. Dairy Tech.* 2001, *56*, 83-92.

Meisel, H. Multifunctional peptides encrypted in milk proteins. *BioFactors,* 2004a, *21*, 55-61.

Meisel, H.and FitzGerald, R.J. Opioid peptides encrypted in intact milk protein sequences. *Brit. J. Nutr.* 2004b, *84*, 27-31.

Meisel, H. Biochemical properties of peptides encrypted in bovine milk proteins. *Curr. Med. Chem.* 2005, *12*, 1905-1919.

Meisel, H.; Walsh, D.J.; Murray, B.A.; FitzGerald, R.J. *ACE inhibitory peptides.* In Mine, Y. and Shahidi, F. (eds.). *Nutraceutical proteins and peptides in health and disease. Nutraceutical science and technology,* Canada: CRC Press, 2006.

Mellander, O. The physiological importance of the casein phosphopeptide calcium salts II. Peroral calcium dosage of infants. *Acta of the Society of Medicine of Uppsala.* 1950, *55*, 247-255.

Mercier, A.; Gauthier, S.F.; Fliss, I. Immunomodulating effects on whey proteins and their enzymatic digests. *Int. Dairy J.* 2004, *14*, 175-183.

Miguel, M.; Contreras, M.M.; Recio, I.; Aleixandre, A. ACE-Inhibitory and antihypertensive properties of a bovine casein hydrolysate. *Food Chem.* 2009, *112*, 211-214.

Minhalma, M.; Maqueijo, V.; Queiroz, D.P.; de Pinho, M.N. Optimization of "Serpa" cheese whey nanofiltration for effluent minimization and by-products recovery. *J. Environ. Manage.* 2007, *82*, 200-206.

Mota, M.V.T.; Ferreira, I.M.P.L.V.O.; Oliveira, M.B.P.; Rocha, C.; Teixeira, J.A.; Torres, D.; Goncalves, M.P. Trypsin hydrolysis of whey protein concentrates: Characterization using multivariate data analysis. *Food Chem.* 2006, *94*, 278-286.

Mullally, M.M.; Meisel, H.; FitzGerald, R.J. Synthetic peptides corresponding to α-LA and β-LG sequences with angiotensin-I-converting enzyme inhibitory activity. *Biol. Chem. Hoppe Seyler*, 1996, *377*, 259–260.

Mullally, M.M.; Meisel, H.; FitzGerald, R.J. Identification of a novel angiotensin-I-converting enzyme enhibitory peptide corresponding to a tryptic fragment of bovine β-lactoglobulin. *FEBS Lett.* 1997, *402*, 99-101.

Murakami, M., Tonouchi, H.; Takahashi, R.; Kitazawa, H.; Kawai, Y.; Negishi, H.; Saito, T. Structural analysis of a new antihypertensive peptide (β-lactosin B) isolated from a commercial whey product. *J. Dairy Sci.* 2004, *87*, 1967–1974.

Muro, C.; Álvarez, R.; Riera-Rodríguez; F.; Arana, A.; Téllez, A. Production and functionality of active peptides from milk. Review. *Food Sci. Technol. Int.* 2011, *17*, 293-317.

Nagaoka, S.; Futamura, Y.; Miwa, K.; Awano, T.; Yamauchi, K.; Kanamaru, Y.; Tadashi, K.; Kuwata, T. Identification of novel hypocholesterolemic peptides derived from bovine milk β-lactoglobulin. *Biochem. Bioph. Res. Co.* 2001, *218*, 11–17.

Neyestani, T.R.; Jalali, M.; Pezeshki, M. Isolation of α-lactalbumin, β-lactoglobulin and bovine serum albumin from cow´s milk using gel filtration and anion-exchange chromatography including evaluation of their antigenicity. *Protein Expres. Purif.* 2003, *29*, 202-208.

Nielsen, P.M.; Petersen, D.; Dambmann, C. Improved method for determining food protein degree of hydrolysis. *J. Food Sci.* 2001, *66*, 642-646.

Nurminen, M.L.; Sipola, M.; Kaarto, H.; Pihlanto-Leppälä, A.; Piilola, K.; Korpela, R. Tossavainen, O.; Korhonen, H.; Vappatalo, H. α-lactorphin lowers blood pressure via radiotelemetry in normotensive and spontaneously hypertensive rats. *Life Sci.* 2000, *66*, 1535–1543.

Oevermann, A.; Engels, M.; Thomas, U.; Pellegrini, A. The antiviral activity of naturally occurring proteins and their peptide fragments after chemical modification. *Antiviral Res.* 2003, *59*, 23-33.

Ohinata, K.; Inui, A.; Asakawa, A.; Wada, K.; Wada, E.; Yoshikawa, M. Albutensin A and complement C3a decrease food intake in mice. *Peptides*, 2002, *27*, 127–133.

Ohnuki, H. and Otani, H. A humoral immunoregulatory mechanism of bovine milk immunoglobulin G via Fc γ receptors in mice. *Milchwissenschaft,* 2007, *62* , 450-453.

Omata, Y.; Satake, M.; Maeda, R.; Saito, A.; Shimazaki, K.; Yamauchi, K. Reduction of the infectivity of *Toxoplasma gondii* and *Eimeria stiedai sporozoites* by treatment with bovine lactoferricin. *J.Vet. Med. Sci.* 2001, *63*, 187-190.

Orsi, N. The antimicrobial activity of lactoferrin: Current status and perspectives. *BioMetals,* 2004, *17*, 189-196.

Ortiz-Chao, P.; Gómez-Ruíz, J.A.; Rastall, A.; Mills, D.; Cramer, R.; Pihlanto-Leppälä, A.; Korhonen, H.; Jauregi, P. Production of novel ACE inhibitory peptides from β-lactoglobulin using Protease N Amano. *Int. Dairy J.* 2009, *19*, 69-76.

Otte, J.; Shalaby, S.M.; Zakora, M.; Nielsen, S.M. Fractionation and identification of ACE-inhibitory peptides from α-lactalbumin and β-casein produced by thermolysin-catalysed hydrolysis. *Int. Dairy J.* 2007a, *17*, 1460-1472.

Otte, J.; Shalaby, S.M.; Zakora, M.; Prippa, A.H.; Shabrawyb, S.A. Angiotensin-converting enzyme inhibitory activity of milk protein hydrolysates: Effect of substrate, enzyme and time of hydrolysis. *Int. Dairy J.* 2007b, *17*, 488-503.

Pan, D. and Guo, Y. Optimization of sour milk fermentation for the production of ACE-inhibitory peptides and purification of a novel peptide from whey protein hydrolysate. *Int. Dairy J.* 2010, *20*, 472-479.

Pan, D.; Cao, J.; Guo, H.; Zhao, B. Studies on purification and the molecular mechanism of a novel ACE inhibitory peptide from whey protein hydrolysate. *Food Chem.* 2012, *130*, 121-128.

Paolucci-Jeanjean, D.; Belleville, M.P.; Rios, G.M.A comprehensive study of the loss of enzyme activity in a continuous membrane reactor. Application to starch hydrolysis. *J. Chem. Technol. Biotechnol.* 2001, *76*, 273-278.

Park, Y.W. *Bioactive components in milk and dairy products;* Bioactive components in goat milk. Wiley-Blackwell/John Wiley and Sons, Ltd. Publication, 2009, pp.43-81.

Pedroche, J.; Yust, M.M.; Lqari, H.; Megías, C.; Girón-Calle, J.; Alaiz, M.; Vioque, J.; Millán, F. Obtaining of *Brassica carinata* protein hydrolysates enriched in bioactive peptides using immobilized digestive proteases. *Food Res. Int.* 2007, *40*, 931-938.

Pellegrini, A.; Thomas, U.; Bramaz, N.; Hunziker, P.; von Fellenberg, R. Isolation and identification of three bactericidal domains in the bovine α-lactalbumin molecule. *Biochim. Biophys. Acta,* 1999, *1426*, 439–448.

Pellegrini, A.; Dettling, C.; Thomas, U.; Hunziker, P. Isolation and characterisation of four bactericidal domains in the bovine α-lactoglobulin. *Biochim. Biophys. Acta,* 2000, *1526*, 131-140.

Pellegrini, A. Antimicrobial peptides from food proteins. *Curr. Pharm. Des.* 2003, *9*, 1225-1238.

Peña- Ramos, E. and Xiong, Y.L. Whey and soy protein hydrolysates inhibit lipid oxidation in cooked pork patties. *Meat Sci.* 2003, *64*, 259-263.

Peña-Ramos, E.A.; Xiong, Y.L.; Arteaga, G.E. Fractionation and characterisation for antioxidant activity of hydrolysed whey protein. *J. Sci. Food Agric.* 2004, *84*, 1908-1918.

Peng, J.; Tang, C.E.; Zhen, W.D.; Chen, Z. Physicochemical and antioxidant properties of buckwheat (*Fagopyrum esculentum Moench*) protein hydrolysates. *Food Chem.* 2009, *115*, 672-678.

Perea, A. and Ugalde, U. Continuous hydrolysis of whey proteins in a membrane recycle reactor. *Enzyme Microb. Tech.* 1996, *18*, 29–34.

Perpetuo, E.A.; Juliano, L.; Lebrun, I. Biochemical and pharmacological aspects of two bradykinin-potentiating peptides from tryptic hydrolysis of casein. *J. Protein Chem.* 2003, *22*, 601–606.

Petitclerc, D.; Lauzon, K.; Cochu, A.; Ster, C.; Diarra, M.S.; Lacasse, P. Efficacy of a lactoferrin-penicillin combination to treat β-lactam-resistant *Staphylococcus aureus* mastitis. *J. Dairy Sci.* 2007, *90*, 2778–2787.

Phelan, M.; Aherme, S.A.; FitzGerald, R.J.; O'Brien, N.M. Casein-derive bioactive peptides: Biological effects, industrial uses, safety aspects and regulatory status. *Int. Dairy J.* 2009, *19*, 643-654.

Phelan, M.; Aherrne, S.A.; O'Sullivan, D.; FitzGerald, R.J.; O'Brien, N.M. Growth inhibitory effects of casein hydrolysates on human cancer cell lines. *J. Dairy Res.* 2010, *77*, 1-7.

Phillips, S.M.; Tang, J.E.; Moore, D.R. The role of milk and soy based protein in support of muscle protein synthesis and muscle protein accretion in young and elderly persons. *J. Am. Coll. Nutr.* 2009, *28*, 343-354.

Pihlanto- Leppälä, A.; Paakkari, I.; Rinta-Koski, M.; Antila, P. Bioactive peptide derived from *"in vitro"* proteolysis of bovine β-lactoglobulin and its effect on smooth muscle. *J. Dairy Res.* 1997, *64*, 149–155.

Pihlanto-Leppälä, A.; Rokka, T.; Korhonen, H. Angiotensin I-converting enzyme inhibitory peptides derived from bovine milk proteins. *Int. Dairy J.* 1998, *8*, 325–331.

Pihlanto-Leppälä, A.; Koskinen, P.; Piilola, K.; Tupasela, T.; Korhonen, H. Angiotensin I-converting enzyme inhibitory properties of whey protein digests: Concentration and characterization of active peptides. *J. Dairy Res.* 2000, *67*, 53–64.

Pihlanto-Leppälä, A. Bioactive peptides derived from bovine whey proteins: Opioid and ACE-inhibitory peptides. *Trends Food Sci.Tech.* 2001, *11*, 347-356.

Pihlanto-Leppälä, A. Review: Antioxidative peptides derived from milk proteins. *Int. Dairy J.* 2006, *16*, 1306-1314.

Pins, J.J. and Keenan, J.M. Effects of whey peptides on cardiovascular disease risk factors. *J. Clin. Hypertens.* 2006, *8*, 775-782.

Poulin, J.F.; Amiot, J.; Bazinet, L. Simultaneous separation of acid and basic bioactive peptides by electrodialysis with ultrafiltration membrane. *J. Biotechnol.* 2006, *123*, 314-328.

Pouliot, Y.; Wijers, M.C.; Gauthier, S.F.; Nadeau, L. Fractionation of whey protein hydrolysates using charged UF/NF membranes. *J. Membrane Sci.* 1999, *158*, 105-114.

Pouliot, Y.; Gauthier, S.F.; L'Heureux, J. Effect of peptide distribution on the fractionation of whey protein hydrolysates by nanofiltration membranes. *Lait.* 2000, *80*, 113-120.

Prata-Vidal, M.; Bouhallab, S.; Henry, G.; Aimar, P. An experimental study of caseinomacropeptide hydrolysis by tripsin in a continuous membrane reactor. *Biochem. Eng. J.* 2001, *8*, 195-202.

Prieto, C.A.; Guadix, A.; González-Tello, P.; Guadix, E.M. A cyclic batch membrane reactor for the hydrolysis of whey protein. *J. Food Eng.* 2007, *78*, 257-265.

Prieto, C.A.; Guadix, E.M.; Guadix, A. Recent patents on whey protein hydrolysates manufactured by proteolysis coupled to membrane ultrafiltration. *Recent Pat. Chem. Eng.* 2010, *3*, 115-128.

Prioult, G.; Pecquet, S.; Fliss, I. Stimulation of interleukin-10 production by acidic beta-lactoglobulin-derived peptides hydrolyzed with *Lactobacillus paracasei* NCC2461 peptidases. *Clin. Diagn. Lab. Immun.* 2004, *11*, 266-271.

Pripp, A.H.; Isaksson, T.; Stepaniak, L.; Sørhaug, T. Quantitative structure-activity relationship modeling of ACE-inhibitory peptides derived from milk proteins. *Eur. Food Res. Technol.* 2004, *8*, 579-583.

Quirós, A.; Ramos, M.; Muguerza, B.; Delgado, M.A.; Miguel, M.; Aleixandre, M.A.; Recio, I. Identification of novel antihypertensive peptides in milk fermented with *Enterococus faecalis*. *Int. Dairy J.* 2007, *17*, 33-41.

Recio, I. and Visser, S. Two ion-exchange methods for the isolation of antibacterial peptides from lactoferrin-in situ enzymatic hydrolysis on an ion-exchange membrane. *J. Chromatogr.* 1999, *831*, 191–201.

Rezende, M.; Elias-Argote, X.E.; Jiménez-Flores, R. Use of ultrafiltration and supercritical fluid extraction to obtain a whey buttermilk powder enriched in milk fat globule membrane phospoholipids. *Int. Dairy J.* 2010, *20*, 598-602.

Rigo, J.; Boehm, G., Georgi, G.; Jelinek, J.; Nyambugabo, K.; Sawatzki, G. An infant formula free of glycomacropeptide prevents hyperthreonimenia in formula-fed preterm infants. *J. Ped. Gastr. Nutr.* 2001, *32*, 127-130.

Rios, G.M.; Belleville, M.P.; Paolucci, D.; Sánchez, J. Progress in enzymatic membrane reactors – a review. *J. Membrane Sci.* 2004, *242*, 189-196.

Rival, S.G.; Boeriu, C.G.; Wichers, H.J. Caseins and casein hydrolysates. 2. Antioxidative properties and relevance to lipoxygenase inhibition. *J. Agric. Food Chem.* 2001, *4*, 295-302.

Rizzello, C.; Losito, I.; Bobbetti, M.; Carbonara, T.; de Bari, M.; Zamboni, P. Antibacterial activities of peptides from the water-soluble extracts of italian cheese varieties. *J. Dairy Sci.* 2005, *88*, 2348-2360.

Rosaneli, C.F.; Bighetti, A.E.; Antonio, M.A.; Carvalho, J.E.; Sgarbieri, V.C. Efficacy of a whey protein concentrate on the inhibition of stomach ulcerative lesions caused by ethanol ingestion. *J. Med. Food*, 2002, *5*, 221-228.

Ruiz-Giménez, P.; Salom, J. B.; Marcos, J. F.; Vallés, S.; Martínez-Maqueda, D.; Recio, I.; Torregrosa, G.; Alborch, E.; Manzanares, P. Antihypertensive effect of a bovine lactoferrin pepsin hydrolysate: Identification of novel active peptides. *Food Chem.* 2012, *131*, 266-273.

Sadat, L.; Cakir-Kiefer, C.; N'Negue, M.A.; Gaillard, J.L.; Girardet, J.L.; Miclo, L. Isolation and identification of antioxidative peptides from bovine α-lactalbumin. *Int. Dairy J.* 2011, *21*, 214-221.

Saint-Sauveur, D.; Gauthier, S.F.; Boutin, Y.; Montoni, A. Immunomodulating properties of a whey protein isolate, its enzymatic digest and peptide fractions. *Int. Dairy J.* 2008, *18*, 260-270.

Saint-Sauveur, D.; Gauthier, S..; Boutin, Y.; Montoni, A.; Fliss, I. Effect of feeding whey peptide fractions on the immune response in healthy and *Escherichia coli* infected mice. *Int. Dairy J.* 2009, *19*, 537-544.

Saito, T. Antihypertensive peptides derived from bovine casein and whey proteins. Part III. Milk peptides In: *Advances in experimental medicine and biology: Bioactive components of milk*. Bösze, Z., Eds; Springer Science + Business Media: New York, 2008, pp. 295-317.

Saksena, A.; Kumar, M.; Tripathi, B.P.; Shahi, V.K. Organic-inorganic hybrid charged membranes for protein separation: Isoelectric separation of proteins under coupled driving forces. *Sep. Pur. Technol.* 2010, *70*, 280-290.

Samuelsen, Ø.; Haukland, H.H.; Ulvatne, H.; Vorland, L.H. Anti-complement effects of lactoferrin-derived peptides. *FEMS Immunol. Med. Microbiol.* 2004, *41*, 141–148.

Sarker, S.A.; Caswall, T.H.; Mahalanabis, D.; Lam, N.H.; Albert, M.J.; Brüssow, H.; Fuchs, G.J.; Hammarström, L.; Successful treatment of rotavirus diarrhea in children with immunoglobulin from immunized bovine colostrum. *The Ped. Infect. Dis. J.* 1998, *17*, 1149-1154.

Scrutton, H.; Carbonnier, A.; Cowen, P.J. Harmer, C. Effects of α-lactalbumin on emotional processing in healthy women. *J. Psychopharmacology*, 2007, *21*, 519-524.

Seppo, L.; Jauhiainen, T.; Poussa, T.; Korpela, R. A fermented milk high in bioactive peptides has a blood pressure-lowering effect in hypertensive subjects. *Am. J. Clin. Nutr.* 2003, *77*, 326-330.

Setarehnejad, A.; Kanekanian, A.; Tatham, A.; Abedi, A.H. The protective effect of caseinomacropeptide against dental erosion using hydroxyapatite as a model system. *Int. Dairy J.,* 2010, *20*, 652-656.

Sfeir, R.M.; Dubarry, M.; Boyaka, P.N.; Rautureau, M.; Tomé, D. The mode of oral bovine lactoferrin administration influences mucosal and systemic immune responses in mice. *J. Nutr.* 2004, *134*, 403-409.

Shin, K.; Wakabayashi, H.; Teraguchi, S.; Tamura, Y.; Kurokawa, M.; Shiraki, K. Effects of orally administered bovine lactoferrin and lactoperoxidase on influenza virus infection in mice. *J. Med. Microbiol.* 2005, *54*, 717-723.

Sipola, M.; Finckenberg, P.; Santisteban, J.; Korpela, R.; Vapäätalo, H.; Nurminen, M.A. Long-term intake of milk peptides attenuates development of hypertension in spontaneously hypertensive rats. *J. Physiol. Pharmacol.* 2001, *52*, 745-754.

Sipola, M.; Finckenberg, P.; Korpela, R.; Vapäätalo, H.; Nurminen, M.A. Effect of long-term intake of milk products on blood pressure in hypertensive rats. *Dairy Res. J.* 2002, *69*, 103-111.

Smithers, G.W. Whey and whey proteins –From "gutter to gold". *Int. Dairy J.* 2008, *18*, 695-704.

Sousa, R.; Lopes, G.P.; Tardioli, P.W.; Giordano, R.L.C.; Almeida, P.I.F.; Giordano, R.C. Kinetic model for whey protein hydrolysis by alcalase multipoint-immobilized on agarose gel particles. *Braz. J. Chem. Eng.* 2004, *21*, 147-153.

Suárez, E.; Lobo, A.; Álvarez, S.; Riera, F.A.; Alvarez, R. Partial demineralization of whey and milk ultrafiltration permeate by nanofiltration at pilot plant scale. *Desalination*, 2006, *198*, 274-281.

Sugahara, T.; Onda., H.; Shinohara, Y.; Horii, M.; Akiyama, K.; Nakamoto, K.; Hara, K. Immunostimulation effects of proteose-peptone component 3 fragment on human hybridomas and pheripheral blood lymphocytes. *Biochim. Biophys.* 2005, *1725*, 233-240.

Sutton, L.F. and Alston-Mills, B. β-lactoglobulin as a potential modulator of intestinal activity and morphology in neonatal piglets. *Anat. Rec. A Discov. Mol. Cell. Evol. Biol.* 2006, *288*, 601-608.

Tamura, Y. Production and application of bovine lactoferrin. *IDF Bull.* 2004, *389*, 64-68.

Tani, F.; Shiota, A.; Chiba, H.; Yoshikawa, M. *β-Casomorphins and Related Peptides: Recent Developments.* Weinheim, Germany: VCH-Verlag. 1993.

Tauzin, J.; Miclo, L.; Gaillard, J. Angiotensin I-converting enzyme inhibitory peptides from tryptic hydrolysate of bovine casein. *FEBS Lett.* 2002, *531*, 369-374.

Tavares, T.; Contreras, M.M.; Amorim, M.; Pintado, M.; Recio, I.; Malcata, F.X. Novel whey-derived peptides with inhibitory effect against angiotensin-converting enzyme: *"in vitro"* effect and stability to gastrointestinal enzymes. *Peptides,* 2011, *32*, 1013-1019.

Teschemacher, H. Opioid receptor ligands derived from food proteins. *Curr. Pharm. Des.* 2003, *9*, 1331-1334.

Timmer, J.M.K.; Speelmans, M.P.J.; van der Horst, H.C. Separation of aminoacids by nanofiltration and ultrafiltration membranes. *Sep. Pur. Technol.,* 1998, *14*, 133-144.

Tolkach, A. and Kulozik, U. Fractionation of whey proteins and caseinomacropeptide by means of enzymatic crosslinking and membrane separation techniques. *J. Food Eng.* 2005, *67*, 13-20.

Townsend, R.R.; McFadden, C.B.; Ford, V.; Cadeé, J.A. A randomized, doubled-blind, placebo controlled trial of casein protein hydrolysate (C12 peptide) in human essential hypertension. *Am. J. Hypertens.* 2004, *17*, 1056-1058.

Tsai, Y.T.; Cheng, P.C.; Fan, C.K.; Pan, T.M. Anthypertensive effect of bioactive peptides produced by protease-facilitated lactic acid fermentation of milk. *Food Chem.* 2008, *106*, 552-558.

Vanhoute, M.; Firdaous, L.; Bazinet, L.; Froidevaux, R.; Lecouturier, D.; Guillochon, D.; Dhulster, P. Effect of haem on the fractionation of bovine haemoglobin peptic hydrolysate by electrodialysis with ultrafiltration membranes. *J. Membrane Sci.,* 2010, *365*, 16-24.

van der Kraan, M.I.A.; Nazmi, K.; Teeken, A.; Groenink, J.; van't Hoff, W.; Veerman, E..I. Lactoferrampin an antimicrobial peptide of bovine lactoferrin exhibits its candidacidal activity by a cluster of positively charged residues at the C-terminus in combination with a helix facilitating N-terminal part. *J. Biol. Chem.* 2005, *386*, 137–142.

van der Zander, K.; Bots, M.L.; Bak, A.A.A.; Koning, M.M.G.; de Leeuw, P.W. Enzymatically hydrolyzed lactotripeptides do not lower blood pressure in mildly hypertensive subjects. *Am. J. Clin. Nutr.* 2008, *88*, 1697-1702.

van Mierlo, L.A.J.; Koning, M.M.G.; van der Zander, K.; Draijer, R. Lactotripeptides do not lower blood pressure in untreated whites: Results from 2 controlled multicenter crossover studies. *Am. J. Clin. Nutr.* 2009, *89*, 617-623.

Vinderola, G.; de Moreno, A.; Perdigón, G.; Matar, C. *Biologically active peptides released in fermented milk: Role and functions* in E.R.Farnworth (ed.). *Handbook of fermented functional foods.* New York: CRC Press. 2003.

Vorland, L.H.; Ulvatne, H.; Rekdal, O.; Svendsen, J.S. Initial binding sites of antimicrobial peptides in *Staphylococcus aureus* and *Escherichia coli*. *Scand. J. Infect. Dis.* 1999, *31*, 467–473.

Wakabayashi, H.; Takase, M.; Tomita, M. Lactoferricin derived from milk protein lactoferrin. *Curr. Pharm. Design.* 2003, *9*, 1277–1287.

Wakabayashi, H.; Yamauchi, K.; Takase, M. Lactoferrin research, technology and applications. *Int. Dairy Res.* 2006, *16*, 1241-1251.

Walsh, D.J., Bernard, H.; Murray, B.A.; MacDonald, J.; Pentzien, A.K.; Wright, G.A.; Wal, J.M.; Struthers, A.D.; Meisel, H.; FitzGerald, R. J. *"in vitro"* generation and stability of the lactokinins beta-lactoglobulin fragment (142-148). *J. Dairy Sci.* 2004, *87*, 3845-3857.

Wang, B.; Yu, B.; Karim, M.; Hu, H.; Sun, Y.; McGreevy, P.; Petocz, P.; Held, S.; Brand Miller, J. Dietary sialic acid supplementation improves learning and memory in piglets. *Am. J. Clin. Nutr.* 2007a, *85*, 561-569.

Wang, Ch. K.; Cadée, J.; Chang, Ch.; Chien, Ch.; Huang, Ch.; Chen, S. Bovine casein hydrolysate (C12 peptide) reduces blood pressure in prehypertensive subjects. *Am. J. Hypertens.* 2007b, *20*, 1-5.

Wu, J. and Ding, X. Characterization of inhibition and stability of soy-protein-derived angiotensin I-converting enzyme inhibitory peptides. *Food Res. Int.* 2002, *35*, 367-375.

Xiaoa, R.; Cartera, J.A.; Lnza, A.; Fergusona, M.; Badgera, T.M.; Simmena, F.A. Dietary whey protein lowers serum C-peptide concentration and duodenal SREBP-1c mRNA abundance, and reduces occurrence of duodenal tumors and colon aberrant crypt foci in azoxymethane-treated male rats. *J. Nutr. Biochem.* 2006, *17*, 626-634.

Xu, J.Y.; Qin, L.Q.; Wang, P.Y.; Li, W.; Chang, C. Effect of milk tri-peptides on blood pressure: A meta-analysis of randomized controlled trials. *Nutrition*, 2008, *24*, 933-940.

Yamaguchi, N.; Kawaguchi, K.; Yamamoto, N. Study of the mechanism of antihypertensive peptide VPP and IPP in spontaneously hypertensive rats by DNA microarray analysis. *Eur. J. Pharmacol.* 2009, *620*, 71-77.

Yamamoto, N.; Ejiri, M.; Mizuno, S. Biogenic peptides and their potential use. *Curr. Pharm. Design.* 2003, *9*, 1345-1355.

Yamauchi, K. Biologically functional proteins of milk and peptides derived from milk proteins. *IDF Bull.* 1992, *272*, 51–58.

Yamauchi, K.; Wakabayashi, H.; Shin, K.; Takase, M. Bovine lactoferrin: Benefits and mechanism of action against infections. *Biochem. Cell Biol.* 2006, *84*, 291-296.

Yamauchi, R.; Usui, H.; Yunden, J.; Takenaka, Y.; Tani, F.; Yoshikawa, M. Characterization of β-lactotensin a bioactive peptide derived from bovine β- lactoglobulin as a neurotensin agonist. *Biosci. Biotechnol. Biochem.* 2003, *67*, 940–943.

Yoo, Y.C.; Watanabe, S.; Watanabe, R.; Hata, K.; Shimazaki, K.; Azuma, I. Bovine lactoferrin and lactoferricin inhibit tumor metastasis in mice. *Adv. Exp. Med. Biol.* 1998, *443*, 285-291.

Yvon, M.; Beucher, S.; Guilloteau, P.; le Huerou-Luron, I.; Corring, T. Effects of caseinomacropeptide (CMP) on digestion regulation. *Reprod. Nutr. Dev.* 1994, *34*, 527–537.

Zhang, G.; Li, W.; Holle, L.; Chen, N.; Chen, W.Y. A novel design of targeted endocrine and cytokine therapy for breast cancer. *Clin. Cancer Res.* 2002, *8*, 1196-1205.

Zhang, R.Z.; Xu, X.H.; Chen, T.B.; Rao, P.F. An assay for angiotensin converting enzyme using capillary zone electrophoresis. *Anal. Biochem.* 2000, *280*, 286-290.

Zimecki, M.; Artym, J.; Chodaczek, G.; Kocieba, M.; Kruzel, M. Effects of lactoferrin on the immune response modified by the immobilization stress. *Pharm. Reports*, 2005, *57*, 811-817.

Zimecki, M. and Kruzel, M.L. Milk-derived proteins and peptides of potential therapeutic and nutritive value. *J. Exp. Ther. Oncology*, 2007, *6*, 89-106.

Zydney, A.L. Protein separations using membrane filtration: New opportunities for whey fractionation. *Int. Dairy J.*, 1998, *8*, 243-250.

In: Whey: Types, Composition and Health Implications   ISBN: 978-1-61942-862-1
Editors: Rafael M. Benitez and Gustavo M. Ortero   © 2012 Nova Science Publishers, Inc.

Chapter 2

WHEY- ATTRACTIVE SUBSTRATE FOR MICROBIAL PRODUCTION OF SUBSTANCES AND MATERIALS FOR MEDICAL APPLICATIONS

Stanislav Obruca[1], Ivana Marova[1,2] and Milan Certik[3]

[1]Centre for Materials ResearchFaculty of Chemistry,
Brno University of Technology, Brno, Czech Republic
[2]Department of Food Chemistry and Biotechnology, Faculty of Chemistry,
Brno University of Technology, Brno, Czech Republic
[3]Faculty of Biochemical Technology, Slovak Technical
University , Bratislava, Slovak Republic

ABSTRACT

Whey is an important surplus product of the food industry. Based on the point of view, huge quantities of whey produced worldwide can represent an environmental problem with its disposal, or, due to the fact that whey is rich in fermentable nutrients, it can be considered as an attractive substrate for microbial production of various industrially interesting products. Therefore, this chapter is intended to summarize possible up-stream processing methods, general principles and fermentation strategies for the microbial productions using whey as a substrate. Further, among huge amount of potential products, this review focuses on the production of high value substances and materials which find applications especially in the fields of health care, medicine and pharmacy. At first, many biologically active substances such as vitamins, carotenoids, antibiotics etc. can be produced from whey employing various microorganisms (bacteria, yeasts as well as fungi) and cultivation strategies. Moreover, also number of biopolymers which can be used in form of drug carriers, scaffolds, sutures, adhesives *etc.* can be produced by using whey as a cheap complex substrate. Apart from poly (lactic acid), these materials include bacterial polyesters- polyhydroxyalkanoates and also several polysaccharides such as xanthan, alginate, hyaluronic acid, gellan, pullulan, dextran or chitosan. In addition, the aim of this review is also to provide basic economical consideration of fermentation processes. In conclusion,utilization of whey as a substrate for microbial productions of high value products could result in a very promising process meeting both economic and ecological requirements.

1. INTRODUCTION

Cheese whey is a by-product of dairy industry; particularly, it represents the watery portion which is formed during coagulation of major cheese proteins – casein – in cheese manufacturing or caseins production (Guimaraes et al., 2010). Because cheese whey constitutesapproximately80-90% (v/v) of the total milk used and, moreover, whey retains about 55% of total milk nutrients, huge amounts of liquid waste with high organic compounds content (BOD_5 = 30 000–50 000 ppm, COD = 60 000–80 000 ppm) are formed. Apart from lactose, which is predominantly responsible for high BOD_5 and COD values, cheese whey also contains soluble proteins, lipids and mineral salts. Although several possibilities of cheese whey utilization have been explored, a major portion of the world cheese whey production is discarded as an effluent. Its disposal as a waste is serious pollution problem for the surrounding environment since it affects the physical and chemical structure of soil which results in decreased potential of crop yields. In addition, release of whey into the water bodies harms aquatic life due to depleting the dissolved oxygen (Siso, 1996; Panesar et al., 2007). Therefore, to overcome problems associated with whey disposal in both economic and ecological meanings, it would be very reasonable to use cheap whey as a substrate for production of high value product(s). Availability of the utilizable lactose in whey as well as the presence of other essential nutrients supporting the growth of various microorganisms make the whey potential excellent raw material for biotechnological productions of high value commodities.Additionally,the process would significantly decrease BOD_5 and COD values of entering waste and, thus, minimize the impact of the whey on the environment. This chapter is intended to provide an overviewof the potential processes enabling transformation of waste whey into the high value materials and substances which find applications especially in the fields of pharmaceutical industry and medicine.

2. WHEY TYPES AND THEIR COMPOSITION

Whey contains most of the water-soluble components (lactose, whey proteins, milk salts, *etc.*) of milk transformed and, of course, water. The precise whey composition is dependent on the method of cheese or caseins manufacturing and it also varies during the season of milk production. Generally, whey is often classified as "*sweet*" if derived from precipitation of caseins by rennet, or as "*acid*", when caseincoagulation was carried out by acidification of milk either by partial fermentation of lactose to lactic acid or by the addition of mineral acids (HCl, H_2SO_4, *etc.*)(Mawson, 1993).In general, whey produced from rennet-coagulated cheeses is low in acidity (pH about 6.5), while the production of acid cheeses (such as ricotta or cottage cheese) or caseins yields acid whey with pH lower than 5. Cheese-whey salts are comprised of NaCl and KCI (more than 50% of total salts), calcium salts (primarily phosphate) and others. Cheese whey also contains appreciable quantities of other com-ponents, such as lactic (0.05% w/v) and citric acids, non-protein nitrogen compounds (urea and uric acid), some of vitamins belonging to B group, free amino acid *etc.* (Siso, 1996).Table 1 summarizes typical composition of sweet and acid whey.

Whey proteins represent about 20% of the milk proteins. The most abundant of whey proteins are β-lactoglobulin (50%), α-lactoalbumin (12%), immunoglobulins (10%), serum albumin (5%) and proteose peptones (0.23%). The Protein Efficiency Ratio value and essential amino acid content of whey proteins are higher than those of caseins. Moreover; their biological value exceeds even that of whole egg proteins (Kilara et al., 2005).

The main differences between the two types of whey are in the mineral content, pH and composition of whey protein fraction. The acid coagulation approach results in the decrease of pH to the value about 4.5, which is necessary for casein precipitation. At this low pH, calcium presented in casein micelles is partially solubilized and released into the solution. This causes higher calcium content of acid whey.

Table 1. Typical composition of sweet and acid whey (Jelen, 2003)

Component	Sweet whey [g/l]	Acid whey [g/l]
Total solids	63-70	63-70
Lactose	46-52	44-46
Protein	6-10	6-8
Calcium	0.4-0.6	1.2-1.6
Phosphate	1.3	2.4.2005
Lactate	2	6.4
Chloride	1.1	1.1

On the other side, precipitation of casein *via* action of rennet results in releasing of specific fragment of κ-kasein molecule. This fragment is termed glycomacropeptide (GMP) and due to its solubility it ends up in the whey. GMP is important protein of sweet whey, because it constitutes approximately 20% of its protein content, however, it is not present in acid whey (Panesar et al., 2007).

3. CHEESE WHEY AS A FERMENTATION MEDIUM

Dairy industry all over the world generates huge amount of whey per litter of milk processed. About 50% of total world cheese-whey production is treated and transformed into various food products (of which 45% is used directly in liquid form, 30% in the form of powdered cheese whey 15% as lactose and byproducts from its removal, and the rest as cheese-whey-protein concentrates) the remaining 50% is disposed as a waste (Marwaha and Kennedy, 1988). This potentially danger waste can be used for production of various bio-technological products *via* microbial fermentation. Generally, the processes based on microbial cultures on cheese whey are considered as the most profitable alternatives for the transformation of cheese whey surplus (Siso, 1996). However, there are many potential facts and risks that should be taken into account prior utilization of cheese whey as a fermentation medium.

Whey is foremost a dilute solution and many difficulties encountered in whey handling stem from this fact. First of all, it complicates the transportation of whey and, secondly, cheese whey tends to spoil by action of naturally occurring microorganisms which signi-ficantly devaluates it potential application as a fermentation medium. Therefore, it is worthy decreasing concentration of water resulting in preparation of cheese whey concentrate. During the procedure of pre-concentration, the cheese whey is, at least, partially sterilized. Moreover, due to high osmotic pressure, this form of cheese whey is much more microbially stable and, in addition, because of the decrease of the whey weight it also simplifies the process of whey transportation.

Since most of biotechnological productions employ microbial monoculture, it is necessary to overcome any possible contaminations of fermentation medium by undesired microorganisms. Hence, the medium must be sterilized prior cultivation. Sterilization of whole cheese whey is problematic, because heating of whey to as high temperature as 121°C results in precipitation of whey proteins (Parris et al., 1993). The protein precipitate seriously complicates the fermentation as well as recovery of the biomass or the down-stream processing of the fermentations products. Therefore, it is usually needed to remove the excessive proteins prior sterilization. This can be done by decreasing pH by mineral acids and boiling (Obruca et al., 2011). On the other side, the whey proteins dispose with high nutritive value which would be reduced by any improper treatment. It is reasonable to remove proteins by more gentle method which allows their subsequent application in human diet or in animal feeding. The most commonly used methods nowadays are ultrafiltration and diafiltration because of their advantages of cost reduction, high processes speed, the absence of denaturation or protein structure modification and the fact that protein concentrate is free of salts, thereby making it suitable for all kinds of human foods (Evans and Gordon, 1980). The process of protein removal ends up with two products. The first is called whey protein concentrate and it contains almost exclusively protein fracture of whole whey. The second products, termed whey permeate, contains lactose and all the other soluble substances. Protein recovery can be highly profitable and reduces effluent load of the whey about 10 000 ppm of COD. However; the whey permeate still contains about 50 000- 60 000 ppm of COD, mostly represented by lactose (Mawson, 1993).

Another option how to overcome the precipitation of cheese whey proteins during sterilization is their hydrolysis*in situ* by proteolytic enzymes or microbes (Vasala et al., 2005). Whey protein hydrolysis yields peptide mixture with increased solubility and altered foaming characteristics. In addition, the peptides can be utilized by microbes during fermentation as carbon, nitrogen and essential amino acids source and, thus, they could represent very important factor supporting the growth of microorganisms and the fermentation process (Margot et al., 1994; Senthuran et al., 1997).

Some microbial strains suitable for production of various substances do not dispose with β-galactosidase activity, in other words, these microbes are not capable of utilizing lactose directly. On the other side, they can utilize glucose and/or galactose and, hence, they can be used for fermentation using whey with pre-hydrolyzed lactose. The lactose can be cleaved by acids or by simple application of β-galactosidase into the cheese whey prior or after sterilization (Kohler et al., 2008; Marangoni et al., 2001) or by using immobilized enzyme or whole cell system (Kosseva et al., 2009).The question is whether the process of biotechnological production remains profitable even after inclusion of relatively expensive process of whey lactose hydrolysis.

Whole whey or whey permeate are usually not sufficient medium for optimal microbial growth and production of desired metabolites. Hence, whey medium is supplemented with various substances serving as additional nitrogen source and by specific growth factors required by particular microorganism. Generally, yeast extract and yeast autolysate are used as complex nitrogen sources (Amrane, 2005; Obruca et al. 2011, Marova et al., 2011) or nitrogen can be also added in the form of mineral salts such as $(NH_4)_2SO_4$, NH_4NO_3, NH_4Cl *etc.* (Aksu and Eren, 2005; Nath et al., 2008; Obruca et al., 2011) depending on preferences of the particular microbe. Introduction of inorganic phosphate was also found to be beneficial for some biotechnological productions using whey as a substrate (Amrane, 2000; Liu et al., 2003; Nikel et al., 2005). Besides mentioned supplements, addition of other nutrients (molasses, corn steep molasses), vitamins, minerals, amino acids and inorganic supplements to whey or whey permeate were also investigated (Amrane, 2000; Liu et al., 2003; Nikel at al. 2005; Khanafari and Sepahei, 2007; Obruca et al. 2011). Of course, it is crucial to take into account demands of the microbes to be employed. The supplementation strategies of whey based medium for particular microorganisms will be mentioned in the following parts of this chapter.

4. FERMENTATION STRATEGIES

Generally, there are few fermentation strategies which can be applied for microbial utilization of whey or any other substrate and production of various commodities. This part of the book chapter is intended to briefly describe individual strategies with respect to particular details stemming from the utilization of cheese whey as a culture medium.

Batch Cultivation

At first, probably the simplest and the most often applied fermentation strategy is a batch cultivation, which is characterized by the growth of microorganisms without supply of additional substrate after inoculation (Figure 1A). While the substrate is metabolized, biomass and products are formed during cultivation. Thebatch is stopped and harvested when the desired product concentration is maximal. Thereafter, the reactor is cleaned and sterilized for the next batch. When the process is carried out in the bio-reactor (also termed fermenter), during batch cultivation several components other than substrate might be added. In aerobic cultivation air or O_2 is continuously added through a sparger. To maintain constant pH, alkalior acid components are added to the broth. Antifoam agents are required for foam control and other agents might be added to the broth to induce the production of a desired metabolite (Ullmann; 2005).

Batch cultivation reveals typical stages of microbial growth and metabolites production. First phase is called "*lag-phase*" and it is characterized by adaptation of microorganisms to conditions within bioreactor. During lag-phase neither growth nor production occurs and, therefore, there is an attempt to maintain this phase as short as possible. Whenever using cheese whey as fermentation medium, there is a risk that antibiotics and other undesired substances stemming from milk will inhibit growth of microorganisms and prolong the lag phase or even stop the fermentation (McEwen et al., 1992). Thereby, the composition of the whey should be precisely analyzed in order to prevent these obstacles. Furthermore, due to the high lactose and salt content, whey possesses relatively high osmotic pressure which could have inhibiting effect on microbes as well. Taking into account abilities of microbes to face high osmotic pressure and also economic demands of process, whey medium can be diluted or desalted.

When microorganisms fully adapt to environment, they start to growth very intensively, usually the biomass concentration increases exponentially. This stage of cultivation is termed "*growth phase*". Besides biomass, also primary metabolites (these which production is growth associated such as ethanol, lactic acid *etc.*) are produced (Ullmann; 2005).

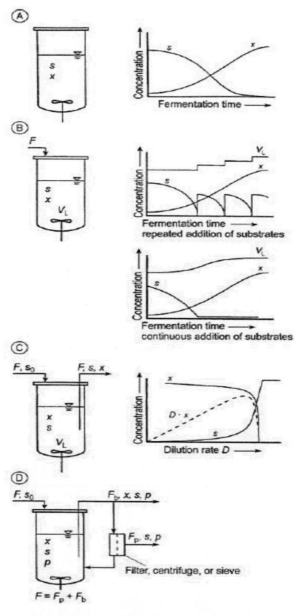

Figure 1.Standard fermentation stretegies. A) Batch cultivation; B) Fed-Batch; C) Continuous cultivation; D) Continuous cultivation with cell recycle.V_L = Working volume; F = flow of fresh substrate; Fp = Permeate flow, cells free; F_b = Bleed flow with cells; s = substrate concentration; x = biomass concentration, p = product concentration; s_0 = concentration of substrate in the flow. Ullmann (2005).Reproduced with permission.

Finally, when either the substrates of the medium are depleted or accumulation of metabolism products possessing inhibiting effect on microbial culture reaches certain level, the growth of microorganism is stopped and so called "*stationary phase*" is about to begin. During stationary phase no biomass growth occurs, however, production of secondary metabolites starts. Because number of desired products such as carotenoids, polyhydro-xyalkanoates *etc.* are traditionally considered as secondary metabolites, it is crucial to precisely optimize the time, when concentration of desired products reaches its maximum. Any unnecessary prolongation of fermentation process could result in the decrease of yields and in the increase of production cost (Oka, 1999).

Fed-Batch Cultivation

To overcome the growth limitations due to the initial substrate concentration, substrates can be added to the broth during cultivation. This mode of operation is termed as fed-batch cultivation. Substrates can be either supplied stepwise during the cultivation or continuously (see Figure1B). Fed-batch technique is the state of the art for the efficient production employing bacteria, fungi as well as yeasts. Modern biotechnology processes with genetically engineered microorganisms often use fed-batch techniques to reach high cell densities before adding the inducing agent to start the production of the desired product. Nevertheless, fed-batch mode of fermentation is also commonly used for cultivation of non-genetically engineered strains (Ullmann, 2005).

To overcome significant volume increases during fermentation, the feeding solution usually contains high concentration of carbon substrate. There are many reports on utilization of whey concentrate for fed-batch feeding (Ahn et al., 2000; Ahn et al., 2001;Viitanen et al., 2003).To counter this, the lactose concentration is increased by pre-concentration of the whey for instance by the addition of concentrated lactose or by using reverse osmosis or other technique (Mawson, 1993). However, it should be kept in mind that apart from lactose also salts are concentrated. This can easily result in a significant increase of osmotic pressure within the bioreactor inhibiting both the cell growth and production of the metabolites of interest. Therefore, whey should be at least partially desalted prior pre-concentration.

In comparison with batch cultivation, fed-batch process can provide improved productivity as a whole because of the enhanced yields and reduced fermentation time. On the other side, production of metabolites which enhance viscosity (such as extracellular poly-saccharides) of media results in significantly decreased oxygen availability in fermentation media. This could be serious complication especially in high density cell cultivations obtained in fed-batch mode. Therefore, batch-cultivation is not the mode of choice for all the fermentation productions (Oka, 1999).

Continuous Fermentation

In continuous fermentation, a complete medium is fed toa fermentor after an appropriate period of batch fermentation, and the same quantity of broth is continuously taken from the fermentor to maintain the fermentation broth at a fixed volume (Figure 1C and D). This may be performed either by the "chemostat" method using a substrate or limiting substance at certain concentration level, or by the "turbidostat" method in which the cell level is adjusted to maintain constant cell mass. Because the continuous fermentation process allows improvement of productivity compared with the ordinary fermentation, the initial investment in equipment is small relative to the production volume, and operation cost is low. However, the first drawback is that it is not suitable for small-scale production. Secondly, the challenges of sterile operation and equipment maintenance are more necessary than they are for batch and fed-batch fermentation. Finally, it is rather difficult to set conditions of continuous fermentation for production of metabolites which are not growth-associated (Oka, 1999). The utilization of whey as a medium in continuous fermentation systems has been recently reported for ethanol (Agustriyanto and Fatwanti, 2009), bio-hydrogen (Azbar et al., 2009; Davila-Vazquez et al., 2009) or methane (Venetsaneas et al., 2009) productions.

An alternative mode of fermentation which can be in principal also considered as a variety of continuous cultivation is application of immobilized cells system. The immobilized cells are defined as "the microbial cells physically confined or localized in a certain defined region of space with retention of their catalytic activities, and which can be used repeatedly and/or continuously". The medium flow through the reactor with immobilized cells and is converted into desired product(s). Immobilization technology has several advantages, because it permits higher cell densities in bioreactors, improves stability, makesre-utilization and continuous operation possible, and precludes the need to separate the cells from the substrate products following processing (Kosseva et al., 2009). Of course, immobilized cells systems are suitable for production of extracellular products. There is great number of the published articles dealing with production of ethanol and lactic acids by cells immobilized systems of various microorganisms using cheese whey medium (Goksungur et al., 2005;Schepers et al., 2006; Panesar et al., 2007;Mirdamadi et al., 2008; Staniszewski et al., 2009;Kosseva et al., 2009, Guo et al., 2010). In addition, also some antibiotics such as nisin and pediocin PA-1 were produced from cheese whey using immobilized cells of *Lactococcus lactis* and *Pediococcus acidilactici* UL5, respectively (Liu et al., 2005; Naghmouchi et al., 2008).

5. PRODUCTION OF SELECTED BIO-SUBSTANCES

Vitamins

According to a recent World Health Organisation (WHO) review, vitamin B_{12}(Figure 2) and folate (also called vitamin B_9) (Figure 3) deficiencies may be a public health problems affecting millions of people (WHO, 2008). Anemia and increased risk of birth defects in newborn are some of the health consequences of low folate and vitamins B_{12} status. The low level of folate may also cause higher risk of cardiovascular diseases, dementia and Alzheimer´s disease (Gisondi et al.2007), moreover, there is some evidence for an increased cancer risk (Mitchell et al., 2004). Vitamins B_{12} deficiency additionally leads to neurological damage and has been linked with psychiatric disorders (Truswell, 2007).

Folate can be produced by plants and microorganisms, whereas vitamin B_{12} is only synthetized by some bacteria and archae. Moreover, folates can be also produced by chemical synthesis by reacting malondialdehyde derivatives with aminobenzoyl-L-glutamic acid and triaminopyrimidinone derivatives, however, a number of studies have reported possible adverse effects caused by high intake of synthetic form of folic acid (Osterhues et al., 2009). Both vitamins can be produced *via* fermentation using either lactic acid bacteria or propionic acid bacteria for production of folate. Vitamin B_{12} can be biotechnologically produced by propionic bacteria and some pseudomonas(Hugenschmidt et al., 2010).

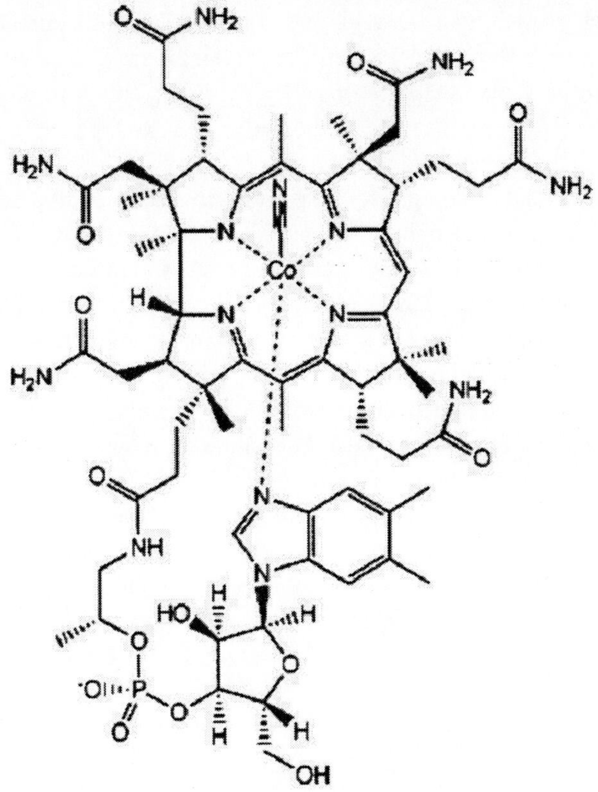

Figure2. Stucture of Vitamin B_{12}(Jin et al., 2009) Reproduced with permission.

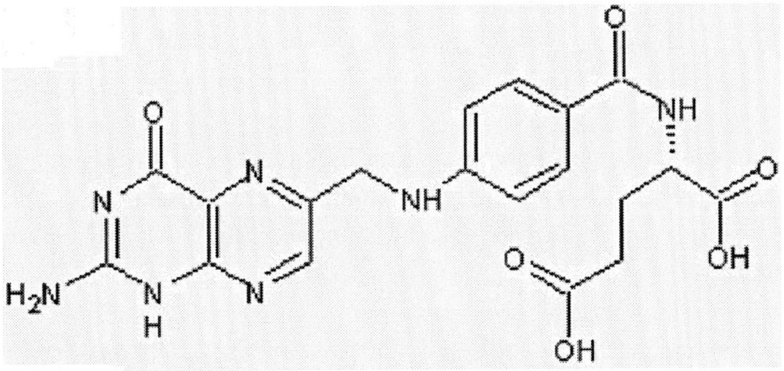

Figure 3.Structure of folic acid (Mote at al., 2011).Reproduced with permission.

There have been several reports on biosynthesis of both folate and vitamin B_{12} by bacteria fermentation using whey as a substrate. Study was carried out in Erlenmeyer flasks and focused on optimization of cultivation conditions. Vitamin yields were significantly increased by medium supplementation with 1.5% of yeast extract and 5 ppm of cobalt was adequate to give good levels of vitamin B_{12}. The vitamin B_{12} precursor 5,6-dimethyl-benzimidazole was found to be adequate at 10 ppm in the absence of aeration, while in the presence of aeration, a zero level of precursor was found to be most desirable. The vitamin formation was observed during the latter part of the fermentation after the organism approached maximal growth.Staniszewski and Kujawski (2007) screened capabilities of selected propionic bacteria to produce vitamin B_{12} in single culture as well as the possibility of strain co-operation in a mixed culture on whey medium. The most significant changes in the content of vitamin B_{12} were observed in the early phase of logarithmic growth up to 72 h of incubation, in all cultures examined.

Propionibacteria produce vitamin B_{12} intracellularly when cultivated anaerobically and simultaneously excrete mainly propionic acid and acetic acid extracellularly. The primary problem for vitamin B_{12} production using propionic bacteria is that the end products such as propionic acid *etc.* inhibit cell growth. It is, therefore, crucial to remove the end products *in situ* and, thus, improve the cell growth which results in the significantly improved vitamin yields (Hatanaka et al., 1998).Under conditions of aerobic growth the synthesis of propionic acid is suppressed; however, oxygen presence inhibits vitamin B_{12} production as well. The propionic acid level can be kept at low level by using cell recycle system. Nevertheless, the major drawback of employing the cell recycle system is that part of the culture medium is drawn off through hollow fiber membrane without efficient use. This problem has hindered the practical application of the cell recycle system. Interesting solution was suggested by Miyano et al. (2000). The propionic acid bacterium *Propionibacterium freudenreichii* was cultivated in mixed culture with *Cupriavidus necator* to keep propionic acid at low level noting that propionic acid produced by propionic bacteria can be assimilated by the second microorganism.

Hugenschmidt et al. (2010) screened intracellular production of vitamin B_{12} and extracellular production of folate by 151 lactic acid bacteria and 100 propionic acid bacteria of different origin using supplemented whey permeate as a substrate. Five lactic bacteria strains belonging to the species *Lactobacillus plantarum*, *Lactobacillus reuteri*, *Lactobacillus brevis* and *Lactobacillus fermentum* exhibited high extracellular folate productions, with a maximum yield of 397 ± 60 ng mL^{-1} for *L. plantarum* SM39. The highest vitamin B_{12} production was measured for *Propionibacterium freudenreichii*DF15with 2.5 mg mL^{-1}.

Vitamin B_{12} and folate can be produced in one fermentation employing co-culture of *Lactobacillus plantarum* SM39 and *Propionibacterium freudenreichii* DF13 on whey permeate supplemented with yeast extract. The cultivations were carried out in two-step mode (3 days anaerobic followed by 4 days aerobic) which led to high vitamin B_{12} and folate yield, 751 and 8399 ng mL^{-1}, respectively (Hugenschmidt et al., 2011).

Riboflavin is another vitamin which can be prepared by fermentation. Buzzini and Rossi (1997) reported riboflavin production by yeasts using various agro-industrial residues including whey as substrates. The highest yields (1.135 mg L^{-1} in 10 days) were reached using *Torulopsis candida* 4253 in fed-batch mode. Cheese whey can be also used for production of riboflavin employing *Ashbya gossypii*. The production can be increased by addition of sugar alcohol and vitamins into the fermentation media (Ozbas and Kutsal, 1991).

Carotenoids

Carotenoids are naturally occurring lipid-soluble pigments, the majority being C40 terpenoids. They act asmembrane-protective antioxidants that efficiently scavenge$^1O_2$ and peroxyl- radicals. Their antioxidative efficiency is apparently related to their structure. The most significant part in the molecule is the conjugated double bond system that determines their color and biological action. Carotenoid pigments occur universally in photosynthetic systems of higher plants, algae and phototrophic bacteria. In non-photosynthetic organisms,carotenoids are important in protecting againstphotooxidative damage. Thus, many non-phototrophicbacteria, yeasts and fungi rely on carotenoids for protection when growing in light and air (Marova et. al., 2010).

Commercially, carotenoids are used as precursors of vitamin A, in nutrient supplementation, for pharmaceutical purposes, in various cosmetic products, as food colorants and in animal feeds. There is an increased interest in carotenoids as natural antioxidants and free radical scavengers because of their ability to reduce and alleviate chronic diseases, various pathological stages and aging. Furthermore, epidemiological evidence and experimental results suggest that dietary carotenoids inhibit the onset of many diseases in which free radicals are thought to play arole in initiation, such as arteriosclerosis, cataracts, multiple sclerosis and cancer (Hughes, 1999).

Due to their wide application in pharmacy, the demand and market for carotenoids is constantly growing. However, the application of chemical synthetic methods to prepare carotenoid compounds as food additives has been strictly regulated in recent years. Therefore, attention is paid to the finding of suitable natural methods for its production. One possibility lies in biotechnological techniques employing the potential of microorganisms that are able to convert various substrates into carotenoid pigments, even if this approach is restricted by a number of useful species and also the carotenoid yield can hardly compete with the chemical synthesis or with plant material extraction (Lee and Schmidt-Dannert, 2002; Marova et al., 2010).

Since an important aspect of the fermentation process is the development of a suitable culture medium to obtain the maximum amount of desired product, cheap raw materials and by-products of agro-industrial origin have been proposed as a low-cost alternative carbohydrate sources for microbial carotenoids production. This is beneficial strategy also from the point of view of minimizing environmental and energetic problems related to residues and effluent disposal. During the product recovery process, the biomass is isolated from the fermentation broth and transformed into a form suitable for carotenoids isolation. Recovery involves extraction of carotenoids from biomass by appropriate solvent, their concentration and purification. Generally, cell disruption prior extraction is recommended to increase efficiency of recovery process (Marova et al., 2011).

There are many reports on utilization of cheese whey for carotenoids production. At first, Frengova et al. (2004) studied carotenoids production by lactose-negative strain yeast *Rhodotorula rubra* GED5 in co-culture with lactose-positive yeast strain *Kluyveromyces lactis* MP11 in whey permeate supplemented with $(NH_4)_2SO_4$, $MgSO_4$, KH_2PO_4, $MnSO_4$ and yeast extract. Maximum yields of cell mass (24.3 gL^{-1})and carotenoids (10.2 mgL^{-1} of culture fluid or 0.421 µgg^{-1} of dry cells) were obtained by growing the microbial association in whey permeate containing lactose at concentration of 50 g L^{-1} ina fermentor with an airflow rate of 0.8 LL^{-1}min^{-1}, agitation of 220 rpm, and temperature of 30°C. The identified carotenoid pigments were β-carotene,torulene, and torularhodin. In another paper the same group reported successful production of carotenoids from whey permeate (supplemented as described above) by co-cultivation of *Rhodotorula rubra* GED5 and yoghurt starter cultures *Lactobacillus bulgaricus* 2–11 and *Streptococcus thermophilus* 15HA. In associated cultivation under intensive aeration (1.3 Lmin^{-1} airflow rate), initial pH 5.5, 30° C,the lactose-negative strain *R. rubra* GED8 synthesized large amounts of carotenoids (13.09 mg L^{-1} of culture fluid). The carotenoid yield was approximately two-fold higher in association with a mixed yoghurt culture than in association with single yoghurt bacteria. The majorcarotenoid pigments comprising the total carotenoidswere β-carotene (50%), torulene (12.3%) and torularhodin(35.2%)(Simova et al., 2004; Frengova et al., 2006).

Aksu and Eren (2005) focused on carotenoids production employing different yeast strain - *Rhodotorula mucilaginosa*. This yeast is lactose positive, hence, no co-culture is needed to be added. Optimum pH and temperature for total carotenoids production were determined as 7.0 and 30°C, respectively. Total carotenoidsconcentration and pigment production yield were significantly increased with increasing aeration rate up to 2.4 vvm. An initial ammoniumsulphate concentration of 2 g L^{-1}gave the maximum carotenoids production. Further, cotton seed oil significantly activated carotenoids accumulation in the yeast cells. Among carbon sources tested, the highest product yield (35.0 mg total carotenoids per gram of dry cells) was achieved when 13.2 g L^{-1}lactose containing whey was the carbon source in the broth. One year later, the same authors published very similar study with another member of *Rhodotorula* yeast genus – *Rhodotorula glutinis*. Also this yeast possesses sufficient β-galactosidase activity and is, therefore, capable of utilizing lactose directly. The optimal pH was determined as 6 and temperature was optimized at 30°C. Again, ammonium sulfate and cotton seed oil addition significantly supported carotenoids biosynthesis. Cultivation of *R. glutinis* in whey containing 13.2 g L^{-1} of lactose yielded 56.8 mg L^{-1} of carotenoids (Aksu and Eren, 2006).

Valduga et al. (2009) tested acid and enzymatic hydrolysis of whey lactose and application of hydrolysate for subsequent bio-production of carotenoids by *Sporidiobolus salmonicolor* CBS 2636. The carotenoids were recovered using liquid N_2 combined with dimethyl sulfoxide for cell rupture and an acetone/methanol mixture (7 : 3 v/v) for extraction. The maximum concentration of total carotenoids obtained was 0.59 mg L^{-1}in pre-hydrolyzed cheese whey supplemented with 4 g L^{-1} of K_2HPO_4 at180 rpm, 25° C and pH4.The use of enzyme-hydrolyzed cheese whey was more effective in carotenoid bio-production by *S. salmonicolor* CBS 2636 than use of acid-hydrolyzed cheese whey. Hydrolyzed cheese whey was also used as carbon substrate for carotenoids production by *Blakeslea trispora*. The aim of the study was to optimize introduction of non-ionic surfactants and β-ionone as activators of carotenoids accumulation. Maximum production was obtained when whey medium was supplemented with Tween 80 (33.6 g L^{-1}), Span 80 (68.7 g L^{-1}) and β-ionone (2.6 g L^{-1}) (Varzakakou et al., 2010; Varzakakou and Roukas, 2010).

Nasrabadi abd Razavi (2011) employed random mutagenesis in order to isolate efficient β-carotene producing strain of *Rhodotorula acheniorum*. The lactose-positive mutant strain named MRN was tested on its ability to produce carotenoids on whey. Conditions for carotenoids production were optimized as follow: lactose concentration 55 g L^{-1}, pH 5.85, $(NH_4)_2SO_4$3.5 g L^{-1}, temperature 23°C and aeration 1.56 vvm. Under these conditions, the strain produced 262.1 mg L^{-1} of β-carotene.

Due to the fact that stress response of red yeasts is usually associated with carotenoids overproduction, very efficient strategy to enhance carotenoids accumulation in various red-yeast strains is an introduction of exogenous stress factors such as ethanol, hydrogen peroxide or high osmotic pressure into the fermentation media (Marova et al., 2010).

Table 2. Summary of carotenoids productions from whey media reported inliterature

Microorganism	Fermantation strategy	Substrate	Biomass [g L^{-1}]	Yields[*] [mg L^{-1}]	Reference
Rhodotorula rubra GED5	Batch, co-culture with *Kluyveromyces lactis*	Whey permeate, $(NH_4)_2SO_4$, KH_2PO_4, $MgSO_4$, yeast extract	24.3	10.2	Frengova et al. (2004)
Rhodotorula rubra GED5	Batch, Co-culture with *Lactobacillus bulgaricus* 2–11 and *Streptococcus thermophilus* 15HA	Whey permeate, $(NH_4)_2SO_4$, KH_2PO_4, $MgSO_4$, yeast extract	26.0	13.1	Simonova et al. (2004); Frengova et al. (2006)
Rhodotorula mucilaginosa	Batch culture	Whey, yeast extract, malt extract, $(NH_4)_2SO_4$, KH_2PO_4, $MgSO_4$	1.8	63.0	Aksu and Eren (2005)
Rhodotorula glutinis	Batch culture	Whey, yeast extract, malt extract, $(NH_4)_2SO_4$, KH_2PO_4, $MgSO_4$	1.6	56.8	Aksu and Eren (2006)
Sporidiobolus salminicolor CBS 2636	Batch culture	Hydrolyzed cheese whey, KH_2PO_4	[2]*n.a.*	0.6	Valduga et al. (2008)
Blakeslea trispora	Batch culture, surfactants and b-ionone	Hydrolyzed cheese whey	*n.a.*	*n.a.*	Varzakakou et al., (2010); Varzakakou and Roukas (2010)
Rhodotorula achenior MRN	Batch culture	Whey permeate, $(NH_4)_2SO_4$	24.5	262.1	Nasrabadi and Razavi (2011)
Rhodotorula glutinis CCY 20-2-26	Bath culture, fermentor, salt stress	Deproteinized whey	44.7	45.7	Marova et al. 2011
Rhodotorula mucilaginosa CCY 20-7-31	Batch culture, fermentor	Deproteinized whey	29.8	11.3	Marova et al. 2011
Sporobolomyces roseus CCY 19-4-8	Batch culture, fermentor	Deproteinized whey	10.2	29.4	Marova et al. 2011

Note: [1] Total yields of carotenoids expressed as mg L^{-1}, [2]*n.a.* stands for: data not available.

Therefore, several red yeast strains (*Sporobolomyces roseus*, *Rhodotorula glutinis*, *Rhodotorula mucilaginosa*) were enrolled into a comparative screening study. To increase the yields of these pigments, several types of exogenous as well as nutrition stress were tested. As inexpensive substrates, whey and potato extract were tested. Stress conditions induced by peroxide and salt stresses were applied too. The production of carotene enriched biomass was carried out in flasks as well as in laboratory bio-reactor. The highest yields were obtained in whey medium using *Rhodotorula glutinis* CCY 20-2-26 (45 g L^{-1} of biomass and 46 mg L^{-1} of β-carotene) in laboratory fermentor (Marova et al., 2011).

The table 2 provides summary of fermentation strategies and yields of carotenoids from cheese whey-based substrates. According to the number of studies aimed at biotechnological production of carotenoids using cheese whey, it seems that whey represents very attractive substrate. This intensive research demonstrates the enormous potential in its application and creates new economic competitiveness and market of microbial carotenoids.

Antibiotics

Antibiotics are wide family of diverse compounds enabling efficient inactivation of various microorganisms, mostly bacteria but also yeasts and fungi. It is the reason why antibiotics find many applications especially in medicine, but also in food industry or agriculture. Many of these compounds are naturally produced by some bacteria and fungi. Therefore, there have been a lot of attempts to improve the antibiotic production by fermentation in terms of process yields and economics and also in these cases, cheese whey and cheese whey permeate were considered as attractive substrates for fermentation.

Probably the most deeply studied antibiotic is penicillin which is commercially produced by fungal strain *Penicillium chrysogenum*, a filamentous microorganism consisting of multi-compartment structure of morphologically heterogenous hyphae (Mou and Cooney, 1983; Paul et al., 1998). *Penicillium chrysogenum* is able to utilize lactose directly, thus, Paul et al. (1998) studied its growth and penicillin production in fed-batch mode using cheese whey with glucose as substrates. Furthermore, cheese whey can be used as an additional co-substrate and moisturizer when penicillin is produced in solid state fermentation mode by*Penicillium* sp. (Hamzan et al., 2009).

Bacteriocins are bacterial peptides that inhibit or kill microorganisms that are usually, but not exclusively, closely related to producer strain. Among producing strains, especially lactic bacteria and members of *Bacillus* genus are in the middle of the attention, since both bacterial groups include a wide variety of industrially important species and have history of safe use in both food and industry (Paik et al., 1997). Although bacteriocin production is often performed in complex media which promote abundant growth and relatively high bacteriocin levels it seems more economical to use some of the wastes of food industry as the raw material for the basis of culture media (Lee et al., 2003). Hence, Cladera-Olivera at al. (2004) produced bacteriocin employing *Bacillus licheniformis* P40 in cheese whey. The medium composition and cultivation conditions were optimized using response surface methodology. Data showed maximum bacteriocin production at initial pH between 6.5 – 7.5 and temperature in range 26-37°C when the cheese whey concentration was 70 g L^{-1}. Sharma and Gautam (2008) isolated, from cheese whey, strain of *Bacillus mycoides* able to excrete bacteriocin which showed strong inhibition activity against food borne serious pathogen *Listeria monocytogenes* and *Leuconostoc mesenteroides*. The bacteriocin withstood temperature up to 100°C and was active at wide pH range.*Enterococcus faecalis* A-48-32 is also capable of production of bacteriocin using cheese whey as a substrate. Medium composition was optimized and various factors, such as whey concentration, glucose, pH and inoculum size were adjusted. The critical factors for maximal production were stabilization of pH at 6.55 and addition of 1% glucose (Ananou et al., 2008). Another very promising peptide antibiotic is mutacin that is naturally produced by common oral bacterium *Streptomyces mutans*. Mutacin disposes with antimicrobial mode action towards a wide range of pathogenic Gram-positive bacteria due to inhibition of their cell wall synthesis. Since lactose was observed to be optimal carbon source for mutacin production (Dahal et al., 2010), it is possible to produce this antibiotic in cheese whey as well. Pediocin PA-1 is peptide antibiotic produced by *Pediococcus acidilactici*. Naghmouchi et al. (2008) aimed at its production by cells immobilized in κ-carrageenan/locust bean gum gel beads. The production was studied during repeated-cycle batch (RCB) culture with pH control in Man Rogosa and Sharpe broth supplemented with either 1% glucose or sweet whey permeate medium. The maximum pediocin PA-1 activity obtained during RCB fermentation was 4096 AU mL^{-1}; it was attained after only 2 h of cultivation in sweet whey medium. Pediocin PA-1 production in the repeated-cycle batch culture was highly stable over 12 fermentation cycles.

Finally, nisin is peptide antibiotic produced by *Lactoococcus lactis*. Nisin´s antimicrobial activity against Gram-positive bacteria is due to pore formation in the membrane, which cases leakage of cytoplasmic contents. Continuous production of nisin in laboratory media and whey permeate was investigated by Liu et al. (2005) using a packed-bed bioreactor. Optimal conditions for continuous nisin production in whey permeate were pH 5.5, 31°C, 10-20 g L^{-1} casein hydrolysate, and 0.2h^{-1} dilution rate. Under these conditions, a maximum nisin titre of 5.1×10^4 AU mL^{-1} was observed. The bioreactor was operated continuously for 6 months without encountering any clogging, degeneration, or contamination problems.De Aurazs et al. (2008)also produced nisin in whey medium. The results showed that *L. lactis* preferred not-filtrated whey where nisin yields reached 11120 AU L^{-1}. In another study concerning nisin production from cheese whey, medium composition was optimized using statistical approach. Optimized conditions were used for constant pH fermentations, where a maximum activity of 575 AUmL^{-1} was achieved at pH 6.5 after 12 h (Gonzalez-Toledo et al., 2010).

Lactic Acid

Lactic acid is considered as one of the most useful chemicals, it is used in the food industry as a preservative, acidulant and flavouring, in the textile and pharmaceutical industries, and in the chemical industry. Moreover, lactic acid consumption has increased considerably because of its role as a monomer in the production of biodegradable polymer – poly (lactic acid) (PLA), which is well-known as a sustainable bioplasticmaterial with many applications in medicine (Datta et al., 1995; Wee et al., 2006).

Of the80 000 tonnes of lactic acid produced worldwide every year, about 90% is made by lactic acid bacteria fermentation and the rest is produced synthetically by the hydrolysis of lactonitrile(Hofvendahl and Hahn-Hagerdal, 2000). Microbial fermentationhas a significant advantage in that by choosing a bacteria strain only one enantiomer, an optically pure product can be obtained, whereas synthetic production results in a racemic mixture of DL-lactic acid. As the physical properties of PLA strongly depend on theenantiomeric composition of lactic acid, the production of optically pure lactic acid is essential. For example, optically pure L-lactic acid is polymerized to a high crystal polymer suitable for fiber and oriented film production and is expected to be useful in production of liquid crystal as well(Hofvendahl and Hahn-Hagerdal, 2000; Panesar et al., 2007).

Lactic acid offers natural ingredients for cosmetic applications. Although primarily used as moisturizers andpH regulators, it possesses multiple other properties such as antimicrobial activity, skin lightening, and skin hydration. The moisturizing effect is related directly to lactate's water retaining capacity, and the skin-lightening action of lactic acid is produced by the suppression of the formation of tyrosinase.Lactic acid is also used in the pharmaceutical industry as an electrolyte in many intravenous solutions that are intended to replenish the bodily fluids or electrolytes. In addition, lactic acidis used in a wide variety of mineral preparations, which include tablets, prostheses, surgical sutures, and controlled drug delivery systems. Finally, as the fully biodegradable and biocompatible material, PLA finds wide range of potential applications in medicine in the form of scaffolds, implants, sutures, bone fixation, fibers, or micro-particles for targeted drug delivery. The polymer is derived from monomers that are natural metabolites of the body, thus, degradation of the material yields the corresponding hydroxyl- acids, making it safe for *in vivo* use. Because the naturally occurring lactic acid is in L-form, polymer consisting of L-lacticacid is considered being more biocompatible (Nampoothiri et al., 2010).

Lactic acid is excreted as a final product of anaerobic metabolism by number of microorganisms. Probably the most important group of these microbes is termed as lactic acid bacteria. Lactic acid bacteria are recognized as "generally regarded as safe" bacteria. This status underlines their increasing use in traditional foods and in an expanding range of novel foods and products designed to have specific nutritional or other health-enhancing benefits (nutriceuticals, prebiotics,probiotics, *etc.*).The key property in defining lactic acid bacteria is that these bacteria produce lactic acid as the major or sole fermentation product. A typical lactic acid bacterium can be described as Gram positive,non-spore forming, catalase-negative, devoid of cytochromes,of non-aerobic habit but aero-tolerant, fastidiously acid tolerant, and strictly fermentative, with lactic acid as the major end products during sugar fermentation (Panesar et al., 2007).

Batch, fed-batch, repeated batch, and continuous fermentations are the most frequently used methods for lactic acid production (Wee et al., 2006). Moreover, employment of cell immobilized techniques attracts attention of many researchers. Various matrixes such as agar, polyacrylamide, alginate, κ-Carrageenan or glass beads were used for cell entrapment (Panesar et al., 2007; Kosseva et al., 2009). The fermentative production of lactic acid is associated with serious complication – lactic acid reveals significant inhibitory effect on microbes to be employed. The inhibitory have been alleviated to a certain extent by conducting fermentation in a continuous dialysis process, in a hollow fiber fermenter or inan electro dialysis system (Panesar et al., 2007).

In order to make the biotechnological production of lactic acid economically feasible, cheap raw materials are necessary, because polymer producers and other industrial users usually require large quantities of lactic acid at a relatively low cost. Raw materials for lactic acid productions should have the following characteristics: cheap, low levels of contaminants, rapid production rate, high yield, little or no by-product formation, ability to be fermented with little or no pre-treatment and year-round availability. When refined materials are used for production, the costs of product purification should be significantly reduced.

Table 3. Productions of lactic acid from cheese whey

Microorganism	Fermentation	Lactic acid[1] [g L^{-1}]	Qv[2] [g L^{-1} h^{-1}]	Reference
Streptococcus thermophilus	Immobilized cell system (k-Carrageenan)	18.0	5.9	Audet et al., 1988
Streptococcus thermophilus	Immobilized cell system (k-Carrageenan)	19.0	6.0	Audet et al., 1989
Lactobacillus rhamnosus ATCC 7469	Batch culture	30.0	1.9	Mulligan and Gibbs, 1991
Lactococcus lactis sp. *cremoris* 2487	Batch culture	37.0	4.6	Mulligan and Gibbs, 1991
Lactobacillus casei	Immobilized cell system (agar), continuous cultivation	22.0	7.3	Mostafa, 1996
Lactobacillus casei	Immobilized cell system (agar), continuous cultivation, cell recycle	28.0	9.4	Mostafa, 1996
Lactobacillus casei and *Lactococcus lactis* co-culture	Immobilized cell system (Ca-alginate beads), continuous cultivation	20.0	2.0	Roukas and Kotzekidou, 1996
Lactobacillus casei and *Lactococcus lactis* co-culture	Immobilized cells system (Ca-alginate), fed-batch cultivation	46.0	1.9	Roukas and Kotzekidou, 1998
Lactobacillus helveticus R211	Batch culture, pH control	66.0	1.4	Schepers et al., 2002
Lactobacillus casei NRRL B-441	Batch culture	46.0	4.0	Buyukkilci and Harsa, 2004
Lactococcus lactis spp. *lactis* ATCC 11454	Batch culture. Nisin-coproduction	19.3	*n.a.*	Liu et al., 2004
Lactobacillus casei	Immobilized cell system (pectate), Batch culture	33.0	0.7	Panesar et al., 2007
Kluyveromyces marxianus IFO 288, *Lactobacillus delbrueckii* ssp. *bulgaricus* ATCC 11842 and *Lactobacillus helveticus* ATCC 15009 co-culture	Batch culture	19.8	0.5	Plessas et al., 2008
Entercoccus flavescens	Batch culture, pH control	12.6	0.4	Agarwal et al., 2008
Lactobacillus bulgaricus	Batch culture	20.8	0.3	Ghasemi et al., 2009
Lactococcus lactis TISTR 1401 and *Lactobacillus casei* TISTR 1341 co-culture	Immobilize cell system (Na-alginate), repeated batch cultivation	29.9	0.7	Choojun and Suttisuwan, 2010
Lactobacillus sp. LMI8	Batch culture	52.4	1.7	de Lima et al., 2010
Lactobacillus plantarum	Batch culture	120.0	2.4	Brinques et al., 2010
Lactobacillus casei	Batch culture, no-pH control	33.7	0.9	Panesar et al., 2010
Lactobacillus delbrueckii NCIM2025 and *Lactobacillus pentosus* NCIM 2912 co-culture	Immobilized cell system (pine needles),	44.9	*n.a.*	Ghosh and Ghosh, 2011

Notes: [1] concentration [g L^{-1}] of lactic acid produced by the process; [2]productivity of the process.

However, it is still economically unfavorable because the refined carbohydrates are so expensive that they eventually result in higher production costs (Wee et al., 2006). Among the cheap raw materials, cheese whey is probably the most widely used for lactic acid production. Therefore, a lot of recent works deals with bioconversion of whey into the lactic acid.

Different lactobacilli cultures (*L. helveticus*, *L. delbrueckii*subsp. *bulgaricus*, *L. acidophilus*, *L. casei*, etc.)have been used for the utilization of whey for lactic acid production. Generally, *L. heleveticus* is the generally preferred microorganism, as it produces almost twice the amount of lactic acid from milk, compared to other common lactic acid bacteria. In addition, *L. heleveticus* is homolactic fermentative and produces a racemic mixture (DL) as compared to only dextrorotatory lactic acid (D) produced by *L. delbrueckii*. Moreover, it also provides an alternative solution to the phase contamination in dairy industries, which is generally encountered during *L. delbrueckii* subsp. *bulgaricus* fermentation. Employment of *S. thermophilus* has some drawbacks, because only a few strains of this bacterium are capable of fermentation of galactose, and it requires some growth factors for lactic acid production in milk-based medium (Roy et al., 1986). In recent studies other organisms such as *L. delbrueckii* and *Bifidobacterium longum* have also shown considerable promise (Satyanarayana and Venkateshwar, 2004; Li et al. 2006).

The table 3 sums up recent studies on whey transformation into lactic acid employing various bacteria strains as well as fermentation strategies. Generally, it can be stated that higher lactic acid concentrations may be obtained in batch and fed-batch cultures than in continuous cultures, whereas higher productivity may be achieved by the use of continuous cultures.

6. PRODUCTION F SELECTED BIO-MATERIALS

Polysaccharide Based Materials

Xanthan Gum

Xanthan gum is a natural polysaccharide and an important industrial biopolymer. It was discovered in 1963 at Northern Regional Research Center (now called The National Center for Agricultural Utilization Research) of the United States Department of Agriculture (USDA). Xanthan gum, produced by the bacterium *Xanthomonas campestris* was extensively studied because of its properties that would allow it to supplement other known natural and synthetic water-soluble gums. Substantial commercial production began in early 1964 (Palaniraj and Jayaraman, 2011).

The primary structure of xanthan gum shown in Figure 3 is a linear (1→4) linked β-D-glucose backbone (as in cellulose) with a trisaccharide side chain on every other glucose at C-3, containing a glucuronic acid residue linked (1→4) to a terminal mannose unit and (1→2) to a second mannose that connects to the backbone. Approximately 50% of the terminal mannose residues are pyruvated and the non-terminal residue usually carries an acetyl group at C-6 (Becker et al., 1998; Palaniraj and Jayaraman, 2011).

Besides many applications in food manufacturing and various industry fields, xanthan is used also in medicine, pharmacy and cosmetics. It serves as a stabilizer of a variety of insoluble drugs and materials such as barium sulfate (X-ray diagnoses), complexed dextromethorphan (for cough preparations) or thiabendazol. Further, xanthan can be also employed for preparation of hydrogels for sustained release of encapsulated drugs (Coviello et al., 2007).

As was mentioned above, xanthan is produced extracellularly by *Xantomonas campesteris*. Because this bacterium possesses very low level of β-galactosidase activity, there have been a lot of efforts to construct strains that are able to utilize lactose directly and produce xanthan using inexpensive medium. Schwartz and Bodie (1985) isolated lactose-utilizing strain after serial sub-culturing the wild-type strain in lactose medium, although the strain was unstable.Thorne et al.(1988),Fu and Tseng (1990)and Papoutsopoulou et al. (1994) exploited insertion of *Escherichia coli*β-galactosidase gene into the *Xantomonas campesteris* and studied its xanthan production abilities in whey-based medium. The xanthan yields were comparable with those obtained in glucose medium.

Slightly different strategy was used by Ekateriniadou et al. (1994) who transferred phospho-β-galactosidase, maturation protein and proteinase P genes from *Lactobacillus lactis* into *X. campesteris*. The transgenic strain was stable and capable of xanthan production on whey. This constructed strain was used for production of xanthan gum in batch reactor using whey medium. Very high xanthan yields (17.3 g L^{-1}) were observed when pH was maintained at 8.0 (Liakopoulou-Kyriakides et al., 1997).

To overcome application of genetically modified strain Yang et al. (2002) focused on induced mutagenesis using nitrous acid as a mutagen and consequently selected mutant strains based on their ability to utilize lactose. Mutants encoded as *Xantomonas campestris* Xc17L possessed 3.5-fold higher β-galactosidase activity than wild strain and, in addition, the ability of β-galactosidase expression was stable for at least 100 generations. The amounts of xanthan produced in whey medium were comparable with those obtained in glucose-based medium (about 2.0 g L^{-1}).

Finally, Mesomo et al. (2009) as well as Silva et al. (2009) employed *Xanthomonas campestris*p.*magiferaeidicae* for xanthan production on whey. This strain featured sufficient β-galactosidase activity to utilize lactose as the only carbon substrate. The whey-based medium composition and cultivation conditions were optimized in terms of maximal production by addition of 1 g L^{-1} magnesium sulphate, 20 g L^{-1} potassium phosphate, 28° C temperature; initial pH was set at 7.2 and agitation at 390 rpm with 1.5 vvm aeration. These condition yielded 36 g L^{-1} of xanthan at the 72nd hour of cultivation (Mesomo et al., 2009). Silva et al. (2009) tested supplementation of whey medium with sucrose, however, it resulted in lowered xanthan yields as compared to cheese whey as a sole carbon source. The strain produced the highest yields of xanthan (25 g L^{-1}) on whey with 0.1% $MgSO_4$ $7H_2O$ and 2.0% K_2HPO_4.

Dextran

Dextrans can be defined as glucose homopolysaccharides that feature a substantial number of consecutive α-(1→6) linkages in their major chains, usually more than 50% of the total linkages. These α-D-glucans possess also side chains stemming from α-(1→2), α-(1→3), or α-(1→4) branch linkages(Coviello et al., 2007).

Dextrans, mostly in partially hydrolyzed form, find a great number of applications in the fields of medicine and pharmacy. This biopolymer has significant commercial values in blood plasma substitute formulations. Anemia associated with chronic kidney disease is being treated with parenteral iron-dextran complex formulations such as DexFerrum® (Sawale and Lele, 2010).Furthermore, it is also very promising material for drug delivery systems. Dextran and its derivatives are among the main promising candidates for the preparation of networks capable of giving a sustained release of proteins (Coviello et al., 2007).

Dextran for human applications is usually produced by *Leuconostoc mesenteroides*. The bacterium growing in sucrose rich media releases enzyme, dextransucrase, which converts excess of sucrose into dextran and fructose.Schwartz and Bodie (1984) developed fermentation system with sucrose-supplemented whey medium for dextran production employing *Leuconostoc mesenteroides* ATCC 14935. The optimal whey-based medium consisted of4% Teklac, 10% sucrose, 0.1% K_2HPO_4, and 0.05% yeast extract. Also Santos et al. (2005) reported dextran production by *Leuconostoc mesenteroides* in cheap medium consisting of carob extract and cheese whey. The process yielded 7.23 g $L^{-1}$of dextran with mean molecular weight of 326kDa (Santos et al., 2005).

Pullulan

Pullulan is a linear homopolysaccharide of glucose that is often described as α-(1→6) linked maltotriose (Figure 4), synthesized primarily by strains of the yeast-like micro-organism*Aureobasidium pullulans*. The unique linkage pattern of pullulan endows the polymer with distinctive physical traits, including adhesive properties and the capacity to form fibers, compression moldings, and strong, oxygen-impermeable films. Unlike bacterial dextrans, which are synthesized extracellularly by secreted enzymes, pullulan is synthesized intracellularly and secreted by *A. pullulans* into fermentation broth. Culture conditions and strain selection are important in obtaining high molecular weight pullulan that is relatively free of melanin (black stain co-produced in*A. pullulans*)(Leathers, 2003).

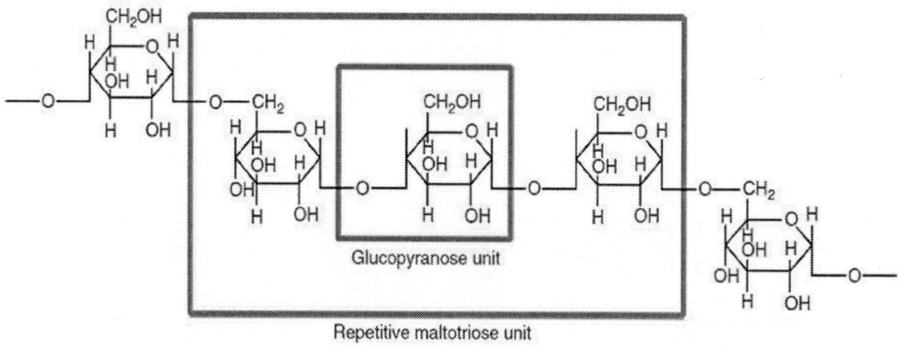

Figure 4.Chemical structure of pullulan.Lin et al. (1999).Reproduced with permission.

Pullulan is now extensively studied forvarious applications in biomedical field. This is mainly due to its non-toxic, non-immunogenic and biodegradable properties. In comparison with a similar but more popular polysaccharide, dextran, the degradation rate of pullulan in serum is faster than that ofdextran (Rekha and Sharma, 2007). Due to its adhesive properties, pullulan and its derivatives can be used in wound-healing compositions. Further, pullulan can be used in pharmaceutical coatings, including sustained-release formulations. For instance, Akiyoshi et al. (1998)developed insulin delivery system of the size in range of 20-30 nm by complexing the hydrogelnanoparticle of cholesterol bearing pullulan.These nanoparticles were stableand protected insulin from the enzymaticdegradation and, moreover, they suppressed insulin aggregation. It was proved *in vivo* that thebiological activity of the entrapped insulin remained intact. Furthermore, several oral care products (such as Listerine®) based on pullulan films have recently been commercialized (Leathers, 2003; Coviello et al., 2007).

In order to reduce cost of fermentation medium, Hafez et al.(2007) studied bioconversion of various industrial by-products into pullulan. When whole sweet whey containing 5% of lactose was used, *A. pullulan* produced 5.5 g L^{-1} of pullulan. The yields were more than doubled by using hydrolyzed sweet whey supplemented with 0.05% glutamic acid and 0.298 KH_2PO_4 as a fermentation medium. After that, pullulan yields reached 12.4 g L^{-1}.

Roukas (1999) studied bio-production of pullulan from deproteinized whey. Different fermentation strategies were used, however, neither adaptation technique nor mixed culture system of *A. pullulans* and/or *Lactobacillus brevis* X20, *Debaryomyces hansenii* 194 and *Aspergillus niger* increased production of desired polysaccharide.The maximal yields were achieved when lactose was enzymatically hydrolyzed and medium was supplemented with 0.5% KH_2PO_4, 1% L-glutamic acid, 2.5% olive oil and0.5% Tween 80. In this medium, pullulan yield was 11.0 g L^{-1} and sugar utilization reached 93.2%.

Alginate

Alginates form an important family of biopolymers of both technological and scientific interest. These polymers are linear polysaccharides, which are composed of variable amounts of (1–4)-β-D-mannuronic acid and itsepimer, α-L-guluronic acid. Alginates present a wide of applications, acting for example as stabilizing, thickening, gel or film-forming agents in various industrial fields. Currently, commercial alginates are extracted from marine brown algae and are used for a wide variety of applications, mainly in the food and pharmaceutical industries. Alginates extracted from algae are relatively cheap products, having selling prices in the range of 5–20$kg^{-1} for the majority of the application, however, alginates of very high purity are used in the pharmaceutical field and these are sold for up to 40 000 $ kg^{-1}. The algal alginates have several problems concerning their production which may limit their use in many interesting contexts, especially in the pharmacy where polymers with a very well defined composition are required (Rehm and Valla, 1997;Galindo et al., 2007).

Aside from algae, alginates are also produced by bacteria and many of their physico chemical characteristics are similar to those ofalgae, so that they can be used for the same applications as algal alginates, as well as in other more sophisticated contexts. Alginates produced by microorganisms differ from those of algae because bacterial polymers are acetylated. In addition, bacterial alginates usually have a higher molecular mass than the algal polymers (ranging from 48 to 186 kDa). A molecular mass as high as 4 000kDa for the polymer synthesized by a mutant strain of *A. vinelandii* has been reported. Both acetylation and molecular mass directly affect the viscosity and other rheological properties of alginate solutions and, therefore, this would determine its utility in specific applications of alginate in the food and pharmaceutical fields(Galindo et al., 2007).

Khanafari and Sepahei (2007) reported production of alginate employing *Azotobacter chroooccum*. The genus *Azotobacter* seems to be the best candidate for the fermentative production of alginate molecules characterized by a chemical composition, molecular mass and molecular mass distribution suited to well-defined applications, especially required in the biotechnological, biomedical and pharmaceutical fields. Of the three strains tested for whey degradation ability, only *Azotobacter chroococcum* 1723 produced significant apparent growth on the whey broth. After optimizing environmental factors such as pH, salt concentration and temperature, this strain was able to produce exopolysaccharidegreater than 5 gL^{-1}. Optimum results were obtained when using whey broth as a fermentation medium without extra salt, temperature at 35 °C and pH 7. Increasing inorganic and organic nitrogen sources (yeast extract and NH_4NO_3) reduced whey utilization and alginate production at least 30%.

Chitosan

Chitosan, a linear hydrophilic polysaccharide of β–(1→4) glucosamine (Figure 5), is obtained by thermo-chemical deacetylation of chitin, which is found in the exoskeleton of crab, shrimp, lobster, crawfish and insects. Chitosan can also be isolated from the cell wall of certain groups of fungi, particularly zygomycetes. Chitosan isolated from fungi is of more uniform physicochemical properties than obtained by deacetylation of crustacean chitin. Recent research is therefore focused on the production of chitosan by fermentation of fungus. Another advantage of fungal chitosan is that the production as well as physico-chemical properties *e.g.* molecular weight of this chitosan can be manipulated by changing the parameters of the fermentation (Chatterjee et al., 2005; Chaterjee et al., 2008).

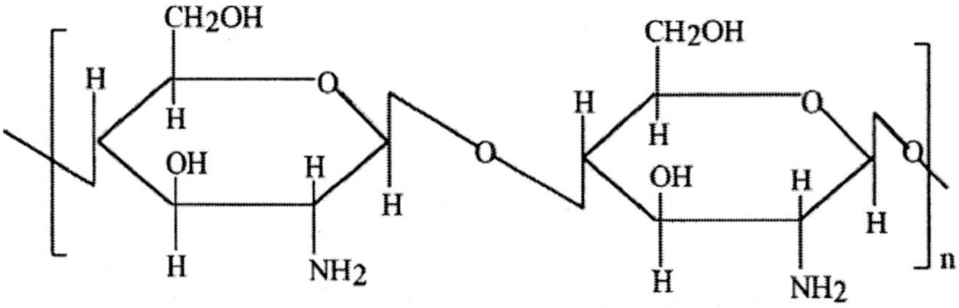

Figure 5.Structure of chitosan, Kumar (2000).Reproduced with permission.

A wide variety of applications for chitosan and its derivatives have been reported over the last three decades. For instance, it has been suggested that chitosan may be used to inhibit fibroplasia in wound healing and to promote tissue growth and differentiation in tissue culture. Fibers made of chitosan are useful as absorbable sutures and wound-dressing materials. Chitosan may be also applied as an artificial skin for persons who suffered extensive losses of skin (Kumar, 2000).

Chatterjee et al. (2007) induced chitosan production by introduction of plant growth hormones such as gibberellic acid, indole-3-acetic acid, indole-3-butyric acid into cultivations of *Rhizopus oryzae* in deproteinized whey. Hormones, at different concentrations, increased the mycelial growth by 19–32%. However, the increase of chitosan content of the mycelia was relatively small (1.7–14.3%) over the control. Maximum enhancement was observed with gibberellic acid that at concentration of 0.1 mg L^{-1} enhanced chitosan production about fifty percent. Nevertheless, hormones, at higher doses, instead of stimulation inhibited both growth and mycelial chitosan content.

Hyaluronic Acid

Hyaluronic acid is an unbranched unsulfated glycosaminoglycanecomposed of repeating disaccharide units of D-glucuronicacid and N-acetylglucosamine linked α-(1→4)and β-(1→3), respectively. While hyaluronicacid is produced from streptococci for industrial purposes, it is also present in human connective tissues, where it plays an important role in many biological mechanisms.Hyaluronic acid is mainly found in the cartilage and in thevitreous, where it primarily lubricates body tissue and blocks the spread of invading microorganisms (Coviello et al., 2007).

Hyaluronic acid is used as a viscoelastic material in ophthalmologic surgery and as an injectable solution for the treatment of joint diseases in orthopedics. The remarkable viscoelasticproperties of hyaluronic acid and its complete lack of immunogenicity make it an attractive biomaterial. Hyaluronic acid also possesses several pharmacological properties, as it inhibits platelet adhesion and aggregation, and stimulates angiogenesis, making it suitable for vascular applications. Its efficiency as a drug carrier matrix has been demonstrated through the vestibular delivery of gentamicin, ocular delivery of pilocarpine,intranasal insulin release, and vaginal delivery of calcitonin (Larsen and Balasz, 1991;Coviello et al., 2007).,

The bacteria employed for biosynthesis of hyaluronic acid are nutritionally fastidious microorganisms which require complexnutrients due to their limited ability to synthesize specific amino acids and B-group vitamins. Additionally, there is the nutritionalrequirement with respect to organic nitrogen, which also suppliesa large portion of carbon for their cellular biosynthesis.In general, the culture media used for the microbial productionof hyaluronic acid contain glucose as a carbon source and appreciable amounts of complex nitrogen sources andgrowth factors like yeast extract and bacterial peptones (Gao et al., 2006; Pires et al., 2010). In order to find cheaper alternative to these expensive complex substrates, Pires et al. (2010) tested hydrolysate soy protein concentrate, whey protein concentrate and cashew apple juice with focus on the production of hyaluronicacid by *Streptococcus zooepidemicus*. Application of whey protein concentrate strongly increased biomass growth; however, the yields of hyaluronic acids were lower than in control culture containing yeast extract.

Gellan

Gellan gum is a bacterial exopolysaccharide commercially prepared by aerobic submerged fermentation of *Sphingomonas*sp. From chemical point of view, gellan gum is a linear tetrasaccharide built up by →4)-L-rhamnopyranosyl-(α-1→3)-D-glucopyranosyl-(β-1→4)-Dglucuronopyranosyl-(β-1→4)-D-glucopyranosyl-(β-1→ withO(2) L-glyceryl and O(6) acetyl substituents on the 3-linkedglucose (Figure 6). It consists of about 50000 residues and it is normally de-esterified by alkali treatment before use. Gellangum forms a 3-fold double helix from two left-handed chains with the acetate residues on the periphery, and glyceryl groups and hydrogen-bonds stabilizing the inter-chain associations (Coviello et al., 2007).

Besides wide range of applications in food industry such as manufacturing of dairy products, fabricated foods, jams or pet foods, gellan attracts attention of pharmaceutical industry as well. It seems to be very promising material for formulation of controlled release systems controlling bioavailability of administrated drugs for instance in ophthalmology (Bajaj et al., 2007).

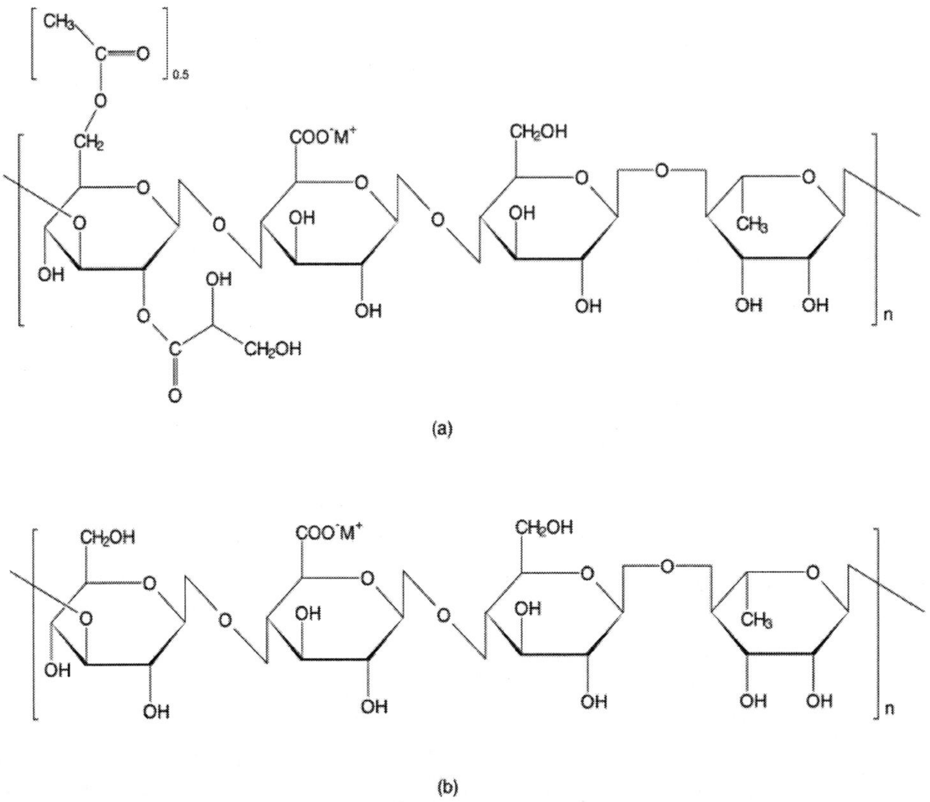

(a)

(b)

Figure 6. The chemical structure of gellan gum: (a) native form (high acyl); (b) deacylated form (low acyl) (Mao et al., 2000). Reproduced with permission.

In order to produce gellan from lactose base substrates including sweet cheese whey, Dlamini and Peirs (1996)employed improved strain of *Sphingomonas elodea* ATCC 31461 capable of producing high broth viscosities when grown in enriched whey permeate and enriched sweet whey media. Maximum biopolymer productions were observed in 25% whey solution (v/v). Study on enzyme activities suggested that transport of lactose into the cells is by permease system as opposed to phosphotransferase system. Fialho et al. (1999)aimed at gellan production from whey and lactose employing other bacterial strain, *Sphigomonas paucimobilis*ATCC 31461.They found that altering the growth medium can markedly affect the polysaccharide yield, acyl substitution level, polymer rheological properties, and susceptibility to degradation. Depression of gellan production from lactose compared with gellan production from glucose (approximately 30%) did not appear to occur at the level of synthesis of sugar nucleotides, which are the donors of monomers used for biosynthesis of the repetitive tetrasaccharide unit of gellan. The lactose-derived biopolymer had the highest total acyl content, the glucose- and whey-derived gellans had similar totalacyl contents but differed markedly in their acetate and glycerate levels. The process of gellan production resulted in production of 8 g L^{-1} of gellan at the 100th hour of cultivation using 25% (v/v) cheese whey as a medium.

Polyhydroxyalkanoates

Polyhydroxyalkanoates (PHA) are a family of linear polyesters of usually 3- but also 4, 5 and 6-hydroxyacids, synthesized by a wide variety of variety of fermentation of sugars, lipids, alkanes and alkanoic acids. Bacteria accumulate PHA as a source of carbon, energy and reducing power intracellularly in form of cytoplasmic inclusion termed PHA granules. Once extracted from the cells, PHA exhibit thermoplastic and elastomeric properties similar to polypropylene or polyethylene *etc.*Nevertheless, unlike the plastics of petrochemical origin, PHA can be easily biodegraded to carbon dioxide and water. In addition, these polymersare biocompatible and hence have a number of medical applications. Furthermore, all of the monomeric units of PHAs are enantiomericallypure and in the R-configuration. R-hydroxyalkanoic acids produced by the hydrolysis ofPHA can also be used as chiral starting materialsin fine chemical, pharmaceutical and medical industries (Sudech et al., 2000; Philip et al., 2007).

Mechanical and physical properties of PHA strongly depend on the monomer composition. From chemical point of view, PHA are polyesters of hydroxyalkanoic acids. PHA can be classified according to number of carbon atoms in monomer unit: short chain lengths (scl) PHA consist of 3-5 carbon atoms and medium-chain length (mcl) PHA contain 6-14 carbon atoms per monomer unit. More than 100 monomers have been found in the naturally synthesized polyester polymers (Steinbuchel and Valentin, 1995; Sudech et al., 2000).

Hence, a range of designer PHA with desirable properties can be obtained. The polymer can be hard and crystalline or elastic and rubbery. The most widespread PHA is homopolymer of 3-hydroxybuytric acid, poly(3-hydroxybutyrate) (PHB). This material is highly crystalline, brittle and stiff with a melting temperature of 180° C. However, the introduction of different hydroxyacids monomers such as 3-hydroxyvalerate (3HV) or 3-hydroxyhexanoate (3HHx) into the PHB chain greatly improves the material properties. PHB is optically pure and possesses piezoelectricity which helps in osteoinduction, the process of inducing osteogenesis. Poly(3-hydroxybutyrate-*co*-3-hydroxyvalerate), P(3HB-*co*-3HV), has a lower melting temperature and lower crystallinity than PHB. The mole percentage of 3HV in the polymer is important in determining the properties of the copolymer. P(3HB-*co*-3HV) containing more than 20 mol% of 3HV units can be used to make films and fibers with different elasticity by controlling the processing conditions (Flickinger and Drew, 1999; Sudech et al., 2000; Philip et al. 2007).

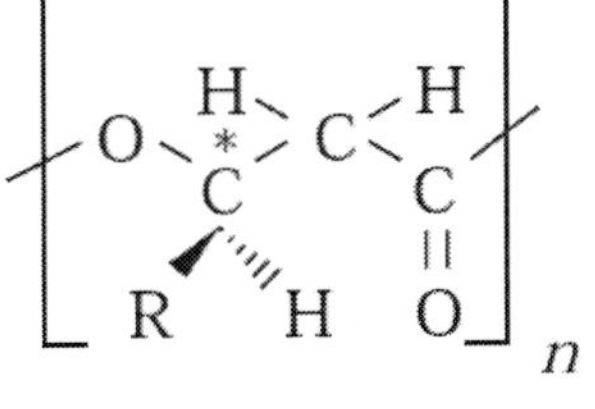

$$R = CH_3\text{-}C_2H_5 \qquad \text{Short-chain-length PHAs}$$
$$R = C_3H_7\text{-}C_{14}H_{29} \qquad \text{Medium-chain-length PHAs}$$

Figure 7. General structure of PHA .Flickinger and Drew (1999).Reproduced with permission.

Besides the fact that PHA are considered as an alternative to traditional petrochemical plastics, they have also many medical applications. PHA are frequently used in tissue engineering as bone plates, osteosynthetic materials and surgical sutures. They are useful in the slow release of drugs and hormones. PHA fibers are especially sought after to make swabs and dressing materials for surgery. PHA are produced by fermentations and, hence, do not contain the left-over undesirable metal catalysts used in chemical synthesis. The greatest contribution of PHA to medicine has been in the cardiovascular area. Tepha, Inc. specializes in manufacturing pericardial patches, artery augments, cardiological stents, vascular grafts, heart valves, implants and tablets, sutures, dressings, dusting powders, pro-drugs and micro particulate carriers using PHA (Williams and Martin, 2002; Philip et al., 2007).

Analysis and economic evaluation of the bacterial PHA productions suggested, that the cost of substrate (mainly carbon source) contributed the most significantly (up to 50%) to the overall production cost. Thus, cheap waste substrates attract attention of both scientific researches and industrial companies in order to reduce PHA production cost. Many agriculture and food industry by-products and wastes such as molasses (Page, 1992), waste frying plant oils (Obruca et al., 2010; Budde et al., 2011) or waste glycerol stemming from biodiesel production (Ashby et al., 2005) have been studied for PHA production. Among them, whey seems to be probably the most promising cheap substrate facilitating cheap PHA production. Thereby, there is high number of studies dealing with PHA production from whey.

PHA Production by Naturally Producing Bacteria

PHA production from cheese whey by naturally PHA producing and lactose utilizing strain was studied by Yellore and Desai (1998) who studied PHB production employing *Methylobacterium* sp. ZP24, isolated from a local pond. The isolate was able to utilize deproteinized whey and produce 1.1 g L^{-1} of polymer. Introduction of $(NH_4)_2SO_4$ enhanced the PHB yields 2.5-fold, so the bacterium produced 2.6 g L^{-1} of PHB which represented 44% of cell dry mass. Further, the production process was scaled-up by Nath et al. (2008). Since *Methylobacterium* sp. ZP24 showed growth associated PHB production, an intermittent feeding strategy having lactose and ammonium sulfate at varying concentration was used towards reaching higher yield of the polymer. About 1.5-fold increase in PHB production was obtained by this feeding strategy. Further increase in PHB production by 0.8-fold could be achieved by limiting the dissolved oxygen levels in the fermentor. The decreased oxygen level is thought to increase flux of acetyl-CoA towards PHB accumulation over TCA cycle. Maximal yields reached 3.91 g L^{-1} when *Methylobacterium* sp. ZP24 was able to convert 1 g lactose into 0.32 g of PHB.

Another bacterium which is capable of direct transformation of lactose into PHB is *Bacillus megaterium*. Obruca et al. (2011) employed *B. megaterium* CCM 2037. Optimization of medium composition in terms of whey dilution, Mg^{2+}, $(NH_4)_2SO_4$ and PO_4^{2-} supplement-ation improved PHB yields about 50-fold (biomass and PHB yields 2.82 and 1.05 g L^{-1}, respectively) as compared to whey alone. Furthermore, PHB yields were improved by about 40% by introducing 1% ethanol into the medium at the beginning of the stationary phase of growth(biomass 2.87 g L^{-1}, PHB 1.48 g L^{-1}).Pandian et al. (2010) converted whey into PHB using *Bacillus megaterium* isolated from brackish water. Medium was supplemented with rice bran and see water and also fed-batch fermentation strategy was developed so the maximum production of PHB (11.32 g L^{-1}) occurred at the 36th hour of cultivation.

Azotobacter vinelandii was used for PHB production on whey using bacterial peptone as nitrogen source. It was observed that by increasing the inoculum size the time of incubation can be reduced considerably (Dhanasekar et al., 2001). Further, *Pseudomonas hydrogenovora* produced PHA on enzymatically cleaved lactose in whey permeate. The application of hydrolyzed whey permeate turned out to be advantageous as compared to the utilization of pure sugars. Sodium valerate was introduced into fermentation media to incorporate 3HV units into PHA structure and form P(3HB-*co*-3HV) copolymer. The process yielded 1.44 g L^{-1} of copolymer containing 21% of 3HV (Koller et al., 2008). Pantazaki et al. (2009) focused on mcl-PHA production from cheese whey employing *Thermus thermophilus* HB8 under nitrogen limitation. PHA was accumulated up to 35% of its biomass after 24 h of cultivation. Heteropolymer consisted of the short chain length 3-hydroxyvalerate and the medium chain length 3-hydroxyheptanoate, 3-hydroxynanoate and 3-hydroxyundecanoate.

PHA Production by Genetically Engineered Bacteria

Apart from those microbes mentioned in the previous text, there is a great number of bacterial strain which are either not able to utilize lactose or they do not accumulate PHA. Therefore, a lot of efforts were targeted on genetic modification of particular bacterial strain in order to reach highly efficient production of PHA from cheese whey.

Cupriavidus necator is a well-known PHA producer, but unable to grow on lactose. Thus,Povolo at al. (2010) choose one of intracellular PHB depolymerases, enzyme degrading intracellular stocks of PHA, to insert *lac*genes of *E. coli*. This would have the effect to allow polymer production on lactose and, in the same time, to remove part of the PHA intracellular degradation system. Disruption of PHA depolymerase was achieved by gene replacement after isolating a fragment of this gene and interrupting it with a cartridge containing the *lac* genes and a synthetic promoter. Growth and polymer production studies of the genetically modified strain mRePTin whey permeate and hydrolyzed whey permeate as carbon sources, were performed. LowerPHA degradation and higher yields were obtained as compared to the wild-type strain.

Finally, many researchers reported very efficient PHA production using *Escherichia coli* harboring PHA biosynthetic genes of various natural PHA producers. Fermentation strategies for the production of PHB from whey by recombinant *Escherichia coli* strain CGSC 4401 harboring the *Alcaligenes latus* PHA biosynthesis genes were developed by An et al. (2000). The pH-stat fed-batch cultures were carried out with a concentrated whey solution containing 280 g of lactose equivalent per liter. Cell and PHB concentrations of 119.5 and 96.2 g L^{-1}, respectively, were obtained at the 37.5th hour of cultivation. In the second study, An et al. (2001) even improved the fermentation strategy. The same *E. coli* strain was employed for PHB production using cell recycle membrane system. The final cell concentration, PHB concentration and PHB content of 194 gL^{-1}, 168 gL^{-1} and 87%, respectively, were obtained at the 36.5thh by the pH-stat cell recycle fed-batch culture using whey solution concentrated to contain 280 glactoseL^{-1} as a feeding solution.

Different recombinant *E. coli* strain was used for PHB accumulation in whey-based broth. The timing of PHB biosynthesis in recombinant *E. coli* was controlled using the agitation speed of a stirred tank fermentor. PHB content of 80% could be obtained with oxygen limitation by decreasing the agitation speed to only 500 rpm. Final yields reached were 31 g L^{-1} of biomass containing 80% of PHB (Kim, 2000). Nikel et al. (2005) aimed at statistical optimization of culture medium using powdered cheese whey by recombinant *E.*

*coli*strain harboring biosynthetic geneses from a natural isolate of *Azotobacter* sp. The study demonstrated that the optimal concentrations of the three components, defined as those yielding maximal biomass and PHB production in shaken flasks, were 37.96 g $L^{-1}$of deproteinated milk whey powder, 29.39 g L⁻1of corn steep liquor and 23.76 g L^{-1} phosphates. The cultivation in the optimized medium yielded9.41 g L^{-1} biomass and 6.12 gL^{-1} of PHB in the culture broth.

Table 4. Summary of PHB productions on cheese whey published in literature

Producent	Substrate	Fermentation mode	Biomass [g L^{-1}]	PHB [%]	PHB [g L^{-1}]	$Y_{p/s}$[1] [g g^{-1}]	Reference
Methylobacterium sp. ZP24	Deproteinized whey $(NH_4)_2SO_4$	Erlenmayer flask, Batch	5,9	44	2,6	*n.a.*[2]	Yellore and Desai (1998)
Methylobacterium sp. ZP24	Deproteinized whey $(NH_4)_2SO_4$	Fermentor, Fed-batch	*n.a.*	*n.a.*	3,9	0,32	Nath et al., 2008
Bacillus megaterium CCM 2037	Deproteinized whey $(NH_4)_2SO_4$, phosphate	Erlenmayer flask, Batch	2,87	52	1,5	0,08	Obruca et al. (2011)
Bacillus megaterium SRKP-3	Whey Rice Bran, Sea Water	Fermentor, Fed-batch	*n.a.*	*n.a.*	11,3	*n.a.*	Pandian et al. (2010)
Azotobacter vinelandii MTCC 124	Whey Bacterial peptone	Erlenmayer flask, Batch	*n.a.*	*n.a.*	1,4	*n.a.*	Dhanasekar et al.(2001)
Pseudomonas hydrogenovora	Hydrolyzed whey permeate	Fermentor, Fed-batch	*n.a.*	12	1,4	*n.a.*	Koller et al. (2008)
Thermus thermophilus HB8	Deproteinized whey	Erlenmayer flask, Batch	1,6	35	0,5	*n.a.*	Pantazaki et al. (2009)
Cupriavidus necator (*E. coli* lac genes)	Whey	Erlenmayer flask, Batch	8,8	23	2,0	*n.a.*	Povolo et al. (2010)
Escherichia coli (*A. latus* PHA biosynthetic genes)	Concetrated whey	Fermentor, Fed-batch	119,5	81	96,2	*n.a.*	Ahn et al. (2000)
Escherichia coli (*A. latus* PHA biosynthetic genes)	Concetrated whey	Fermentor, Fed-batch, Cell recycle system	194	87	168,0	*n.a.*	Ahn et al. (2001)
Escherichia coli (*C. necator*PHA biosynthetic genes)	Whey	Fermentor, Fed-batch, Oxygen limitation	31	80	25,0	*n.a.*	Kim (2000)
Escherichia coli (*Azotobacter* sp. biosynthetic genes)	Deproteinized whey powder Corn steep liquor	Erlenmayer flask, Batch	9,4	65	6,1	*n.a.*	Nikel et al. (2005)
Escherichia coli (*Azotobacter* sp. biosynthetic genes)	Deproteinized whey concetrate	Fermentor, Fed-batch	70	73	51,1	*n.a.*	Nikel et al. (2006)

Notes: [1] Yield in terms of g of PHA per g of substrate; [2]*n.a.* stands for: data not available.

In another study Nikel at al. (2006) employed the same recombinant strain for PHB production fed-batch mode using concentrated and deproteinated whey solution containing 25% lactose as a feeding solution.

The table 4 provides summary of PHA production processes from cheese whey reported in literature. Despite the legislative restrictions stemming from the application of genetically modified strains, it seems that recombinant *E. coli* is the most promising candidate for industrial production of PHA using whey. Employing these recombinant strains, it is possible to achieve very high cell densities in relatively short time. Because PHA production is, in these cases, growth associated PHA contents in cells reach up to 87% of cell dry weight that is furthermost of all the bacterial strains tested so far. This is very important factor influencing the economics of PHA production, because PHA content of the produced biomass strongly affects the efficiency and the price of the down-stream process. For example, Lee and Choi (1999) reported that a relatively low PHB content in cells – 50% results in a high recovery cost of 4.8 $kg^{-1} PHB. On the other hand, the recovery cost for a process with 88% PHB cell content was only 0.92 $ kg^{-1} PHB. A lower PHB content clearly resulted in a high recovery cost. This is mainly due to requirement of large amounts of digesting agents for breaking the cell walls and to the increased cost of waste disposal.

7. ECONOMIC CONSIDERATION

In general, fermentative production of any substance or material can hardly compete with its chemical synthesis (if possible) in terms of productivity and economic parameters. A fermentation process requires relatively high capital and operating cost for the process of production as well as for the process of product separation and purification. Therefore, fermentative productions can be economically reasonable in those commodities which cannot be efficiently synthetized *via* chemical synthesis or the chemical synthesis yields product with undesired properties. Actually, this chapter focuses on this type of products.

The table 5 shows the market prize of some of the substances and materials include in this chapter. It is important to note that these prices are more or less orientational and the real price of high purity and highly defined commodity can be simply several times higher depending on its potential application.

Because the cost of fermentation medium is one of the most important operating costs for biotechnological production (representing up to 40 % of the process cost), there is always an effort to reduce it as much as possible. Among cheap substrates, whey is one of the most promising candidates. For instance Lee (1996) suggested cheese whey as the most promising substrate for PHB production (see table 6).Similarly, van Wegen et al.(1998) reported that the process of PHB production employing recombinant *E. col*i harboring PHA biosynthetic genes was profitable if 60 % of glucose substrate had been be substituted by evaporator-concentrated cheese whey. The cost of whey based medium is significantly lower than those of pure or waste substrates. Moreover, if the cheese whey can be used as the sole carbon source as has been described for instance in carotenoids, lactic acid or polyhydro-xyalkanaotes, the utilization of whey not only decreases the price of final products, but it may also improve the process in terms of yields and also enhance quality of the final product.

Table 5.Market prices of some of the substances mentionedin this chapter

Substance	Price [$/kg]
Vitamin B12	10 - 30
β-carotene	10 - 200
Nisin	50 - 600
Xanthan (food grade)	1,8 - 3
Dextran	1 - 200
Pullulan	15 - 30
Hyaluronic acid	5000 - 7500
PHB	3 - 10

Table 6. Costs of substrates for PHB production (Lee, 1996)

Substrate	Substrate cost [$ kg^{-1} of PHB]
Glucose	1.35
Sucrose	0.72
Methanol	0.42
Acetic acid	1.56
Ethanol	1.00
Cane molasses	0.52
Hydrolyzed corn starch	0.58
Hemicelluloze hydrolyzate	0.34
Cheese whey	0.22

Gonzales et al. (2006) evaluated production of lactic acid from the economic point of view. The highest contribution to the total investment cost corresponds to the concentration step, representing 40% of the total cost, whereas the fermentation step requires the highest operating cost (47% of the total operating cost). Thanks to the fact that cheap ultrafiltred whey was used as a substrate, the proposed process was demonstrated to be economically viable. The cost resulted to be 1.25 $ kg^{-1} for 50% (w/w) lactic acid.

Wolf-Hall et al. (2009) focused on the development of a low-cost medium for production of nisin by *Lactococcus lactis* subsp. *lactis* using either condensed corn soluble or cheese whey as inexpensive growth media.The use of cheap substrates reduced the medium costs for nisin production from 600 $ kg^{-1} nisin (based on Laurel–Tryptose broth medium) to 35–40$kg^{-1}.This represents a 93% reduction in costs. With further development of pH control methods and carbohydrate supplementation, there is a perspective of the further increase of nisin yields to levels comparable to, or even exceeding those, of commercially used media, thereby further reducingnisin production costs.

To sum up, extensive research has been, and is continuing to be, conducted on profitablebio-products that can be obtained from cheese whey. The process of whey conversion into the high valuable products can not only be economically feasible but it would also provide very efficient solution of surplus whey disposal.

ACKNOWLEDGMENT

This work was suported by project "Centre for Materials Research at FCH BUT" No. CZ.1.05/2.1.00/01.0012 from ERDF.

REFERENCES

Agarwal, L; Dutt, K; Meghwanshi, GK; Saxena, RK.Anaerobic fermentative production of lactic acid using cheese whey and corn steep liquor.*Biotechnology Letters*.2008, 30, 631-365.

Agustriyanto, R; Fatmawati, A. Model of continuous cheese whey fermentation by *Candida pseudotropicalis*.*Proceedings of World Academy of Science, Engineering and Technology*. 2009, 57, 213-217.

Ahn, WS; Park, SJ; Lee, SY. Production of poly(3-hydroxybutyrate) by fed-batch culture of recombinant *Escherichia coli* with highly concentrated whey solution. *Applied and Environmental Microbiology*.2000, 66, 3624-2627.

Ahn, WS; Park, SJ; Lee, SY. Production of poly(3-hydroxybutyrate) from whey by cell recycle fed-batch culture of recombinant *Escherichia coli*. *Biotechnology Letters*, 2001, 23, 235-240.

Akiyoshi, K; Kobayashi, S; Schichibe, S; Mix, D; Baudys, M; Kim, SW; Sunamoto, J. Self-assembled hydrogel nanoparticle of cholesterol-bearing pullulan as a carrier of protein drugs: Complexation and stabilization of insulin. *Journal of Controlled Release*. 1998, 54, 313-320.

Aksu, Z; Eren, AT. Carotenoids production by the yeast Rhodotorula mucilaginosa: use of agricultural wastes as a carbon source. *Process Biochemistry*. 2005, 40, 2985-2991.

Aksu, Z; Eren, AT.Production of carotenoids by the isolated yeast of *Rhodotorula glutinis*.*Biochemical Engineering Journal*. 2007, 35, 107-113.

Ananou, S; Munoz, A; Galvez, A; Martinez-Bueno, M; Maqueda, M; Valdiva, E. Optimization of enterocin AS-48 production on whey-based substrate.*International Dairy Industry Journal*. 2008, 18, 923-927.

Amrane, A. Effect of inorganic phosphate on lactate production by *Lactobacillus helveticus*. *Journal of General and Applied Microbiology*. 2000,49, 21-27.

Amrane, A. Analysis of the kinetics of growth and lactic acid production for Lactobacillus helveticus growing on supplemented whey permeate. *Journal of Chemical Technology and Biotechnology*. 2005, 80, 345-352.

Ashby, RD; Foglia, TA. Bacterial poly(hydroxyalkanoate) polymer production from the biodiesel coproduct stream. *Journal of Polymers and Environment*. 2005, 12, 105–112.

Audet, P; Paquin, C; Lacroix, C. Immobilized growing lactic acid bacteria with κ-carrageenan-locust gum gel.*Applied Microbiology and Biotechnology*. 1988, 29, 11-18.

Audet, P; Paquin, C; Lacroix, C.Sugar utilization and acid production by free and entrapped cells of *Streptococcus salivarius* spp. *thermophilus*, *Lactobacillus delbrueckii* spp. *bulgaricus*, and *Lactococcus lactis* spp. *lactis* in a whey permeate medium. *Applied and Environmental Microbiology*. 1989, 55, 185–189.

Azbar, N; Cetinkaya Dokgoz, FT; Keskin, T; Korkmaz, KS; Syed, HM. Continuous fermentative hydrogen production from cheese whey wastewater under thermophilic anaerobic conditions.*International Journal of Hydrogen Energy*. 2009, 34, 7441-7447.

Bajaj, IB; Survase, SA; Saudagar, PS; Singhal, RS. Gellan Gum: Fermentative Production, Downstream Processing and Applications. *Food Technology and Biotechnology*. 2007, 45, 341-354.

Becker, A; Katzen, F; Puhler, A; Ielpi, L. Xanthan gum biosynthesis and application: a biochemical/genetic perspective. *Applied Microbiology and Biotechnology*.1998, 50, 145-152.

Berry, EC; Bullerman, LB. Use of cheese whey for vitamin B12 production. II. Cobalt precursors and aeration levels. *Applied Microbiology*. 1966, 14, 356-357.

Brinques, GB; Peralba, MC; Ayub, MAZ.Optimization of probiotic and lactic acid production by *Lactobacillus plantarum* in submerged bioreactor systems.*Journal of Industrial Microbiology and Biotechnology*. 2010, 37, 205-212.

Budde, CF; Riedel, SL; Hubner, F; Risch, S; Popovic, MK; Rha, C; Sinskey, AJ. Growth and polyhydroxybutyrate production by *Ralstonia eutropha* in emulsified plant oil medium. *Applied Microbiology and Biotechnology*. 2011, 89, 1611-1619.

Bullerman, LB; Berry, EC.Use of cheese whey for vitamin B12 production. I. Whey solids and yeast extract levels. *Applied Microbiology*. 1966, 14, 356-357.

Bullerman, LB; Berry, EC.Use of cheese whey for vitamin B12 production. III. Growth studies and dry-weight activity. *Applied Microbiology*. 1966, 14, 356-357.

Büyükkilci, AO; Harsa, S. Batch production of L(+)-lactic acid from whey by *Lactobacillus casei* (NRRL B-441). *Journal of Chemical Technology and Biotechnology*. 2004, 79, 1036–1040.

Buzzini, P; Rossi, J. Riboflavin production by yeasts as an alternative approach for the utilization of agro-industrial residues.*Agro Food Industry HI-TECH*. 1997, 8, 30-32.

Choojun, S; Suttisuwan, R. Lactic acid production by coimmobilized cells of Lactococcus lactis TISTR 1401 and *Lactobacillus casei* TISTR 1341 using whey as substrate. *Chiang Mai University Journal of Natural Sciences*. 2010, 9, 245-254.

Cladera-Olivera, F; Caron, GR; Brandelli, A. Bacteriocin production by Bacillus licheniformis strain P40 in cheese whey using response surface methodology.*Biochemical Engineering Journal*. 2004, 21, 53-58.

Coviello, T; Matricardi, P; Marianecci, C; Alhaique, F. Polysaccharide hydrogels for modified release formulation.*Journal of Controlled Release*.2007, 119, 5-24.

Dahal, N; Chaney, N; Ellis, D; Lu, SE; Smith, L. Optimization of the production of the lantibiotic mutacin 1140 in minimal media. *Process Biochemistry*. 2010, 45, 1187-1191.

Datta, R;Tsai, SP; Bonsignore, P; Moon, SH; Frank, JR. Technological and economic potential of poly(lactic acid) and lactic acid derivatives. *FEMS MicrobiologyReviews*. 1995, 16, 221-231.

Davila-Vazquez, G; Cota-Navarro, CB; Rosales-Colunga, LM; de Leon-Rodriquez, A; Razo-Flores, E. Continuous biohydrogen production using cheese whey: Improving the hydrogen production rate. *International Journal of Hydrogen Energy*. 2009, 34, 4296-4304.

De Arauz, LJ; Jozala, AF; Pinheiro, GS; Mazzola, PG; Pessoa, A; Penna, TCV.Nisin expression production from *Lactococcus lactis* in milk whey medium.*Journal of Chemical Technology and Biotechnology*. 2008, 83, 325-328.

De Lima, CJB; Coelho, LF; Contiero, J. The use of response surface methodology in optimization of lactic acid production: Focus on medium supplementation, temperature and pH control. *Food Technology and Biotechnology*. 2010, 48, 175-181.

Dhanasekar, R; Viruthagiri, T; Sabarathinam, PL. Biosynthesis of poly(3-hydroxybutyrate) from cheese whey using *Azotobacter vinelandii.Indian Journal of Chemical Technology*. 2001, 8, 68-71.

Dlamini, AM; Peiris, PS. Production of exopolysaccharide by *Pseudomonas* sp. ATCC 31461 (*Pseudomonas elodea*) using whey as fermentation substrate. *Applied Microbiology and Biotechnology*. 1997, 47, 52-57.

Ekateriniadou, LV; Papoutsopoulou, SV; Kyriakidis, DA. High production if xanthan gum by a strain of *Xanthomonas campesteris* conjugated with *Lactococcus lactis*. *Biotechnology Letters*. 1994, 16, 517-522.

Evans, MT; Gordon JF.Whey proteins.In Grant RA editor.*Applied Proteins.*London: Applied Science Publisher; 1980; 31-67.

Fialho, AM; Martins, LO; Donval, ML; Leitao, JH; Ridout, MJ; Jay, AJ; Morris, VJ; Sa-Correira, I. Structure and properties of gellan polymers produced by *Sphingomonas paucimobilis* ATCC 31461 from lactose compared with those produced from glucose and from cheese whey. *Applied and Environmental Microbiology*. 1999, 65, 2485-2491.

Frengova, G; Simova, E; Beshkova, D. Use of whey ultrafiltarte as a substrate for production of carotenoids by the yeast *Rhodotorula rubra.Applied Biochemistry and Biotechnology*. 2004, 112, 133-141.

Frengova, G; Simova, E; Beshkova, D. Beta-carotene-richcarotenoid-proteinpreparation and exopolysaccharideproductionby*Rhodotorularubra*GED8grown witbayogurtstarterculture.*Zeitschrift fur Naturforschung C-A Journal of Biosciences*. 2006, 61, 571-577.

Fu, JF; Tseng, YH.Construction of lactose-utilizing *Xanthomonas campesteris* and production of xanthan gum from whey.*Applied and Environmental Microbiology*. 1990, 56, 919-923.

Galindo, E; Pena, C; Nunez, C; Segura, D; Espin, G. Molecular and bioengineering strategies to improve alginate and polydydroxyalkanoate production by *Azotobacter vinelandii. Microbial Cell Factories*. 2007, 7, doi:10.1186/1475-2859-6-7.

Gao, HJ; Du, GC; Chen, J. Analysis of metabolic fluxes for hyaluronic acid (HA) production by *Streptococcus zoepidemicus*. *World Journal of Microbiology and Biotechnology.*2006, 22, 399-408.

Ghasemi, M; Najafpour, G; Rahimnejad, M; Beigi, PA; Sedighi, M; Hashemiyeh, B.Effect of different media on production of lactic acid from whey by *Lactobacillus bulgaricus*. *African Journal of Biotechnology*. 2009, 8, 81-84.

Ghosh, MK; Ghosh, UK. Utilization of pine needles as bed material in solid state fermentation for production of lactic acid by *Lactobacillus strains*. *BioResources*. 2011, 6, 1556-1575.

Gisondi, P; Fantuzzi, F; Malerba, M; Girolomoni, G. Folic acid in general medicine and dermatology.*Journal of Dermatological Treatment.*2007, 18, 138-146.

Göksungur, Y; Gündüz, M; Harsa, Ş. Optimization of lactic acid production from whey by *L. casei* NRRL B-441 immobilized in chitosan stabilized Ca-alginate beads. *Journal of Chemical Technology and Biotechnology*. 2005, 80, 1282-1290.

Gonzales, MI; Alvarez, S; Riera, F; Alvarez, R. Economic evaluation of an integrated process for lactic acid production from ultrafiltered whey. *Journal of Food Engineering.* 2007, 80, 553-561.

Gonzales-Toledo, SY; Dominguez-Dominguez, J; Garcia-Almendarez, BE; Prado-Barragan, LA; Relegado-Gonzales, C. Optimization of nisin production by *Lactococcus lactis* UQ2 using supplemented whey as alternative culture medium. *Journal of Food Science.* 2010, 75, M347-M353.

Guimaraes, PMR; Teixeira ,JA; Domingues L. Fermentation of lactose to bio-ethanol by yeast as part of integrated solutions for the valorisation of cheese whey. *Biotechnology Advances.* 2010, 28, 375-384.

Guo, X; Zhou, J; Xiao, D.Improved ethanol production by mixed immobilized cells of *Kluyveromyces marxianus* and *Saccharomyces cerevisiae* from cheese whey powder solution fermentation.*Applied Biochemistry and Biotechnology.* 2010, 160, 532-538.

Hafez, AMA; Abdelhady, HM; Sharaf, MS; Tayeb, TSE.Bioconversion of various industrial by-products and agricultural wastes into pullulan.*Journal of Applied Sciences Research.* 2007, 11, 1416-1425.

Hamzah, HM; Ali, AHL; Hassan, HG.Physiological regulation of protease and antibiotics in *Penicillium* sp. using submerged and solid state fermentation techniques.*Journal of Engineering Science and Technology.* 2009, 4, 81-89.

Hatanaka, H; Wang, E; Taniguchi, M; Iijima, S; Kobayashi, T. Production of vitamin B_{12} by fermentation with hollow-fiber module. *Journal of Fermention and Bioengineering.*1998, 27, 470-473.

Hofvendahl, K; Hahn-Hagerdal, B. Factors affecting the fermentative lactic acid production from renewable resources.*Enzyme and Microbial Technology.* 2000, 26, 87-107.

Hugenschmidt, S; Schwenniger, SM;Lacroix, C. Concurrent high production of natural folate and vitamin B_{12} using a co-culture process with *Lactobacillus plantarum* SM39 and *Propionibacterium freudenreichii* DF13. *Process Biochemistry.* 2011, 46, 1063-1070.

Hugenschmidt, S; Schwenniger, SM; Gnehm, N; Lacroix, C. Screening of natural biodiversity of lactic acid bacteria for folate and vitamin B_{12} production by supplemented whey permeate. *International Dairy Journal.*2010, 20, 852-857.

Hughes, DA. Beta-carotene and imunne function: is it a case of defining the rate intake? *Nutrition.* 1999, 15, 405-407.

Jelen, P.Whey processing.In Roginski H, Fuquay JW, Fox PF editors.*Encylcopedia of dairy sciences.* London: Academic Press; 2003; 2739-2751.

Jin, L; Lu, P; You, H; Chen, Q; Dong, J. Vitamin B12 diffusion and binding in crosslinked poly(acrylic acid)sand poly(acrylic acid-co-N-vinyl pyrrolidinone)s. *International Journal of Pharmaceutics.* 2010, 371, 82-88.

Kessler, B; Witholt, B. Polyhydroxyalkanoates.In Flickinger M, Drew SW editors.*Encyclopedia of Bioprocess Technology – Fermetation, Biocatalyst, and Bioseparation.* New York: John Wiley and Sons; 1999, 2024-2133.

Khanafari, A; Sepahei; AA.Alginate biopolymer production by *Azotobacter chroococum* from whey degradation.*International Journal of Environmental Science and Technology*, 2007, 4, 427-432.

Kilara, A; Vaqghela M.N. Whey proteins.In Yada RY editor.*Proteins in food processing.* Woodhead Publishing; 2005; 73-99.

Kim, BS. Production of poly(3-hydroxybutyrate) from inexpensive substrates. *Enzyme and Microbial Technology*. 2000, 27, 774-777.

Kohler, M; Bona, R; Chiellini, E; Fernandes, EG; Horvat, P; Kutschera, C; Hesse, P; Braunegg, G. Polyhydroxyalkanoates production from whey by *Pseudomonas hydrogenovora*. *Bioresource Technology*, 2008, 99, 4854-4863.

Kosseva, MR; Panesar, PS; Kaur, G; Kennedy, JF.Use of immobilised biocatalyst in the processing of cheese whey.*International Journal of Biological Macromolecules*, 2009, 5, 437-447.

Kumar, MNVR. A review of chitin and chitosan applications.*Reactive and Functional Polymers.*2000, 46, 1-27.

Larsen, NE; Balasz, EA. Drug delivery systems using hyaluronan and its derivatives.*Advances in Drug Delivery Reviews*. 1991, 7, 279-293.

Leathers, TD.Biotechnological production and applications of pullulan.*Applied Microbiology and Biotechnology*. 2003, 62, 468-473.

Lee, SY. Plactic bacteria?Progress and prospects for polyhydroxyalkanoate production in bacteria.*Trends in Biotechnology.*1996, 14, 431-438.

Lee, PC; Schmidt-Dannert, C. Metabolic engineering towards biotechnological production of carotenoids in microorganisms.*Applied Microbiology and Biotechnology*. 2002, 60, 1-11.

Lee, SY; Choi, J. Effect of fermentation performance on the economics of poly-(3-hydroxybutyrate) production by *Alcaligenes latus.Polymer Degradation and Stability*. 1999, 59, 387-393.

Li, Y; Shahbazi, A; Coulibaly, S. Separation of cells and proteins from fermentation broth using ultrafiltration.*Journal of Food Engineering*. 2006, 75, 574–580.

Liakopoulou-Kyriakides, M; Tzanakakis, ES;Kiparissidis, C; Ekaterianiadou, LV; Kyriakidis, DA.Kinetics of xanthan gum production from whey by constructed strains of *Xanthomonas campestris* in batch fermentations. *Chemical Engineering and Technology,* 1997, 20, 354-360.

Lin, Y; Thibault, J; LeDuy, A. Pullulan, microbial production methods. In: Flickinger MC; Drew SW. *Encyclopedia of bioprocess technology – fermentation biocatalysis and bioseparation*. New York: John Wiley and Sons; 1999; 4197-4211.

Liu, C; Liu, Y; Liao, W; Wen, Z; Chen, S. Application of statistically-based experimental design for the optimization of nisin production from whey. *Biotechnology Letters,* 2003, 25, 877-882.

Liu, C; Liu, Y; Liao, W; Wen, Z; Chen, S. Simultaneous production of nisin and lactic acid from cheese whey. *Applied Biochemistry and Biotechnology*. 2004, 114, 627-638.

Liu, X; Chung, YK; Yang, ST; Yousef, AE. Continuous nisin production in laboratory media and whey permeate by immobilized *Lactococcus lactis*. *Process Biochemistry*. 2005, 40, 13-24.

Marangoni, C; Furigo, A; Aragao, GMF. Production of poly(3-hydroxybutyrate-co-3-hydroxyvalerate) by *Ralstonia eutropha* in whey and inverted sugar with propionic acid feeding. *Process Biochemistry.*2002, 38, 137-141.

Margot, A; Flaschel, E; Renken A. Continuous monitoring of enzymatic whey protein hydrolysis.Correlation of base consumption with soluble nitrogen content.*Process Biochemistry.*1994, 29, 257-262.

Marova, I; Carnecka, M; Halienova, A; Breierova, E; Koci, R. Production of carotenoid-/ergosterol-supplemented biomass by red yeast *Rhodotorula glutinis* grown under external stress. *Food Technology and Biotechnology*. 2010, 48, 56-61.

Marova, I; Carnecka, M; Halienova, A; Certik, M; Dvorakova, T; Haronikova, A. Use of several waste substrates for carotenoid-rich yeast biomass production.*Journal of Environmental Management.*in press. DOI: 10.1016/j.jenvman.2011.06.018.

Marova, I; Certik, M; Breierova, E. Production of enriched biomass vy carotenogenic yeasts – application of whole-cell yeast biomass to production of pigments and other lipid compounds. In Matovic D editor.*Biomass – detection, production and usage.* Rijeka:InTech; 2011, 345-384.

Marwaha, SS; Kennedy JF.Whey pollution problem and potential utilization.*International Journal of Food Science and Technology*. 1988, 23, 323-336.

Mawson, AJ. Bioconversions for whey utilization and waste abatement.*Bioresource Technology*, 1994, 47, 195-203.

McEwen, SA; Black, WD; Meek, AH. Antibiotic residues (bacterial inhibitory substances) in the milk of cows treated under label and extra-label conditions. *The Canadian Veterinary Journal*. 1992, 33, 527-534.

Mesomo, M; Silva, MF; Boni, G; Padilha, FF; Mazutti, M; Mossi, A; de Oliveira, D; Cansian, RL; Luccio, MD; Treichel, H. Xanthan gum produced by *Xanthomonas campestris* from cheese whey: production, optimization and rheological characterization. *Journal of the Sciences of Food and Agriculture*. 2009, 89, 2440-2445.

Mirdamadi, S; Atashgahi, S; Rajabi, A; Aziz-Mohseni, F; Roayael, M; Hamedi, J.Cell entrapment of *Lactobacillus casei* subsp. *casei* ATCC 39392 for lactic acid production.*Iranian Journal of Biotechnology*. 2008, 6, 16-21.

Mitchel, IE; Adzick, N; Melchione, J; pasquariello, PS; Sutton, IN; Whitehead, AS.Spina bifida.*Lancet*. 2004, 364, 1885-1895.

Miyano, K; Ye, K; Shimidzu, K. Improvement of vitamin B_{12} fermentation by reducing inhibitory metabolites by cell recycle and a mixed culture. *Biochemical Engineering Journal*. 2000, 6, 207-214.

Mostafa, NA. Production of lactic acid from whey with agar immobilized cells in continuous packed tubular reactor. *Energy Conversion Management*. 1996, 37, 253-260.

Mote, US; Patil, SR; Bhosale, SH; Han, SH; Kolekar, GB. Fluorescence resonance energy transfer from tryptophan to folic acidin micellar media and deionised water. *Journal of Photochemistry and Photobiology B: Biology*. 2011, 103, 16-21.

Mou, DG; Cooney, CL. Growth monitoring and control though computer-aided on-line mass balancing in a fed-batch penicillin fermentation. *Biotechnology and Bioengineering*. 1983, 25, 225-255.

Mulligan, CN; Gibbs, BF. Batch conversion of whey permeate to ammonium lactate by *Streptococcus cremosis*. *Biotechnology and Applied Biochemistry*. 1991, 14, 41-53.

Naghmouchi, K; Fliss, I; Drider, D; Lacroix, C. Pediocin PA-1 production during repeated-cycle batch culture of immobilized *Pediococcus acidilactici* UL5 cells.*Journal of Bioscience and Bioengineering*. 2008, 105, 513-517.

Nampoothiri, KM; Nair, NR; John, RP.An overview of the recent developments in polylactide (PLA) research.*Bioresource Technology*, 2010, 101, 8493-8501.

Nasrabadi, MRN; Razavi, SH. Optimization of β-carotene production by a mutant of lactose positive yeast *Rhodotorula acheniorum* from whey ultrafiltrate.*Food Science and Biotechnology.* 2011, 20, 445-454.

Nath, A; Dixit, M; Bandiya, S; Chavda, S; Desai, AJ.Enhanced PHB production and scale up studies using cheese whey in fed batch culture of *Methylobacterium* sp. ZP24.*Bioresource Technology*, 2008, 99, 5749-5755.

Nikel, PI; Pettinari, MJ; Mendez, BS; Galvagno, MA. Statistical optimization of culture medium for biomass and poly(3-hydroxybutyrate) production by recombinant *Escherichia coli* strain using agroindustrial byproducts. *International Microbiology.* 2005, 8, 243-250.

Nikel, PI; de Almeida, A; Melillo, EC; Galvagno, MA; Pettinari, MJ. New recombinant *Escherichia coli* strain tailored for production of poly(3-hydroxybutyrate) from agroindustrial by-products. *Applied and Environmental Microbiology.* 2006,72, 3949-3954.

Norton, S.; Lacroix, C; Vuillemard, JC. Kinetic study of continuous whey permeate fermentation by immobilized *Lactobacillus helveticus* for lactic acid production. *Enzyme and Microbial Technology.* 1994, 16, 457-466.

Obruca, S; Marova, I; Melusova, S; Mravcova, L. Production of polyhydroxyalkanoates from cheese whey by employing Bacillus megaterium CCM 2037.*Annals of Microbiology*, in press. DOI 10.1007/s13213-011-0218-5.

Obruca, S; Marova, I; Snajdar, O; Mravcova, L; Svoboda, Z. Production of poly(3-hydroxybutyrate-co-3-hydroxyvalerate) by *Cupriavidus necator* from waste rapeseed oil using propanol as a precursor of 3-hydroxyvalerate. *Biotechnology Letters.* 2010, 32, 1925-1932.

Oka, T. Amino acids, production processes. In: Flickinger MC; Drew SW. *Encyclopedia of bioprocess technology – fermentation biocatalysis and bioseparation.* New York: John Wiley and Sons; 1999; 89-100.

Osterhues, A; Holzgreve, W; Michels, KB. Shall we put the world of folate? *Lancet.* 2009, 374, 959-961.

Ozbas, T; Kutsal, T. Effect of growth-factors on riboflavin production by *Ashbya gosysypii.Enzyme and Microbial Technology.* 1991, 13, 594-596.

Page, WJ.Production of polyhydroxyalkanoates by *Azotobacter vinelandii* UWD in beet molasses culture.*FEMS Microbiology Reviews.* 1992, 103, 149-157.

Palaniraj, A; Jayaraman, V. Production, recovery and application of xanthan gum by *Xanthomonas campesteris.Journal of Food Engineering.*2011, 106, 1-12.

Pandian, SR; Deepak, V; Kalishwaralal, K; Rameshkumar, N;, Jayaraj, M; Gurunathan, S. Optimization and fed-batch production of PHB utilizing dairy waste and sea water as nutrient sources by *Bacillus megaterium* SRKP-3. *Bioresource Technology.* 2010, 101, 705-711.

Panesar, PS; Kennedy, JF; Gandhi, DN; Bunko, K. Bioutilization of whey for lactic acid production.*Food Chemistry*, 2007, 105, 1-14.

Panesar, PS; Kennedy, JF; Knill, CJ; Kosseva, M.Applicability of pectate-entrapped *Lactobacillus casei* cells for L(+) lactic acid production from whey. *Applied Microbiology and Biotechnology.* 2007, 74, 35-42.

Panesar, PS; Kennedy, JF; Knill, CJ; Kosseva, M. Production of L(+) lactic acid using *Lactobacillus casei* from whey. *Brazilian Archives of Biology and Technology*. 2010, 53, 219-226.

Pantazaki, AA; Papaneophytou, CP; Pritsa, AG; Liakopoulus-Kyriakides, M; Kyriakidis, DA.Production of polyhydroxyalkanoates from whey by *Thermus thermophilus* HB8.*Process Biochemistry*. 2009, 44, 847-853.

Papoutsopoulou, SV; Ekateriniadou, LV; Kyriakidis, DA.Genetic construction of *Xanthomonas campestris* and xanthan gum production from whey.*Biotechnology Letters*. 1994, 16, 1235-1240.

Parris, N; Anema, G; Singh, G; Creamer LK.Aggregation of whey proteins in heated sweet whey.*Journal of Agriculture and Food Chemistry,* 1993, 41, 160-464.

Paul, GC; Syddal, MT; Kent, CA; Thomas, CR. A structured model for penicillin production on mixed substrates. *Biochemical Engineering Journal*. 1998, 2, 11-21.

Philip, S; Keshavarz, T; Roy, I. Polyhydroxyalkanoates: biodegradable polymers with a range of application. *Journal of Chemical Technology and Biotechnology*. 2007, 82, 233-247.

Pires, AMB; Macedo, AC; Eguchi, SY; Santana, MHA.Microbial production of hyaluronic acid from agricultural resource derivatives.*Bioresource Technology*. 2010, 101, 6506-6509.

Plessas, S; Bosnea, L; Psarianos, C; Koutinas, AA; Marchant, R; Banat, IM. Lactic acid production by mixed cultures of *Kluyveromyces marxianus, Lactobacillus delbrueckii* ssp. *bulgaricus* and *Lactobacillus helveticus*. Bioresource Technology. 2008, 99, 5951-5955.

Povolo, S; Toffano, P; Bsaglia, M; Casella, S. Polyhydroxyalkanoates production by engineered *Cupriavidus necator* from waste material containing lactose.*Bioresource Technology*. 2010, 101, 7902-7907.

Rehm, BH; Valla, S. Bacterial alginates: biosynthesis and applications. *Applied Microbiology and Biotechnology.*1997, 48, 281-288.

Rekha, MR; Sharma, CP. Pullulan as a promising biomaterial for biomedical applications: a perspective. *Trends in Biomaterials and Artificial Organs*.2007, 20,116-122.

Roukas, T. Pullulan production from deproteinized whey by *Aureobasidium pullulans.Journal of Industrial Microbiology and Biotechnology*. 1999, 22, 617-621.

Roukas, T; Kotzekidou, R.Continuous production of lactic acid from deproteinized whey by coimmobilized *Lactobacillus casei* and *Lactococcus lactis* cells in a packed-bed reactor. *Food Biotechnology*.1996, 10, 231– 42.

Roukas, T; Kotzekidou, R.Lactic acid production from deproteinized whey by mixed cultures of free and coimmobilized *Lactobacillus casei* and *Lactococcus lactis* cells using fedbatch culture. *Enzyme and Microbial Technology*. 1998, 22, 199-204.

Roy, D; Goulet, J; LeDuy, A. Batch fermentation of whey ultrafiltrate by *Lactobacillus helveticus* for lactic acid production.*Applied Microbiology and Biotechnology*. 1986, 24, 206–213.

Santos, M; Rodrigues, A; Teixeira, JA. Production of dextran and fructose from carob pod extract and cheese whey by *Leuconostoc mesentereoides* NRRL B512(f). *Biochemical Engineering Journal*. 2005, 25, 1-6.

Satyanarayana, D; Venkateshwar, S. Lactic acid production from dairy waste by fermentation using *Lactobacillus delbruekii.Asian Journal of Microbiology Biotechnology and Environmental Sciences*. 2004, 6, 139–140.

Sawale, SD; Lele, SS. Statistical optimization of media for dextran production by *Leuconostoc* sp. isolated from fermented Idle Batter. *Food Science and Biotechnology.* 2010, 19, 471-478.

Schepers, AW; Thibault, J; Lacroix, C. *Lactobacillus heveticus* growth and lactic acid production during pH-controlled batch cultures in whey permeate/yeast extract medium. Part II: Kinetic modeling and model validation. *Enzyme Microbiology and Technology.* 2002, 30, 187–194.

Schepers, AW; Thibault, J; Lacroix, C. Continuous lactic acid production in whey permeate/yeast extract medium with immobilized *Lactobacillus helveticus* in a two-stage process: Model and experiments. *Enzyme and Microbial Technology.* 2006, 38, 324-337.

Schwartz, RD; Bodie, EA. Production of viscous dextran-containing whey-sucrose broths by *Leuconostoc mesenteroides* ATCC 14935.*Applied and Environmental Microbiology.* 1984, 48, 678-697.

Schwartz, RD; Bodie, EA. Production of high-viscosity whey broths by lactose-utilizing *Xanthomonas campesteris* strains.*Applied Microbiology and Biotechnology.* 1985, 50, 1483-1485.

Senthuran, A; Senthuran, V; Mattiasson, B; Kaul, RH. Lactic acid fermentation in cycle batch recycle batch reactor using immobilized *Lactobacillus casei*. *Biotechnology and Bioengineering.*1997, 55, 841-853.

Silva, MF; Fornani, RCG; Mazutti, MA; de Oliveira, D; Padilha, FF; Cichoski, AJ; Cansian, RL; Luccio, MD; Treichel, H. Production and characterization of xanthan gum by *Xanthomonas campestris* using cheese whey as sole carbon source. *Journal of Food Engineering.* 2009, 119-123.

Simova, ED; Frengova, GI; Beshkova, DM. Synthesis of carotenoids by Rhodotorula rubra GED8 co-cultured with yogurt starter cultures in whey ultrafiltrate. *Journal of Industrial Microbiology and Biotechnology.* 2004, 31, 115-121.

Siso, MIG. The biotechnological utilization of cheese whey: a review. *Bioresource Technology.* 1996, 57, 1-11.

Staniszewski, M; Kujawski, W; Lewandowska M.Semi-continuous ethanol production in bioreactor from whey with co-immobilized enzyme and yeast cells followed by pervaporative recovery of product - Kinetic model predictions considering glucose repression. *Journal of Food Engineering.* 2009, 91, 240-249.

Steinbuchel, A; Valentin, HE. Diversity of bacterial polyhydroxyalkanoic acids: minireview, *FEMS Microbiology Letters.* 1995, 125, 219-228.

Sudech, K; Abe, H; Doi, Y. Synthesis, structure and properties of polyhydroxyalkanoates: biological polyesters. *Progress in Polymer Science.* 2000, 25, 1503-1555.

Tian, J; Sinskey, AJ; Stubbe, J. Kinetics studies of polyhydroxybutyrate granule formation in *Wautersia eutropha* H16 by transmission electron microscopy.*Journal of Bacteriology.* 2005, 187, 3814-3824.

Thorne, L; Tansey, L; Pollock, TJ.Direct utilization of lactose in clarified cheese whey for xanthan gum synthesis by *Xanthomonas campesteris.Journal of Industrial Microbiology and Biotechnology.* 1988, 3, 321-328.

Truswell, AS. Vitamin B12.*Nutrition and Dietetics.*2007, 64, S120-S125.

Ullmann, F. Ullmann's Chemical Engineering and Plant Design, Volumes 1-2. 1st Edition. New York: John Wiley and Sons; 2005.

Valduga, E; tatsch, P; Vanzo, LT; Rauber, F; Di Luccio, M; Treichel, H. Assessment of hydrolysis of cheese whey and use of hydrolysate for bioproduction of carotenoids by *Sporidiobolus salminicolor* CBS 2636. *Journal of the Science of Food and Agriculture.* 2009, 89, 1060-1065.

Van Wegen, RJ; Ling, Y; Middelberg, APJ. Industrial production of polyhydroxyalkanoates using *Escherichia coli*: an economic analysis. *Trans IChemE.* 1998, 76, 417-426.

Varzakakou, M; Roukas, T. Identification of carotenoids produced from cheese whey by Blakeslea trispora in submerged fermentation.*Preparative Biochemistry and Biotechnology.* 2010, 40, 76-82.

Varzakakou, M; Roukas, T; Kotzekidou, P; Giamoustaris, A. Effect of non-ionic surfactants and beta-ionone on the morphology of *Blakeslea trispora* and carotenoids production from cheese whey in submerged aerobic growth: a statistical approach. *Food Biotechnology.* 2010, 24, 197-214.

Vasala, A; Panula, J; Neubaueur P. Efficient lactic acid production from high salt containing by-products by *Lactobacillus salivarium* ssp. *salicinius* with pre-treatment by proteolytic microorganisms. *Journal of Biotechnology.* 2005, 117, 421-431.

Venetsaneas, N; Antonopoulou, G; Stamatelatou, K; Kornaros, M; Lyberatos, G. Using cheese whey for hydrogen and methane generation in a two-stage continuous process with alternative pH controlling approaches. *Bioresource Technology.* 2009, 100, 3713-3717.

Viitanen, MI; Vasala, A; Neubauer, P; Alatossava, T. Cheese whey-induced high-cell-density production of recombinant proteins from *Escherichia coli.Microbial Cell Factories.*2003, 2.

Wee, YJ; Kim, JN; Ryu, HW.Biotechnological production of lactic acid bacteria and its recent application.*Food Technology and Biotechnology.*2006, 44, 163-172.

Williams, SF; Martin, DP.Applications of PHAs in medicine and pharmacy.In Doi Y, Steinbuchel A editors, *Biopolymers: Polyesters 3.* Weinheim: Wiley – VCH, Weinheim; 2002, 91–128.

WHO.Conclusions of a WHO technical consultation on folate and vitamins B112 deficiences.*Food and Nutrition Bulletin.*2008, 29, S238-S244.

Yang, TC; Wu, GH; Tseng, YH. Isolation of *Xanthomonas campestris* strain with elevated β-galactosidase activity for direct use of lactose in xanthan gum production. *Letters in Applied Microbiology.*2002, 35.375-379.

Yellore, V; Desai, A. Production of poly-3-hydroxybutyrate from lactose and whey by *Methylobacterium* sp. ZP24.*Letters in Applied Microbiology.* 1998, 26, 391-394.

In: Whey: Types, Composition and Health Implications   ISBN: 978-1-61942-862-1
Editors: Rafael M. Benitez and Gustavo M. Ortero   © 2012 Nova Science Publishers, Inc.

Chapter 3

WHEY PROTEINS AS FUNCTIONAL FOOD AFFECTING GLYCEMIC CONTROL: MOLECULAR DETERMINANTS

Giovanni Tulipano, Lara Faggi, Anna Maria Caroli and Daniela Cocchi*

Department of Biomedical Sciences and Biotechnologies,
University of Brescia, Italy

ABSTRACT

Whey proteins are high nutritional quality proteins and are currently used to prepare a number of commercial products claiming effects on consumer health. Whey proteins have potential as a functional food in the management of obesity and its co-morbidities, in detail non insulin dependent diabetes (NIDD or type-2 diabetes) and high blood pressure. Focusing on the effects of whey protein consumption on the insulinemic and glycemic response to meal in both type-2 diabetic and healthy subjects, preclinical and clinical studies suggest that whey protein intake can ameliorate postprandial glucose control and potentiate insulin release.

The insulinotropic effect of whey proteins can be due to their rapid digestion and to the following fast increase in plasma amino acids, in particular in the so called branched-chain amino acids (leucine, isoleucine, valine, threonine). Most likely, the insulinotropic effect of whey occurs by multiple pathways, including the potentiation of incretin activity mediated by small bioactive peptides released during gastrointestinal digestion or during food processing.

Glucose-dependent insulinotropic polypeptide (GIP) and glucagone-like peptide-1 (GLP-1) are gut derived peptides (so called incretin hormones) that are released after food ingestion and potentiate insulin secretion from the islet β-cells in a glucose-dependent manner. They are both rapidly degraded by the aminopeptidase, dipeptidyl peptidase-4 (DPP-4), after termination of feeding. Noteworthy, the use of injected DPP-4

---

* Corresponding author: Giovanni Tulipano, PhD, Unit of Pharmacology, Dept. Biomedical Sciences and Biotechnologies, University of Brescia, Viale Europa 11, 25123 Brescia (Ital), Fax 0039 030 3717529, e-mail: tulipano@med.unibs.it resistant GLP-1 analogs or, alternatively, the use of orally administered inhibitors of DPP-4 activity in order to increase endogenous incretin levels, are the most recent advances in the pharmacological treatment of type-2 diabetes.

As to the mechanism accounting for the positive effect of whey on the incretin system, there is evidence that products of whey protein digestion have the potential to affect incretin degradation through inhibition of intestinal DPP-4, with the outcome of prolonging their insulinotropic effect.

The aim of the present work is to review recent studies dealing with the effects of whey protein intake on glucose homeostasis and to focus on the molecular determinants for such effects contained within whey protein amino acids sequences. Genetic variants of whey proteins among species and within species which might predict differences in their effects on glycemic control will be also discussed.

1. INTRODUCTION

1.1. Management of Energy Balance

The management of energy balance in mammals is critical for their survival and mainly depends on complex networks involving local factors, circulating hormones and both central- and peripheral nervous system. The sensing of metabolic state and the transfer of information between the main tissues and organs involved in metabolic control (i.e. central nervous system, skeletal muscle, adipose tissue, endocrine pancreas and liver) regulate energy intake, energy store and energy expenditure.

The physiological and molecular mechanisms regulating plasma glucose homeostasis have been extensively reviewed elsewhere (Buse 2008). In the present paragraph, we restrict ourselves to summarize a few basic contents.

Insulin is well known as key regulator of energy metabolism and growth. Remarkably, insulin is unique in lowering plasma glucose after meal by stimulating glucose uptake in skeletal muscle and adipose tissue cells and by suppressing lipolysis and hepatic glucose production. Insulin activity is counterbalanced by circulating factors like glucagon, adrenaline and cortisol.

Pancreatic β-cells are sensitive to changes in plasma glucose concentrations. More precisely, insulin release is triggered by the increase in glucose transport into β-cells mediated by low affinity glucose-transporter (GLUT) subtypes, following glycemic response to meal. Actually, glucose-dependent insulin secretion is influenced by a number of hormones and metabolites like amino acids and free fatty acids (FAA) and by the autonomic nervous system activity.

Insulin acts by binding to insulin receptor, thus activating the receptor's intrinsic tyrosine kinase activity. This results in receptor autophosphorylation and subsequent phosphorylation of intracellular substrates of the IRS family (mainly IRS-1). As to insulin-stimulated glucose transport in skeletal muscle and fat tissue cells, intracellular signal propagation requires the activation of phosphatidylinositol 3-kinase (PI-3K) and its downstream effector Akt/PKB. Akt is central to insulin action by controlling the translocation of glucose transporters (GLUT4 subtype) from intracellular storage vesicles to cell surface. The same signaling pathway plays a role in mediating insulin stimulation of glycogen synthesis and protein synthesis. A number of factors can either enhance or decrease the sensitivity to insulin by acting on the intricate network of signaling pathways in target tissue cells and thus play a role in glycemic control (i.e. adipokines from adipose tissue).

Diabetes mellitus is a pathological condition mainly characterized by high circulating glucose concentrations (hyperglycemia) caused by a decrease in pancreatic release of insulin and/or a decrease in skeletal muscle-, adipose tissue- and liver sensitivity to insulin which leads to resistance to its blood glucose-lowering activity. Type 1 diabetes (insulin-dependent diabetes) is an autoimmune disease causing destruction of pancreatic β-cells. Patients suffering type 1 diabetes are not able to produce insulin and require insulin administration. Type 2 diabetes mellitus (non-insulin dependent diabetes) is an adult-onset metabolic disorder of energy balance and is the outcome of both altered insulin secretion and insulin resistance. Type 2 diabetes is the predominant form of diabetes (up to 90% of cases) and its worldwide prevalence is predicted to rise dramatically in 20 years (Nolan 2011).

The primary pathogenic event in the development of type 2 diabetes is chronic excess in calorie balance due to overnutrition and inactivity, joint to a failure of compensatory mechanisms in genetically or epigenetically susceptible people. Type 2 diabetes arises from inadequate response of pancreatic β-cells to calorie intake, increased glucagon secretion, failed suppression of hepatic glucose production, increased expansion of visceral adipose tissue versus subcutaneous tissue, inflammation of adipose tissue and reduced release of adiponectin, peripheral insulin resistance. The excess in free fatty acids and triglycerides and their ectopic storage in key organs like pancreas, liver and skeletal muscle may induce lipotoxicity events causing tissue damage and worsening islet β-cell function and peripheral insulin resistance (Nolan 2011).

1.2. Incretins in Glycemic Control and in Type 2 Diabetes

The aim of the present paragraph is to summarize the main understandings of incretin system activity since it is believed to play an important role in mediating the metabolic effects of whey protein intake, as discussed afterwards. More detailed information are reviewed in the cited references (mainly, Drucker 2003 and 2006a).

The mucosa of the gastrointestinal (GI) tract plays an important role in the management of energy balance. After meal ingestion, enteroendocrine cells dispersed along the length of the GI tract are locally involved in the regulation of the rate of gastric emptying and small bowel motility and cooperate to regulate pancreatic enzyme- and pancreatic hormone secretion.

Glucose-dependent insulinotropic polypeptide (GIP) and glucagone-like peptide-1 (GLP-1) are gut derived peptides (incretin hormones) that are released within minutes after food ingestion and potentiate insulin secretion from the islet β-cells in a glucose-dependent manner (Drucker 2003). The aminopeptidase dipeptidyl peptidase-4 (DPP-4) is the principal enzyme responsible for the rapid inactivation of these peptides *in vivo* through the removal of their NH_2-terminal dipeptides. DPP-4 exists as a cell surface membrane-spanning enzyme in numerous cell types and as a soluble circulating form (Darmoul 1994; Holst 1998).

Multiple factors are most likely responsible for rapid nutrient-stimulated GLP-1 release in humans, including autonomic nervous system via M1 muscarinic receptor activation, several neuropeptides, hormones and the direct contact of digested nutrients with GIP- and

GLP-1 secreting cells. Specific fats and complex carbohydrates are known to act as effective incretin secretagogues (Drucker 2003; Reimann 2010). Recently, it has been shown that intact or partially digested dietary proteins are able to affect GLP-1 release from *in vitro* cultured murine endocrine cells, too (Geraedts 2011). In fact, high protein diets have been shown to be more satiating than carbohydrates and fats and this effect is consistent with elevated levels of circulating gastrointestinal hormones including GLP-1 (Geraedts 2011).

As to incretin degradation, it is worth to remark that DPP-4 is highly expressed on endothelial cells directly adjacent to incretin-secreting cells in the gastrointestinal tract and it has been shown that the majority of circulating GLP-1 and GIP are cleaved into inactive moieties, suggesting that rapid degradation of incretins occurs soon after their release and before they can traverse the portal system (Hansen 1999; Drucker 2006b; Gunnarsson 2006). More in detail, NH_2-terminally truncated inactive peptides contribute to more than 50% of total immunoreactive GIP and GLP-1 in both the fasting and the postprandial state.

There is strong similarity between the amino acid sequences of GIP and GLP-1. Actually, their properties and physiological actions are not wholly superimposable. GIP-secreting enteroendocrine cells (K-cells) have been found in the proximal bowel (duodenum and proximal jejunum) and can be regarded as exposed to partially digested nutrients. In contrast, GLP-1 is mainly secreted by L-cells in the ileum and colon although L-cells have been also located in the proximal bowel.

In addition to acute potentiation of glucose-dependent insulin secretion, both GIP and GLP-1 promote expansion of β-cell mass by inducing β-cell proliferation and survival. GLP-1 also inhibits glucagon secretion and slows gastric emptying. Finally, GLP-1 has a role in central nervous system (CNS) regulation of food intake. Unlike GLP-1, GIP does not affect glucagon secretion, gastric emptying and food intake. GIP has a role in the control of fat metabolism in adipocytes in that it stimulates fatty acid synthesis and incorporation (Drucker 2003 and 2006a; Laferrere 2011).

Although altered incretin action is unlikely to be a primary defect in the development of type 2 diabetes, it may account for dysfunction in the secretion of glucagon, which fails to suppress after meal in diabetic subjects, and for gradual loss of β-cell mass and β-cell function. Noteworthy, the enhanced post-prandial release of GLP-1 after Roux-en-Y gastric bypass surgery (GBP) is believed to contribute to the improvement of type 2 diabetes as observed in up to 80% of patients which underwent surgical therapy, in parallel with the benefits of weight loss. The mechanism mediating the beneficial effects of GBP on incretin release is largely unknown. Interestingly, as far as the topic of the present paper is concerned, it has been suggested that the rapid exposure of the distal ileum to nutrients which have not been fully digested may be responsible for increased GLP-1 and hence for the recovery of the early phase insulin secretion and better glucose tolerance after meal (Laferrere 2011).

Finally, the use of GLP-1 receptor agonists or, alternatively, the use of orally administered inhibitors of DPP-4 activity in order to increase endogenous incretin levels, are the most recent advances in the pharmacological treatment of type-2 diabetes (Holst 1998; Drab 2010; Drucker 2006a).

1.3. Effects of Amino Acids on Insulin Secretion and Insulin Activity

Diets lower in carbohydrate and higher in protein have shown promising results on short-term weight loss and glycemic control. Remarkable results have been recently achieved by administering a diet containing 46% carbohydrate, 32.5% protein and 20% lipid to type-2 diabetic patients in a trial of acute calorie restriction and negative energy balance (Lim 2011). Actually, concern has been raised about potential adverse long-term effects of high protein intake. Indeed, high intake of protein and processed meat has been recently associated with increased incidence of type 2 diabetes in a large population based study (Ericson 2011). Moreover, an excess of products arising from metabolism of proteins can lead to glomerular hyperfiltration and is of concern for people with any degree of chronic kidney disease. Major nutrition recommendations for diabetic patients have been reported elsewhere (Buse 2008). Remarkably, individualized medical nutrition therapy and mixed meals have been recommended.

Although proteins have long been recognized as a source of short peptides with distinct biological activities which may be released during gastrointestinal digestion (Meisel 1997; Lorenzini 2007; Luhovyy 2007; Hernandez-Ledesma 2008), dietary proteins are basically a source of free amino acids. High-quality proteins, or complete proteins, contain substantial amounts of all essential amino acids. Amino acids are well known for their role as the building blocks of structural and functional proteins. Actually, there is evidence that individual amino acids play also direct roles in the regulation of metabolism. Amino acids, especially branched-chain amino acids (BCAAs), are well known to regulate secretion of hormones involved in the control of energy balance (insulin, glucagon and growth hormone). Current understandings of their effects on insulin secretion have been summarized elsewhere (Nair 2005; Buse 2008; Anuradha 2009). Briefly, amino acids have been shown to stimulate insulin release from pancreatic islets both *in vitro* and *in vivo*, the most potent secretagogues being arginine, lysine, leucine and phenylalanine (Nair 2005; Buse 2008). Actually, the effect of individual amino acids on insulin secretion may vary with physiological conditions, i.e. aging and fasting (Nair 2005).

A number of studies have investigated the relative roles of insulin and free amino acids in the regulation of protein turnover and glucose metabolism. As to the regulation of protein synthesis and degradation, data have been extensively reviewed elsewhere (Nair 2005).

Despite the fact that amino acids can be regarded as insulin secretagogues, data about the impact of free amino acids on the regulation of plasma glucose levels are still controversial. It is worth to remark that distinct amino acids may differ in their effects on glucose transport and glucose metabolism. Moreover, their effects on the sensitivity to insulin may be different in distinct target tissues and in different *in vitro* cultured cells.

Amino acid infusions can inhibit glucose utilization in healthy humans, due to preferential oxidation of amino acids versus glucose (Nair 2005), leading to reduced glucose tolerance. In this line, there is evidence that high protein diets and BCAA excess may increase insulin resistance and diabetes risk in humans (Ericson 2011) and plasma levels of BCAAs have been found higher in obese subjects compared to lean subjects (Newgard 2009; Wang 2011, Xiao 2011). Actually, as to the last data, it has not been clearly established whether high levels of circulating amino acids may be either markers or effectors of impaired control of body weight and plasma glucose. On the other hand, a recent study demonstrated that a higher BCAA intake is associated with a lower prevalence of being obese or overweight in middle-aged individuals (Qin 2011) and it is worth to remark that obesity is linked to the worsening of insulin resistance and to type 2 diabetes development. Moreover, a long-term dietary supplementation with a balanced amino acid formula was shown to improve glycemic control and insulin sensitivity in elderly subjects with type 2 diabetes (Solerte 2008).

With regards to the role played by specific BCAAs, the effects of dietary leucine content on insulin sensitivity have been throughly investigated but controversy still exists (Valerio 2011). Leucine deprivation increased the hepatic insulin sensitivity in *in vitro* cultured hepatocytes (Xiao 2011). Conversely, leucine infusion was shown to decrease the endogenous glucose production in synergy with insulin action and doubling dietary leucine was able to reverse many metabolic alterations (i.e. hepatic steatosis) with a marked improvement in glucose tolerance without altering food intake or weight gain in mice fed on high fat diet (Macotela 2011).

As to the effects of free amino acids on insulin signaling pathways and on insulin-simulated glucose uptake in target tissues, intracellular amino acids excess in skeletal muscle has been shown to determine overactivation of mammalian-target-of-rapamycin (mTOR) cascade with the following serine/threonine phosphorylation of insulin-receptor-substrate-1 (IRS-1) and decreased recruitment and activation of PI-3 kinase, an event normally associated with insulin resistance (Tremblay 2007; Anuradha 2009). In fact, this inhibitory effect on PI-3 kinase/Akt-mediated insulin signaling may account for the reduction of insulin-stimulated glucose transport, as observed in *in vitro* cultured L6 skeletal muscle cells after acute exposure to a balanced amino acid mixture (Tremblay 2001). Actually, in the same study the individual amino acids were found to affect differently the glucose transport, with inhibitory effects of leucine, metionine, threonine and tyrosine and null effects of isoleucine, valine and phenylalanine. It is also noteworthy that BCAAs like leucine, isoleucine and valine may differ significantly in their effects on glucose transport, despite their structural similarity.

On the other hand, a negative modulation of insulin action by exposure to BCAAs is not certain in all the experimental models. Indeed, isoleucine was shown to induce glucose transport in C2C12 skeletal muscle cells in an insulin-independent manner (Doi 2003) and *in vitro* studies on adipocytes from rats made obese by high-fat diet intake and on adipose tissue explants from genetically obese mice showed that amino acids may exert a positive effect in the setting of insulin resistance by enhancing insulin-induced Akt activation and glucose transport independently of PI-3K, which is upstream of Akt in the related insulin signaling pathway (Hinault 2004 and 2006). Furthermore, Kleinert and coworkers have recently reported on the effects of an amino acid mixture containing isoleucine, leucine, valine and sulphur-containing amino acids on glucose uptake in isolated rat epitrochlearis muscle. The amino acid mixture stimulated glucose uptake in the absence of insulin and increased insulin-induced glucose uptake additively. In agreement with data obtained in adipocyte cell cultures, the amino acid mixture induced Akt activation in the absence of insulin without enhancing Akt phosphorylation (Kleinert 2011).

Evidence has been shown suggesting that BCAA-activated mTOR signaling may have beneficial effects accompanied by increased average life span *in vivo* experimental models. In detail, long-term dietary supplementation with a specific BCAA-enriched amino acid mixture was found to increase mitochondrial biogenesis and to up-regulate the reactive oxygen species defence system with reduced tissue oxidative damage both in cardiac and skeletal muscles of mice. These BCAA-induced changes were dependent on endothelial NO synthase activity and were related to activation of mTOR signaling in muscle cells. Remarkably, the effects were tissue-specific in that they were not observed in liver or adipose tissue of the same animals (Valerio 2011). To our purpose, it is important to remark that increased mitochondrial biogenesis and function in skeletal muscles is expected to ameliorate glycemic control in the whole body (Szendroedi 2011).

In summary, the results of preclinical and clinical studies do not allow to draw final conclusions about the role played by amino acid- or more specifically BCAA-intake in the management of glycaemic control, despite their insulinotropic effect.

2. MOLECULAR BASIS FOR THE EFFECTS OF WHEY PROTEINS ON POSTPRANDIAL GLYCEMIC CONTROL

2.1. Effects of Whey Protein Intake on Metabolic Regulation

There has long been interest in the impact of dairy consumption on food intake regulation and glucose homeostasis and there is substantial agreement about the capacity of milk protein to affect appetite and food intake (Luhovyy 2007). In 2002, a population-based prospective study provided evidence that dairy consumption can also reduce the incidence of insulin resistance among overweight individuals (Pereira 2002). The two primary sources of proteins in milk are the caseins and whey. Whey protein intake has been shown to enhance the insulinemic response to carbohydrate-rich food in healthy subjects and in type-2 diabetes suffering patients (Nilsson 2004; Frid 2005; Manders 2006; Petersen 2009; Akhavan 2010).

The inhibitory effect of milk proteins, both caseins and whey, on food intake is most likely mediated by the well documented enhancement of the release of insulin from endocrine pancreas and satiety hormones from enteroendocrine cells in the gastrointestinal tract, namely cholecystokinin (CKK) and GLP-1. Whey protein intake also increases GIP release from K cells in the Duodenum (Nilsson 2004; Frid 2005; Gunnarsson 2006; Manders 2006; Luhovyy 2007; Petersen 2009). GIP and GLP-1 are so called incretins in that their release into the portal system in response to meal cooperates to enhance insulin secretion from pancreatic β-cells in response to plasma glucose increase. The influence of whey proteins on the incretin system activity is likely to play a pivotal role in their effects on glycemic control.

Regardless of dietary sources of proteins, the satiating and insulinotropic effects of protein intake are rather expected, due to the following increase in circulating amino acid levels. Actually, there is growing evidence that these effects are at least partially source-dependent; i.e. differences have been reported between whey and caseins (Luhovyy 2007). Finally, it is worth to consider that the effect of protein intake may be affected by many factors like the physiological or pathological conditions of the subjects (overweight, obesity, insulin resistance or diabetes), the overall macronutrient content of their diet and the overall caloric intake.

Preclinical and clinical studies on the effects of whey on metabolic disorders have been recently reviewed (Luhovyy 2007; Hernandez-Ledesma 2008; Graf 2011). Now, we are focusing on a number of studies published in the last three years which address the differences in the acute effects on appetite, energy intake, plasma glucose- and hormone levels between whey protein supplements and other protein sources.

In lean, healthy men whey protein intake produced a higher increase of plasma insulin as compared with three distinct protein sources (tuna, turkey, egg). The greater postprandial insulin response may account for the more pronounced effect on appetite and the lower *ad libitum* energy intake at a subsequent meal (4 hours later with respect to protein test meal) (Pal 2010).

The strongest acute effect of whey on insulin release compared with other proteins was not new (Veldhorst 2009). Whey also triggered the strongest response in concentrations of active GLP-1 compared with caseins and soy proteins.

A discrepancy exists between the two above mentioned studies in that Veldhorst and coworkers reported no differences in *ad libitum* energy intake (as assessed 2 hours later with respect to the test meal) between the protein sources, despite their differential effects on satiating hormones. Quite precisely, whey decreased hunger more than caseins or soy proteins when subjects had received test meals with low or normal relative protein content (10% energy source) but no differences in appetite ratings were observed after test meals with higher protein content (25% energy source).

As to the effects of different kind of proteins on pancreatic hormone release, Claessens and coworkers reported that both insulin and glucagon responses increased with increasing protein load for soya and whey proteins. Actually, the effect was more pronounced for glucagon so that the insulin:glucagon ratio tended to decrease with higher doses of proteins in test meals (Claessens 2008). These results may suggest potential adverse effect of protein supplements on postprandial glucose control, in disagreement with aforementioned studies. Remarkably, the increase in glucagon release after whey intake is rather unexpected due to the well documented stimulatory effects of whey intake on incretin secretion. In detail, an increase in plasma GLP-1 levels following whey intake would be expected to contribute to postprandial glucagon suppression.

Apart from confirming a greater insulin response after whey meal than after soy- or casein meal and an attenuated glycemic response after consumption of test meals with high protein content versus a glucose meal containing the same glucose load, Acheson and coworkers proved that whey intake was more effective in stimulating thermogenesis and fat oxidation in lean, healthy subjects than soy or caseins (Acheson 2011).

The effects of distinct dietary proteins on metabolic responses have been studies in different physiological or pathological conditions.

Hoppe and coworkers performed a 7-day long supplementation study in prepubertal boys in order to compare the insulinotropic activity of whey versus casein. They showed that whey, but not so caseins, increased fasting insulin. In turn, caseins caused an higher increase of circulating IGF-1 levels vs whey. These results prompted the authors to conclude that the two major milk protein fractions are both involved in the growth-promoting effect of milk (Hoppe 2009). Actually, it is worth to remark that an exaggerated insulinotropic nutrition may have substantial adverse implications in young people because overactivation of insulin signaling may promote pathologies like juvenile acne and an increase in adiposity and body weight which can predispose to metabolic diseases (Melnik 2011).

In type 2 diabetic patients, Mortensen and coworkers showed that a whey supplement to a high-fat meal caused a more marked improvement of postprandial lipemia than casein-, cod- or gluten proteins. No differences were observed in pancreatic hormone- or incretin responses to the different protein test meals (Mortensen 2009).

Bowen and coworkers compared the responses to protein preloads in subjects with high BMI versus subjects with normal BMI. The BMI status did not affect the higher satiating effect of protein intake compared with a reference carbohydrate test meal. Remarkably, no differences were found in the effects on *ad libitum* food intake (as assessed 3 hour later with respect to test meal) and in the effects on postprandial plasma levels of appetite regulating hormones (namely, ghrelin, CKK and GLP-1) between distinct protein sources (Bowen 2006a, 2006b).

Conversely, Baer and coworkers have recently published the results of a clinical trial aimed at evaluating the effects of protein supplementation to free-choice diets on body weight in overweight or obese subjects. The study provided compelling evidence that different protein sources (namely, whey and soy proteins) may differently facilitate weight loss and affect body composition. After 23 weeks of treatment, whey protein but not soy protein supplementation caused a small but significant decrease in body weight and fat mass and significantly reduced waist circumference compared to an isoenergetic carbohydrate-containing supplement (Baer 2011).

The comparison between the effects of different protein supplements on body composition and glycemic response has been investigated in preclinical models, as well. In wistar rats fed a high fat diet for two months, allocation to a high protein diet for six week reduced energy intake and visceral and subcutaneous fat depots. Actually, whey protein diet was more effective than red meat in improving insulin sensitivity (decreased fasting plasma insulin and plasma insulin/glucose ratio versus controls) and reducing body weight (Belobrajdic 2003 and 2004).

Differently from the majority of the aforementioned human studies, data obtained in rats fed a high fat diet suggest that whey protein intake may reduce plasma glucose levels by ameliorating tissue response to insulin, independently of its insulinotropic effect. In agreement with preclinical data, evidence that whey protein intake may contribute to postmeal blood glucose control by both insulin-dependent and insulin-independent mechanisms, has been obtained in young, healthy humans (Akhavan 2010).

It is worth to remark that the results of clinical trials in lean, healthy subjects may be uninformative about the efficacy of whey supplementation in obese-, insulin resistant- or type-2 diabetic subjects. Recent clinical studies have been published which further address this issue. Lan-Pidhainy and Wolever showed that the hypoglycemic and insulinotropic effects of whey were not blunted by the degree of insulin resistance as estimated by fasting serum insulin levels in humans (Lan-Pidhainy 2010). In agreement with these findings, Ma and coworkers showed that whey protein consumed before a carbohydrate meal could stimulate GLP-1 and insulin secretion and could slow gastric emptying in type-2 diabetic patients (Ma 2009). As to the effects in obese, non diabetic subjects, whey protein intake elicited early incretin responses like in lean individuals (Lindgren 2011). Whey protein supplementation of a spontaneous diet improved hepatic steatosis and plasma lipid profiles in obese women after four weeks of treatment, without adverse effects on glucose tolerance (Bortolotti 2011). Finally, Frestedt and coworkers showed that a whey protein supplement in combination with the restriction of calorie intake increased fat loss and spared lean muscle in obese subjects with respect to calorie restriction, only (Frestedt 2008). Actually, in contrast with these data, Bellissimo and coworkers found that the effect of whey-protein preload on satiety was affected by body composition in that whey protein suppressed food intake in normal weight boys but not in obese boys (Bellissimo 2008).

2.2. Molecular Determinants

Dietary proteins have long been recognized as functional foods with direct effects on consumer health, regardless of their role as source of essential metabolic substrates. Whey proteins can be ranked with the most effective proteins in affecting satiety and postprandial glycemic control (see previuos paragraph). Elucidating the molecular factors and the mechanisms involved in the insulinotropic and glucose-lowering activity of whey proteins may be of interest to the preparation of diet supplements aimed at improving postprandial glycemic control.

Whey and caseins are the two primary sources of protein in milk. Whey (milk serum) is defined as the soluble component of milk proteins after precipitation of caseins at pH 4.6 and 20°C. The primary components of whey and the interspecies differences in the composition of whey, as far as the ratio between protein fractions is concerned, have been extensively listed elsewhere (Luhovyy 2007). It is enough to remark that β-lactoglobulin (β-LG) is the major whey protein found in the milk of cows and other ruminants, representing up to 50-55% of total whey protein and 12% of milk protein whereas it is almost absent in human and rat milks. Conversely, bovine milk contains lower levels of α-lactalbumin (α-LA) (as low as 5% whey protein) versus human milk.

Any functional properties of ingested whey is likely to be ascribed either to free amino acids derived from full enzymatic digestion of proteins or to small peptides derived from partial degradation of proteins. Actually, direct effects of intact proteins on cells within the intestinal mucosa cannot be ruled out, as well.

Whey proteins, above all β-lactoglobulin and α-lactalbumin, are ranked within high quality proteins due to their high content of essential amino acids and BCAAs (namely, leu, ile and val), including the well-known insulin secretagogue leucine, with respect to proteins from vegetable sources. Moreover, whey proteins, in particular α-lactalbumin, are rich in sulphur-containing amino acids (cysteine and methionine) which are substrates for the intracellular glutathione synthesis. Indeed, a long-term whey supplementation has been proven useful to increase the glutathione levels in HIV-infected subjects (Micke 2001). As to our topic, it is important to point out that the addition of a cysteine supplement to meal has been proven useful to acutely improve the glycemic control in rats fed a high-sucrose diet (Blouet 2007).

The role of BCAAs in regulating insulin secretion and tissue response to insulin has been extensively discussed in previous paragraphs. The fast increase in plasma amino acid levels following to the rapid digestion of whey can at least partially account for its insulinotropic effect, due to the direct stimulatory action of free amino acids on insulin release form pancreatic islets. The rise of plasma insulin would, in turn, determine the glycemic response and the satiety response to meal after whey preload. Actually, in young healthy subjects, Akhavan and coworkers have recently showed that a preload with intact whey proteins produced better postmeal glycemic control than a preload with the corresponding hydrolysates, by both insulin-dependent and insulin-independent mechanisms (Akhavan 2010). These results support a major role of intact proteins or peptidic hydrolysates versus the corresponding free amino acid mixtures in mediating the effects of whey protein intake on postmeal glycemic response.

Four more papers remarked on the importance of intact or partially digested whey proteins with respect to free amino acids derived from their complete degradation by enzymatic hydrolysis. It is worth to remind that the insulinotropic effect of whey protein is believed to occur by multiple pathways, including the potentiation of incretin activity (see previous paragraph). Nilsson and coworkers showed that the intake of free amino acid mixtures cannot raise plasma incretin levels to the same extent as whey protein intake (Nilsson 2007). Furthermore, Geraedts and coworkers have recently provided evidence that intact whey proteins and proteins partially digested by trypsin were able to directly stimulate the release of the satiating hormone CCK and the incretin hormone GLP-1 from *in vitro* cultured murine entero-endocrine cells (STC-1). In detail, the authors tested various dietary proteins for their *in vitro* effect on CCK and GLP-1 release. Proteins from different animal and vegetable sources were found to enhance hormone secretion and, remarkably, whey protein were not more effective than caseins, egg albumin and pea proteins (Geraedts 2011). The direct effect of whey protein on CCK release from STC-1 cells *in vitro* has been recently confirmed by Catiau and coworkers (Catiau 2011). In detail, they showed that both intact □-lactalbumin and its chymotryptic hydrolysate were able to increase CCK secretion. Interestingly, the chymotryptic hydrolysate proved to be more effective than the intact protein and than egg albumin hydrolysate.

Finally, α-lactalbumin is a cysteine-rich protein and it has been speculated that the enhancement of glutathione synthesis following α-lactalbumin hydrolysis and absorption of cysteine *in vivo*, may account for the improved glycemic control in response to whey protein intake. Actually, Blouet and coworkers proved that the administration of a specific inhibitor of glutathione synthesis abrogated the beneficial effects of cystein supplement on post-prandial glycemic control in rats fed a high-sucrose diet but did not affect those of α-lactalbumin, suggesting a more complex mechanism for α-lactalbumin action (Blouet 2007).

It is well known that the large majority of intact proteins and peptides are likely to be poorly or not in the least absorbed in blood after oral administration. Low bioavailability raises high scepticism about the relevance of dietary proteins or peptides provided with functional properties which need to enter the circulatory system and reach their target tissue in an intact form. Actually, peptides released after partial proteolytic cleavage of dietary proteins may also act locally on cells in close proximity of the lumen of the bowel, without needing to reach high circulating levels to raise an effect. Endocrine cells in the gastro intestinal tract, including the incretin secreting cells in the proximal and distal bowel, can be regarded as a possible target. In particular, GIP-secreting cells (Nilsson 2004; Gunnarsson 2006) in the proximal bowel are likely to be transiently exposed to high local concentrations of whey proteins and whey protein-derived peptides because whey proteins are believed to reach rapidly jejunum after their intake.

To our knowledge, any molecular determinants of the stimulatory effect of whey protein intake on incretin secretion in the proximal and distal bowel have not been identified yet. Furthermore, although *in vitro* experiments suggest that whey proteins and whey protein-derived peptides can directly affect GLP-1 release from entero-endocrine STC-1 cells, any indirect effect mediated by the autonomous nervous system or the endocrine system is equally conceivable *in vivo* and can not be ruled out at present.

A few years ago, data published by Gunnarsson and coworkers suggested that whey protein intake can enhance the incretin response to meal by retarding incretin enzymatic inactivation with the outcome of prolonging their insulinotropic effect. In fact, the peptidase DPP-4 is highly expressed on endothelial cells directly adjacent to increting-secreting cells within the *lamina propria* in the gastrointestinal tract (Hansen 1999; Gunnarsson 2006; Drucker 2006b) and the majority of circulating GLP-1 and GIP are cleaved into inactive molecules, suggesting rapid degradation of incretins before they can traverse the portal system. According to studies in rodents and in humans, whey protein intake has the potential to reduce DPP-4 activity in the proximal small bowel, the main site of GIP synthesis, and to increase plasma levels of intact GIP (Nilsson 2004; Frid 2005; Gunnarsson 2006; Menders 2006; Petersen 2009).

During last decades, it has been clearly shown that milk proteins, both caseins and whey proteins, are a source of short peptides with distinct biological activities which are generated by enzymatic hydrolysis during gastrointestinal digestion or during food processing. Interestingly, a number of bioactive peptides with antihypertensive-, antimicrobial-, hypocholesterolemic- or opiod-like activities have been identified within the products of degradation of β-lactoglobulin, the major whey protein found in the milk of cows and other ruminants (Lorenzini 2007; Hernandez-Ledesma 2008). Based on the above mentioned effects of whey protein intake on incretin degradation, we have recently investigated the presence of moieties with DPP-4 inhibitor activity among the bioactive peptides derived from β-lactoglobulin. We showed that the peptide Ile-Pro-Ala (IPA) is a DPP-4 inhibitor *in vitro* (Tulipano 2011a). IPA (β-lactosin) has been previously identified in β-lactoglobulin hydrolysates prepared using proteinase K. It has been shown to exert a strong antihypertensive effect in rats (Abubakar 1998) and acts as a moderate angiotensin-converting enzyme inhibitor *in vitro*. Back to our studies, two more peptides (Leu-Leu and Leu-Ala) proved to act as DPP-4 inhibitors but their potency was 10-fold lower as compared with IPA (Tulipano 2011a). Leucine-containing dipeptides like Leu-Leu and Leu-Val are products of β-lactoglobulin digestion with bacterial proteases (Morifuji 2009). Leu-Ala has not been identified in whey protein hydrolysates but it can be regarded as a transient product of β-lactoglobulin cleavage by digestive proteases, according to *in silico* analysis (Tulipano 2011a). Although we can not complain a link between the presence of these DPP-4 inhibitors within β-lactoglobulin sequence and the well documented effects of whey protein intake on glycemic control, we suggest that IPA can be a molecular determinant of the inhibitory effect of whey protein ingestion on DPP-4 activity in the proximal bowel. The dipeptides Leu-Leu and Leu-Ala are weak inhibitors but they also may play a role in the regulation of DPP-4 activity because the luminal cleavage of β-lactoglobulin is expected to generate high concentrations of fragments in close proximity to endothelial DPP-4. New data supporting the presence of DPP-4 inhibitors within β-lactoglobulin hydrolysates has been recently published by Uchida and coworkers. They isolated a new DPP-4 inhibitor hexapeptide within β-lactoglobulin hydrolysis products obtained by incubation with trypsin. The authors also reported that, differently from β-lactoglobulin, α-lactalbumin hydrolysates did not show any inhibitory effect on DPP-4 and provided evidence that β-lactoglobulin has a role in the effect of whey protein intake on glycemic response to meal. In detail, they showed that the oral administration of β-lactoglobulin digested with trypsin decreased the plasma glucose peak and AUC vs controls in the oral glucose tolerance test in mice. The DPP-4 inhibitory activity might have contributed to such an effect in that the well-known DPP-4 inhibitor sitagliptin was able to affect the plasma glucose response to the oral glucose load to a similar extent and with the same time-course as β-lactoglobulin hydrolysates (Uchida 2011).

We have already pointed out that low bioavailability of orally administered polypeptides is expected, with high concern about the relevance of bioactive peptides from dietary proteins *in vivo* (Foltz 2010). Actually, it has been recently reported that bioactive tripeptides from a lactotripeptide-enriched milk beverage are absorbed into the circulation (Foltz 2007). As to DPP-4 inhibitor peptides, IPA has been shown to raise a strong antihypertensive effect in rats after oral administration (Abubakar 1998). These data suggest that IPA can be absorbed in blood and can preserve circulating incretins from degradation by DPP-4, which is expressed on cell surface in various tissue and is also released in a soluble form. Furthermore, a novel DPP-4 inhibitor peptide has been recently identified in the water-soluble fraction of Gouda-type cheese homogenates (Uenishi 2012). The authors proved that the peptide was able to reduce the glucose response in a glucose tolerance test after oral administration in rats, suggesting high bioavailability although it consisted of eight amino acid.

Table 1. Well-known DPP-4 inhibitors and N-terminal amino acid sequences of DPP-4 inhibitor peptides from dairy proteins. The proposed consensus sequence. See Molecular Determinants paragraph for details. BCAA, branched chain amino acid. In the third position, amino acids with a aliphatic side-chain, glycine or glutamine are consistent with DPP-4 inhibitory activity

NH₂—ILE—PRO—ILE	(diprotin A, Umezawa 1984)
NH₂—VAL—PRO—LEU	(diprotin B, Umezawa 1984)
NH₂—ILE—PRO—ALA	(Tulipano 2011a)
NH₂—LEU—ALA	(Tulipano 2011b)
NH₂—LEU—PRO—GLN—X—X—	(Uenishi 2012)
NH₂—VAL—ALA—GLY—X—X—	(Uchida 2011)

Site of enzymatic cleavage

↓

NH₂—BCAA—PRO—X—X--

-(ALA)-

The comparison between the amino acid sequences of the DPP-4 inhibitor peptide from Gouda-type cheese and the peptide IPA from β-lactoglobulin reveals that their N-terminal dipeptides (Leu-Pro) are quite similar (Leu-Pro vs Ile-Pro, respectively) in that Leu and Ile are both amino acids with branched hydrophobic side-chains. Again, the N-terminal dipeptide (Val-Ala) of the DPP-4 inhibitor hexapeptide identified by Uchida and coworkers resembles the DPP-4 inhibitor Leu-Ala, due to the presence of a BCAA with aliphatic chain in the first position. The N-terminal amino acids play a central role in the mechanism of DPP-4 inhibition by peptidic compounds. DPP-4 cleaves the N-terminal dipeptides X-Ala or X-Pro from its target proteins, such as GIP and GLP-1. Short peptides carrying proline or alanine as a second amino acid from the N-terminus are likely to act as pseudosubstrates and competitive inhibitors of DPP-4. The remaining amino acids may contribute to determine the binding affinity for the enzyme active site and the potency. We may conclude that the N-terminal amino acid sequences of the DPP-4 inhibitor peptides from dairy proteins joint to the structure of previously characterized DPP-4 inhibitors (Umezawa 1984) suggest a consensus sequence, with a BCAA at the N-terminus and either Pro or Ala in the second position (table 1). It is not possible to rule out that the following amino acids in third or fourth position may be relevant to the inhibitory activity, as well but no consensus can be drawn at present. In agreement with the latter comment, we have previously shown that a moderate DPP-4 inhibitory activity was observed *in vitro* by using a dipeptide containing Leu for Ala in the second position (Leu-Leu peptide). The addition of Phe (Leu-Leu-Phe peptide) completely abolished the inhibitory activity (Tulipano 2011a). Again, data by Uenishi and coworkers suggest that the presence of Pro in the third position is related to decreased inhibition of DPP-4 *in vitro*, regardless the presence of N-terminal dipeptides matching the proposed consensus sequence (Uenishi 2012).

Although further confirmation is required, a consensus sequence may be helpful for searching published amino acid sequences of protein of interest for their content of biopeptides with the potential to affect DPP-4 activity (table 2).

Table 2. Comparison between the published amino acid sequences of β-lactoglobulin (variant B) and α-lactalbumin (ref. http://www.uniprot.org). The two protein sequences do not show any substantial difference in the content of sulphur-containing amino acids (undermarked twice) or BCAAs (bolded). Based on the proposed N-terminal consensus sequence of DPP-4 inhibitor peptides from dairy proteins, a lower amount of DPP-4 inhibitors should be expected among the products of enzymatic cleavage of α-lactalbumin versus β-lactoglobulin (see undermarked dipeptides), in agreement with the results shown by Uchida and coworkers (2011)

P02754 (LACB_BOVIN)

MKCLLLALALTCGAQALIVTQTMKGLDIQKVAGTWYSLAMAASDISLLDAQSAPL
RVYVEELKPTPEGDLEILLQKWENGECAQKKIIAEKTKIPAVFKIDALNENKVLVLD
TDYKKYLLFCMENSAEPEQSLACQCLVRTPEVDDEALEKFDKALKALPMHIRLSFN
PTQLEEQCHI

P00711 (LALBA_BOVIN)

MMSFVSLLLVGILFHATQAEQLTKCEVFRELKDLKGYGGVSLPEWVCTTFHTSGYD
TQAIVQNNDSTEYGLFQINNKIWCKDDQNPHSSNICNISCDKFLDDDLTDDIMCVKK
ILDKVGINYWLAHKALCSEKLDQWLCEKL

Preliminar *in silico* and *in vitro* studies aimed at finding out the theoretical molecular determinants within the amino acid sequences underlying the effects of whey protein intake on plasma intact incretin levels, may be also relevant to predict differences in enhancing incretin activity and hence postmeal insulin response between whey proteins from either different species or genetic variants within species, by searching their published amino acid sequences (Tulipano 2011b). For instance, our results suggest that the differential level of expression of β-lactoglobulin across and within species could significantly affect DPP-4 inhibitor content of whey. We have previously discussed the relative β-lactoglobulin content of milk from different species. Now, it is worth to remark that the most common bovine β-lactoglobulin variants (A and B) differ significantly in their levels of expression, with the outcome of higher amount of β-lactoglobulin in the milk of animals carrying the A variant vs animals carrying the B variants (Cerbulis 1975; Graml 1989; Lum 1997; Ganai 2008). Furthermore, the sequence IPA and the hexapeptide identified by Uchida and coworkers are conserved across bovine, ovine and caprine species and within bovine variants (see Tulipano 2011b for details about sequence alignment). Noteworthy, IPA is absent in β-lactoglobulin from donkey whereas an hexapeptide with strong similarity to the DPP-4 inhibitor isolated by Uchida and coworkers is present in the published amino acid sequence (amino acid residues starting from position-15 to -20: VAG—W— in P13613 LACB1_EQUAS and in P19647 LACB2-EQUAS; http://www.uniprot.org). Actually, before drawing any conclusion, it is worth to remark once more that the insulinotropic and glucose-lowering effects of whey are most likely raised by multiple factors and *in vivo* preclinical studies are required to prove or reject any role played by the DPP-4 inhibitory peptides in mediating the effects of whey protein intake on metabolic regulation. The first step might be the study of the relationships, if any, between the relative β-lactoglobulin content of whey and its effects on postmeal incretin degradation and glycemic response.

The classification of whey proteins as "fast" protein, based on the rate of amino acid absorption in blood and the effect on endogenous protein synthesis, has been extensively discussed elsewhere (Dangin 2001; Luhovyy 2007). Now, it is important to remark that such peculiar properties are relevant to their effects on glycemic control.

After being ingested, whey proteins are believed to reach rapidly the jejunum as intact polypeptides and to be digested slowly as compared to other proteins in the small intestine. Conversely, caseins are prone to clot in the stomach due to the acid environment and their release to the intestine is delayed. Despite the requirement of a longer time for being degraded in the intestine, the digestion of whey and the absorption of its amino acids are still faster than for proteins like caseins, which accordingly have been classified as "slow" proteins. The outcome is a faster and higher but short-lasting increase in plasma amino acid concentrations after whey protein intake. The considerable peak of plasma amino acids, including BCAAs, may account for the observed enhancement of the early postprandial insulin response as observed after whey supplement intake. Furthermore, if whey proteins escape extensive peptic hydrolysis and their degradation mainly depends on the action of the proteases released into the lumen (i.e. trypsin) or exposed on the cell surface in the small intestine, a peculiar set of hydrolysis products may be expected with respect to proteins which are longer exposed to the acid environment. In summary, we may speculate that the peculiar fate of whey protein in the gastrointestinal tract may be relevant to the release of short, functional peptides in the small intestine and to their interaction with enteroendocrine cells over a great length of intestine before being fully degraded and absorbed. Although "slow" proteins like caseins may contain high amounts of essential amino acids as whey proteins and their published amino acid sequences may include short peptides with the potential to affect the incretin system activity, it is highly conceivable that the differences in the time of exposure to peptic hydrolysis and the overall rate of digestion may contribute to determine differences in the functional properties between caseins and whey proteins as far as postprandial glycemic control is concerned.

Finally, it has been reported that complete dairy protein intake attenuated weight gain and improved body composition and insulin sensitivity to a greater extent than whey or casein alone in diet-induced obese rats (Eller 2010). These results suggest a synergistic action of whey protein and caseins which most likely depends on the difference in their fate in the gastrointestinal tract when ingested. Whey proteins provide early signals whereas caseins provide later signals in the regulation of food intake, insulin secretion, glucose metabolism and protein synthesis (Luhovyy 2007).

CONCLUSION

Whey proteins are known to be high nutritional quality proteins and are currently used to prepare a number of commercial products claiming effects on consumer health.

Focusing on the effects of whey protein consumption on plasma glucose homeostasis both in type-2 diabetic patients and healthy subjects, preclinical and clinical studies suggest that whey protein intake can improve the insulinaemic and glycaemic response to meal. Hence, whey protein can be regarded as an excellent dietary protein with additional functional properties in both healthy subjects and subjects with altered glycemic control due to insulin resistance.

More doubts have been raised about the clinical efficacy of whey protein supple-mentation on metabolic diseases. For instance, Graf and coworkers concluded that the clinical evidence are not strong enough to make final recommendations presently as far as the dose and the duration of supplementation is concerned (Graf 2011; Poppit 2011). In support of their comment, among intervention trials addressing the effects of whey protein supplementation on glycemic control, a few studies have examined the acute or subchronic effects, only. Moreover, due to the complex impact of high protein intake and circulating free amino acids on the regulation of plasma glucose, it would be hardly possible to establish the correct dose and duration of whey protein supplementation without carefully regarding the whole diet composition, its protein content and the physiological or pathological condition of subjects.

REFERENCES

[1] Abubakar, A., Saito, T., Kitazawa, H., Kawai, Y., & Itoh, T. (1998). Structural analysis of new antihypertensive peptides derived from cheese whey protein by proteinase K digestion. *Journal of Dairy Science, 81*, 3131-3138.

[2] Acheson, K.J., Blondel-Lubrano, A., Oguey-Araymon, S., Beaumont, M., Emady-Azar, S., Ammon-Zufferey, C., Monnard, I., Pinaud, S., Nielsen-Moennoz, C. &Bovetto, L. (2011). Protein choices targeting thermogenesis and metabolism.*American Journal of Clinical Nutrition, 93*, 525-34.

[3]   Akhavan, T., Luhovyy, B. L., Brown, P. H., Cho, C. E., & Anderson, G. H. (2010). Effect of premeal consumption of whey protein and its hydrolysate on food intake and postmeal glycemia and insulin responses in young adults. *The American Journal of Clinical Nutrition, 91,* 966-975.

[4]   Anuradha, K.V. (2009). Aminoacid support in the prevention of diabetes and diabetic complications. *Current protein and Peptide Science, 10,* 8-17.

[5]   Baer, D.J., Stote, K.S., Paul, D.R., Harris, G.K., Rumpler, W.V. &Clevidence, B.A. (2011). Whey protein but not soy protein supplementation alters body weight and composition in free-living overweight and obese adults. *Journal of Nutrition, 141,* 1489-94.

[6]   Bellissimo, N., Desantadina, M.V., Pencharz, P.B., Berall, G.B., Thomas, S.G. &Anderson, G.H. (2008). A comparison of short-term appetite and energy intakes in normal weight and obese boys following glucose and whey-protein drinks. *International Journal of Obesity, 32,* 362-71.

[7]   Belobrajdic, D., McIntosh, G. &Owens, J. (2003). The effects of dietary protein on rat growth, body composition and insulin sensitivity. *Asia Pacific Journal of Clinical Nutrition,12, Suppl:S42.*

[8]   Belobrajdic DP, McIntosh GH, Owens JA (2004). A high-whey-protein diet reduces body weight gain and alters insulin sensitivity relative to red meat in wistar rats. *Journal of Nutrition, 134,* 1454-8.

[9]   Bortolotti, M., Maiolo, E., Corazza, M., Van Dijke, E., Schneiter, P., Boss, A., Carrel, G., Giusti, V., Lê, K.A., Quo Chong, D.G., Buehler, T., Kreis, R., Boesch, C. &Tappy, L. (2011). Effects of a whey protein supplementation on intrahepatocellular lipids in obese female patients. *Clinical Nutrition, 30,* 494-8.

[10]   Bowen, J., Noakes, M. &Clifton, P.M. (2006a). Appetite regulatory hormone responses to various dietary proteins differ by body mass index status despite similar reductions in ad libitum energy intake. *Journal of Clinical Endocrinology and Metabolism, 91,* 2913-9.

[11]   Bowen, J., Noakes, M., Trenerry, C. &Clifton, P.M. (2006b). Energy intake, ghrelin, and cholecystokinin after different carbohydrate and protein preloads in overweight men. *Journal of Clinical Endocrinology and Metabolism, 91,*1477-83.

[12]   Blouet, C., Mariotti, F., Mikogami, T., Tome, D. &Huneau, J.F. (2007).Meal cysteine improves postprandialglucose control in rats fed a high-sucrose meal. *Journal of Nutritional Biochemistry, 18,* 519-24.

[13]   Buse, J.B., Polonsky, K.S. & Burant, C.F. Type-2 Diabetes Mellitus. In: Kronenberg, H.M., Melmed, S., Polonsky, K.S. & Reed Larsen, P., editors. *Williams Textbook of Endocrinology (ed. 11),* Saunders-Elsevier (2008), 1329-1389.

[14]   Caroli, A. M., Chessa, S., & Erhardt, G. J. (2009). Milk protein genetic variation in cattle: impact on animal breeding and human nutrition. *Journal of Dairy Science, 92,* 5335-5352.

[15]   Catiau, L., Delval-Dubois, V., Guillochon, D. & Nedjar-Arroume, N. (2011). Characterization and identification of a chymotryptic hydrolysate of alpha-lactalbumin stimulating cholecystokinin release in STC-1 cells. *Applied Biochemistry and Biotechnology,* DOI 10-1007/s12010-011-9344-6.

[16] Cerbulis, J., & Farrell Jr., H. M. (1975). Composition of milks of dairy cattle. I. Protein, lactose, and fat contents and distribution of protein fraction. *Journal of Dairy Science,58*, 817-827.

[17] Claessens, M., Saris, W.H. &van Baak, M.A. (2008). Glucagon and insulin responses after ingestion of different amounts of intact and hydrolysed proteins. *British Journal of Nutrition, 100*, 61-9.

[18] Dangin, M., Boirie, Y., Garcia-Rodenas, C., Gachon, P., Fauquant, J., Callier, P., Ballèvre, O., Beaufrère, B. (2001). The digestion rate of protein is an independent regulating factor of postprandial protein retention. *American Journal of Physiology. Endocrinology and Metabolism, 280*, E340-8.

[19] Darmoul, D., Voisin, T., Couvineau, A., Rouyer-Fessard, C., Salomon, R., Wang, Y., Swallow, D. M., & Laburthe, M. (1994). Regional expression of epithelial dipeptidyl peptidase IV in the human intestines. *Biochemical and Biophysical Research Communications, 203,* 1224-1229.

[20] Doi, M., Yamaoka, I., Fukunaga, T., Nakayama, M. (2003). Isoleucine, a potent plasma glucose-lowering amino acid, stimulates glucose uptake in C2C12 myotubes. *Biochemical and Biophysical Research Communications, 312*, 1111-1117.

[21] Drab, S. R. (2010). Incretin-based therapy for type-2 diabetes mellitus: current status and future prospects. *Pharmacotherapy,30*, 609-624.

[22] Drucker, D. J. (2003). Enhancing incretin action for the treatment of type 2 diabetes. *Diabetes Care, 26*, 2929-40.

[23] Drucker, D. J. (2006a).The biology of incretin hormones. *Cell Metabolism,3*, 153-165.

[24] Drucker, D. J. (2006b). Enhancing the action of incretin hormones: a new whey forward? *Endocrinology,147*, 3171-3172.

[25] Eller, L.K. & Reimer, R.A. Dairy protein attenuates weight gain in obese rats better than whey or casein alone. (2010). *Obesity (Silver Spring) 18*, 704-711.

[26] Ericson, U.C., Sonestedt, E., Gullberg, B., Hellstrand, S., Hindy, G., Wirfalt, E. & Orho-Melander M. High intake of protein and processed meat is associated with increased incidence of type 2 diabetes. *Diabetologia, 54* (suppl. 1), S12.

[27] Frid, A. H., Nilsson, M., Holst, J. J., & Bjorck, I. M. (2005). Effect of whey on blood glucose and insulin responses to composite breakfast and lunch meals in type 2 diabetic subjects. *American Journal of Clinical Nutrition,82*, 69-75.

[28] Foltz, M., Meynen, E.E., Bianco, V., Platerrink, C.V., Koning, T.M.M.G. & Kloek, J. (2007). Angiotensin converting enzyme inhibitory peptides from a lactotripeptide-enriched milk beverage are absorbed intact into the circulation. *Journal of Nutrition, 137*, 953-958.

[29] Foltz, M., Van der Pijl, P. C., & Duchateau, G. S. (2010). Current in vitro testing of bioactive peptides is not valuable. *Journal of Nutrition, 140*, 117-118.

[30] Frestedt, J.L., Zenk, J.L., Kuskowski, M.A., Ward, L.S. &Bastian, E.D. (2008). A whey-protein supplement increases fat loss and spares lean muscle in obese subjects: a randomized human clinical study. *Nutrition and Metabolism (London)* doi:10.1186/1743-7075-5-8.

[31] Ganai, N. A., Bovenhuis, H., van Arendonk, J. A. M., & Visker, M. H. P. W. (2008). Novel polymorphisms in the bovine beta-lactoglobulin gene and their effects on beta-lactoglobulin protein concentration in milk. *Animal Genetics, 40*, 127-133.

[32] Geraedts, M.C.P., Troost, F., Fisher, M.A.J.G., Edens, L. & Saris, W.H.M. (2011). Direct induction of CCK and GLP-1 release from murine endocrine cells by intact dietary proteins.*Molecular Nutrition and Food Research, 55*, 476-484.

[33] Graf, S., Egert, S. &Heer, M. (2011). Effects of whey protein supplements on metabolism: evidence from human intervention studies. *Current opinion in clinical nutrition and metabolic care, 14*, 569-580.

[34] Graml, R., Weise, G., Buchberger,J., & Pirchner, F. (1989). Different rates of synthesis of whey protein and casein by alleles of the beta-lactoglobulin and alpha$_{s1}$-casein locus in cattle. *Genetics SelectionEvolution, 21*, 547-554.

[35] Gunnarsson, P. T., Winzell, M. S., Deacon, C. F., Larsen, M. O., Jelic, K., Carr, R. D., & Ahrèn, B. (2006). Glucose-induced incretin hormone release and inactivation are differently modulated by oral fat and protein in mice. *Endocrinology, 147*, 3173-3180.

[36] Hansen, L., Deacon, C. F., Orskov, C., & Holst, J. J. (1999). Glucagone-like peptide-1-(7-36) amide is transformed to glucagon-like-peptide-1-(9-36) amide by dipeptidyl peptidase IV (DPPIV) in the capillaries supplying the L cells on the porcine intestine. *Endocrinology, 140*, 5356-5363.

[37] Hernandez-Ledesma, B., Recio, I., & Amigo, L. (2008). Beta-lactoglobulin as a source of bioactive peptides. *Amino Acids, 35*, 257-265.

[38] Hinault, C., Mothe-Satny, I., Gautier N., Lawrence J.C. jr & Van Obberghen, E. (2004). Amino acids and leucine allow insulin activation of the PKB/mTOR pathway in normal aipocytes treated with wortmannin and in adipocytes from db/db mice. *FASEB Journal, 18*, 1894-1896.

[39] Hinault, C., Van Obberghen, E. & Mothe-Satny, I. (2006). Role of amino acids in insulin signaling in adipocytes and their potential to decrease insulin resistance of adipose tissue. Journal *of Nutritional Biochemistry, 17*, 374-378.

[40] Holst, J. J., & Deacon, C. F. (1998). Inhibition of the activity of dipeptidyl-peptidase IV as a treatment for type 2 diabetes. *Diabetes, 47*, 1663-1670.

[41] Hoppe, C., Mølgaard, C., Dalum, C., Vaag, A., Michaelsen, K.F. (2009). Differential effects of casein versus whey on fasting plasma levels of insulin, IGF-1 and IGF-1/IGFBP-3: results from a randomized 7-day supplementation study in prepubertal boys. *European journal of Clinical Nutrition, 63*, 1076-83.

[42] Kleinert, M., Liao, Y.H., Nelson, J.L., Bernard, J.R., Wang, W. &Ivy, J.L. (2011). An amino acid mixture enhances insulin-stimulated glucose uptake in isolated rat epitrochlearis muscle. *Journal of Applied Physiology, 111*, 163-9.

[43] Laferrere, B. (2011). Do we really know why diabetes remits after gastric bypass surgery? *Endocrine*, DOI 10.1007/s12020-011-9514-x

[44] Lan-Pidhainy, X. &Wolever, T.M. (2010). The hypoglycemic effect of fat and protein is not attenuated by insulin resistance. American Journal of Clinical Nutrition, 91, 98-105.

[45] Lim, E.L., Hollingsworth, K.G., Aribisala, B.S., Chen, M.J., Mathers, J.C. & Taylor, R. (2011). Reversal of type 2 diabetes: normalisation of beta cell function in association with decreased pancreas and liver triacylglycerol. *Diabetologia, 54*, 2506-14.

[46] Lindgren, O., Carr, R.D., Holst, J.J., Deacon, C.F. &Ahrèn, B. (2011). Dissociated incretin hormone response to protein versus fat ingestion in obese subjects. *Diabetes, Obesity and Metabolism, 13*, 863-5.

[47] Lorenzini, E. C., Chessa, S., Chiatti, F., Caroli, A., & Pagnacco, G. (2007). Peptidi bioattivi di latte e derivati. *Scienza e Tecnica Lattiero-Casearia*, *58*, 113-156.

[48] Luhovyy, B. L., Akhavan, T., & Anderson, G.H. (2007). Whey proteins in the regulation of food intake and satiety. *Journal of the American College of Nutrition*, *26*, 704S-712S.

[49] Lum, L. S., Dovč, P., & Medrano, J. F. (1997). Polymorphisms of bovine *β*-lactoglobulin promoter and differences in the binding affinity of activator protein-2 transcription factor. *Journal of Dairy Science*, *80*, 1389-1397.

[50] Ma, J., Stevens, J.E., Cukier, K., Maddox, A.F., Wishart, J.M., Jones, K.L., Clifton, P.M., Horowitz, M. &Rayner, C.K. (2009).Effects of a protein preload on gastric emptying, glycemia, and gut hormones after a carbohydrate meal in diet-controlled type 2 diabetes. Diabetes Care, 32, 1600-2.

[51] Macotela, Y., Emanuelli, B., Bang, A.M., Espinoza, D.O., Boucher, J., Beebe, K., Gall, W. & Kahn C.R. (2011). Dietary Leucine – An environmental modifier of insulin resistance acting on multiple levels of metabolism. *Plos One, 6*, (6) e2187.

[52] Manders, R. J., Koopman, R., Sluijsmans, W. E., van den Berg, R., Verbeek, K., Saris, W. H., Wagenmakers, A. J., & van Loon, L. J. (2006). Co-ingestion of a protein hydrolysate with or without additional leucine effectively reduces postprandial blood glucose excursions in type 2 diabetic men. *The Journal of Nutrition*, *136*, 1294-1299.

[53] Meisel, H. (1997). Biochemical properties of regulatory peptides derived from milk proteins. *Biopolymers*, *43*, 119-128.

[54] Melnik, B.C. (2011). Evidence for acne-promoting effects of milk and other insulinotropic dairy products. *Nestlè Nutrition Workshop Series. Pediatric Programme,67*, 131-145.

[55] Micke, P., Beeth, K.M., Schlaak, J.F. & Buhl, R. (2001). Oral supplementation with whey proteins increase plasma glutathione levels of HIV-infected patients. *European Journal of Clinical Investigation, 31*, 171-178.

[56] Morifuji, M., Koga, J., Kawanaka, K. & Higuchi, M. (2009). Branched-chain amino acid-containing dipeptides, identified from whey protein hydrolysates, stimulate glucose uptake rate in L6 myotubes and isolated skeletal muscles. *Journal of Nutritional Science and Vitaminology, 55*, 81-86.

[57] Mortensen, L.S., Hartvigsen, M.L., Brader, L.J., Astrup, A., Schrezenmeir, J., Holst, J.J., Thomsen, C. &Hermansen, K. (2009). Differential effects of protein quality on postprandial lipemia in response to a fat-rich meal in type 2 diabetes: comparison of whey, casein, gluten, and cod protein. *American Journal of Clinical Nutrition, 90*, 41-8.

[58] Nair Sreekumaran, K. & Short, K.R. (2005). Hormonal and signaling role of branched-chain amino acids. Proceeding of the "4th Amino acid Assessment workshop" published in a supplement to the *Journal of Nutrition*, 1547S-1551S.

[59] Newgard, C.B., An, J., Bain, J.R., Muehlbauer, M.J., Stevens, R.D., Lien, L.F., Haqq, A.M., Shah, S.H., Arlotto, M., Slentz, C.A., Rochon, J., Gallup, D., Ilkayeva, O., Wenner, B.R., Yancy, W.S., Eisenson, H., Musante, G., Surwit, R.S., Millington, D.S., Butler, M.D. & Svetkey L.P. (2009). A branched-chain amino acid-related metabolic signature that differentiates obese and lean humans and contributes to insulin resistance. *Cell Metabolism, 6*, 311-326.

[60] Nilsson, M., Stenberg, M., Frid, A. H., Holst, J. J., & Bjorck, I. M. (2004). Glycemia and insulinemia in healthy subjects after lactose-equivalent meals and other food

proteins: the role of plasma amino acids and incretins. *American Journal of Clinical Nutrition, 80*, 1246-1253.

[61] Nilsson, M., Holst, J. J., & Bjorck, I. M. (2007). Metabolic effects of amino acid mixtures and whey protein in healthy subjects: studies using glucose equivalent drinks. *American Journal of Clinical Nutrition*, 85, 996-1004.

[62] Nolan, C.J., Damm, P., & Prentki, M. (2011). Type 2 diabetes across generations: from pathophysiology to prevention and management. *Lancet, 378*, 168-181.

[63] Pal S. &Ellis V. (2010). The acute effects of four protein meals on insulin, glucose, appetite and energy intake in lean men. *British Journal of Nutrition, 104*, 1241-1248.

[64] Pereira, M.A., Jacobs, D.R. jr, Van Horn, L., Slattery, M.L., Kartashov, A.I. & Ludwig, D.S. Dairy consumption, obesity and the insulin resistance syndrome in young adults: the CARDIA Study. *JAMA 287*, 2081-99.

[65] Petersen, B. L., Ward, L. S., Bastian, E. D., Jenkins, A. L., Campbell, J., & Vuksan V. (2009). A whey protein supplement decreases post-prandial glycemia. *Nutrition Journal, 8*, 47.

[66] Poppitt, S.D., Proctor, J., McGill, A.T., Wiessing, K.R., Falk, S., Xin, L., Budgett, S.C., Darragh, A. &Hall, R.S (2011). Low-dose whey protein-enriched water beverages alter satiety in a study of overweight women. *Appetite, 56*, 456-64.

[67] Qin, L.Q., Xun, P., Bujnowski, D., Daviglus, M.L., Van Horn, L., Stamler, J. & He, K for the INTERMAP Cooperative Research Group. (2011). Higher branched-chain amino acid intake is associated with a lower prevalence of being overweight or obese in middle-aged East Asian and Western adults. *Journal of Nutrition, 141*, 249-254.

[68] Reimann, F. (2010). Molecular mechanisms underlying nutrient detection by incretin secreting cells. *International Dairy Journal, 20*, 236-242.

[69] Sadat, L., Cakir-Kiefer, C., N'Negue, M.-A., Gaillard, J.-L., Girardet, J.-M., & Miclo, L. (2011). Isolation and identification of antioxidative peptides from bovine α-lactalbumin. *International Dairy Journal, 21*, 214-221.

[70] Saltiel, A.R. & Pessin J.E. (2002). Insulin signaling pathways in time and space. *TRENDS in Cell Biology, 12*, 65-71.

[71] Solerte, S.B., Fioravanti, M., Locatelli, E., Bonacasa, R., Zamboni, M., Basso, C., Mazzoleni, A., Mansi, V., Geroutis, N. & Gazzaruso, C. (2008). Improvement of blood glucose control and insulin sensitivity during a long term (60 weeks) randimized study with amino acid dietary supplements in elderly subjects with type 2 diabetes mellitus. *American Journal of Cardiology, 101*, 82E-88E.

[72] Szendroedi, J., Phielix, E. & Roden M. (2011). The role of mitochondria in insulin resistance and type 2 diabetes mellitus. *Nature Reviews. Endocrinology*, DOI 10.1038/nrendo.2011.138.

[73] Tremblay, F. & Marette, A. (2001). Amino acid and insulin signaling via the mTOR/p70 S6 kinase pathway. *Journal of Biological Chemistry, 276*, 38052-60.

[74] Tremblay, F., Lavigne, C., Jacques, H. & Marette, A. (2007). Role of dietary proteins and amino acids in the pathogenesis of insulin resistance. *Annual Review of Nutrition, 27*, 293-310.

[75] Tulipano, G., Sibilia, V., Caroli, A. M., & Cocchi, D. (2011a). Whey proteins as source of dipeptidyl dipeptidase IV (dipeptidyl peptidase-4) inhibitors. *Peptides, 32*, 835-838.

[76] Tulipano, G., Cocchi, D.& Caroli A.M. (2011b). Comparison of goat and sheep beta-lactoglobulin to bovine beta-lactoglobulin as potential source of dipeptidyl peptidase IV (DPP-4) inhibitors. *International Dairy Journal*, DOI 10.1016/j.idairyj.2011.09.004.

[77] Uchida, M., Ohshiba, Y. & Mogami O. (2011). Novel Dipeptidyl Peptidase-4-inhibiting peptide derived from beta-lactoglobulin. *Journal of Pharmacological Sciences, 177*, 63-66.

[78] Uenishi, H., Kabuki, T., Seto, Y., Serizawa, A.& Nakajima, H. (2012). Isolation and identification of casein-derived dipeptidyl-peptidase-4 (DPP-4)-inhibitory peptide LPQNIPPL from gouda-type cheese and its effect on plasma glucose in rats. *International Dairy Journal, 22*, 24-30.

[79] Umezawa, H., Aoyagi, T., Ogawa, K., Naganawa, H., Hamada, M. & Takeuchi, T. (1984). Diprotins A and B, inhibitors of dipeptidyl aminopeptidase IV, produced by bacteria. *Journal of Antibiotics, 37*, 422-425.

[80] Valerio, A., D'Antona, G. & Nisoli, E. (2011). Branched-chain amino acids, mitochondrial biogenesis, and healthspan: an evolutionary perspective. *Aging, 3*, 464-478.

[81] Veldhorst, M.A., Nieuwenhuizen, A.G., Hochstenbach-Waelen, A., van Vught, A.J., Westerterp, K.R., Engelen, M.P., Brummer, R.J., Deutz, N.E.&Westerterp-Plantenga, M.S. (2009). Dose-dependent satiating effect of whey relative to casein or soy. *Physiology and Behavior, 96*, 675-82.

[82] Wang, T.J., Larson, M.G., Vasan, R.S., Cheng, S., Rhee, E.P., McCabe, E., Lewis, G.D., Fox, C.S., Jacques, P.F., Fernandez, C., O'Donnell C.J., Carr, S.A., Mootha, V.K., Florez, J.C., Souza, A., Melander, O., Clish, C.B. & Gerszten, R.E. (2011). Metabolite profiles and the risk of developing diabetes. *Nature Medicine, 17*, 448-453.

[83] Xiao, F., Huang, Z., Li, H., Yu, J., Wang, C., Chen, S., Meng, Q., Cheng, Y., Gao, X., Li, J., Liu, Y. &Guo, F. (2011). Leucine deprivation increases hepatic insulin sensitivity via GCN2/mTOR/S6K1 and AMPK pathways. *Diabetes, 60*, 746-56.

In: Whey: Types, Composition and Health Implications ISBN: 978-1-61942-862-1
Editors: Rafael M. Benitez and Gustavo M. Ortero © 2012 Nova Science Publishers, Inc.

Chapter 4

CONTROLLING THE MICROBIOLOGY OF WHEY AND WHEY PRODUCTS

Steve Flint,[1] Xuemei Tang,[2]
Rod Bennett,[1] and John Brooks[3]

[1]Institute of Food Nutrition and Human Health, Massey
University, Palmerston North, New Zealand
[2]R and D Department, Shenzhen Oceanpower Co.,
Ltd, Shenzhen, China
[3]School of Applied Sciences, AUT University,
Auckland, New Zealand

ABSTRACT

Microbiologically, whey is an interesting product. Traditionally as whey was a waste material in the dairy industry, a by-product of casein and cheese manufacture, the microbiological quality of whey was of little concern. The protein and lactose content of whey is now recognised as a valuable resource and products from the ultrafiltration and reverse osmosis of whey are an integral part of the dairy industry. Maintaining microbiological quality of these whey products to meet customer specifications is challenging.The raw whey leaving the casein or cheese manufacturing plant is often contaminated with bacteria – many originating from the starter cultures used in the manufacture of these products. Changes in the handling of whey have helped improve the quality of products manufactured from whey. However, further challenges exist in the processing of whey which involves large areas of filtration membrane on which biofilm can grow and thence contaminate the product.The composition of the membrane influences biofilm growth, so appropriate selection of membranes may help in controlling biofilm development. Mixed enzyme cleaners and mixed oxidant sanitisers offer the best control of microflora on the membrane surfaces used in whey processing plants.

INTRODUCTION

Whey is the waste stream from the manufacture of cheese and casein. One common method for disposing of whey was to spray it onto pastures, adding to the bio-loading of the environment.

Today, a variety of products are manufactured from whey – including whey protein concentrates (WPC), lactose and ethanol from the fermentation of lactose. The whey products with the most value are whey protein concentrates and isolates, and these are the most challenging to manufacture with an acceptable microbiological quality. This is under-standable, as the raw material has been through several processing steps since the collection of the raw milk. At each step there is potential for microbiological contamination and growth. During the manufacture of casein and cheese, the focus is not on the quality of the whey produced but on the quality of the casein and cheese. Whey product manufacturers therefore often have a less than ideal raw material to process.

There is little published information on the microbiological quality of whey products. In our experience, thermophilic streptococci are often regarded as common contaminants, however in our laboratory, we have isolated a wide range of bacteria from WPC. The actual types of bacteria are likely to vary depending on whether the whey is sweet (from cheese and rennet casein manufacture) or acid (from acid casein manufacture). The temperature of the whey manufacturing process also influences the microflora. The use of poor quality milk for the manufacture of cheese and casein can result in an increase in proteose peptone content of the whey which has been shown to influence the functional properties of the whey products (Hobman, 1992).

In the manufacture of WPC, a heat treatment step, or pasteurisation, is normally one of the first steps in the manufacturing process to help reduce the microbiological load of the raw material.This will be effective in reducing the starter bacteria and heat sensitive contaminants in the raw material. The thermoduric bacteria including spore formers will survive and these can produce acid during the manufacture of whey products (Zadow, 1992).

Key steps in the process are ultrafiltration and reverse osmosis and this is where we believe most of the contamination problems occur. Both these processes involve large surface areas prone to biofilm development and this can be very difficult to control.

A biofilm is a community of microorganisms attached to a surface, producing extra-cellular polymeric substances (EPS) and interacting with each other. It can form on any surface in any environment where the bacteria are present. Biofilms in many food processing plants have been studied, however, the surfaces colonisedwere typically stainless steel, aluminium, glass, Buna-N, Teflon and nylon seals, rather than membranes used for filtration. Studies that have examined biofilms on membrane surfaces have been in aqueous environ-ments rather than food manufacturing plant.

In the dairy processing environment, whey protein with other organic or inorganic molecules can form a conditioning layer on manufacturing plant surfaces. These conditioning layers alter the physico-chemical properties of the surface, including the surface free energy, hydrophobicity and electrostatic charge, with subsequent effects on the adhesion of different microorganisms. The colonisation of a surface by one species is also found to influence the attachment of other species to the same surface. Once the mature biofilm forms, it is difficult to remove using normal cleaning procedures.

Ultrafiltration (UF) and reverse osmosis (RO) membranes are growing in use in the dairy industry. The spiral-wound configuration is most commonly used as it is competitively priced. However, because of the close spacing of the membrane leaves, these assemblies are susceptible to fouling. The large surface area of the membranes provides ample support for the development of biofilms. Previous studies have focused on protein fouling of membranes. With the increase in use of this technology, there is a growing awareness of the limitations imposed by biofilm growth on membrane surfaces. Biofilm growth on membranes has two effects on dairy manufacture. Firstly, when biofilm is present on the membrane surface, colloidal solids and insoluble precipitates can adhere to the biofilm and form a physical barrier that reduces the membrane flux (volumetric flow rate per unit area) which results in reduction of the operating run time of the plants. Secondly, the constant release of micro-organisms from the biofilms increases the cell numbers in the liquid phase and thus has a high probability of contaminating the product stream.

There are many possible sources of contaminating bacteria. These include feed solutions (whey), diafiltration water, the environment of the manufacturing plant, and solutions (e.g. water) used for clean-in-place (CIP) operations. Residual bacteria following CIP procedures may also act as a nidus for subsequent biofilm development.

In this chapter we will focus on biofilm development in whey manufacturing plants, in particular on the membrane surfaces.Our work has focussed on thermoresistant streptococci, believed to be a persistent contaminant in whey processing plants (Flint *et al.* 1999), and more recently on the generalmicrobial populations in the biofilms on the membrane surfaces, developing a fundamental understanding of adhesion of microorganisms and the relationship between the adhesion and the cell surface characteristics, investigating the factors influencing biofilm growth and examining methods for improving CIP strategies used in dairy membrane plants in terms of removing biofilm.

BIOFILMS ON ULTRAFILTRATION AND REVERSE OSMOSIS MEMBRANES USED IN WHEYPROCESSING

Filtration is a process for separating two or more substances, based on differences in their physical size and shape, by allowing liquid to pass through a porous barrier. Membrane filtration technology was adopted early by the dairy industry (D'Souza andMawson, 2005), and ultrafiltration (UF) and reverse osmosis (RO) membranes have been widely used (Kumar andAnand, 1998). However, biofilms on membrane surfaces, the undesirable layer of living microorganisms and their decomposition products on the surfaces, limit the application of membrane technologies (Kumar and Anand, 1998).

The following is a critical review of recent literature about UF and RO membranes and biofilms. The review includes the fundamental working principles and functions of these two membranes in whey plants, the principles of biofilm development and its relationship to the characteristics of microorganisms and membranes, techniques that can be used in biofilm research, and the latest improvements in control.

Ultrafiltration and reverse osmosis membranes are both semi-permeable membranes that have many small pores. Depending on the size of the pores, smaller molecules can pass through the membrane, and larger molecules are retained. The feed stock will generally be split into two streams: molecules that can pass through the membrane are called permeates, those that cannot pass through are called retentates (Bird, 1996).

UF is widely used in the dairy industry (Daufin et al., 2001).The pore size used for UF membranes is larger than that used for RO membranes, allowing the protein and fat to be retained, while permitting the water, lactose and ash to pass through. UF membranes are used for the manufacture of whey protein concentrates (WPCs) and milk protein concentrates (MPCs), milk standardisation before cheese manufacture, liquid milk concentration for market milk product and clarification of cheese brine (Bird, 1996).

RO is a high pressure membrane separation process that operates at between 25-40 bar (Bird, 1996; Hiddink et al., 1980) and allows only water to pass through the membrane.RO membranes are used for the concentration of ultrafiltration permeates for lactose manufacture, milk standardisation, lactose fermentation, recovery of proteins and lactose from casein whey washwaters, recovery of clean-in-place (CIP) water and concentration of whey prior to transportation (Bird, 1996).

Membrane filtration in the dairy industry is almost exclusively operated in a cross-flow modeespecially for the more difficult feeds (Pearce, 2008). The circulation in cross-flow filtration is parallel to the membrane ([Anon], 2007). The shearing effect of the fluid as it passes over the surface of the membrane acts to remove any particles which may have collected at the surface of the membrane and helps to maintain a relatively steady flux through the membrane.

Cross-flow creates consistent turbulent flow on the surface of the membrane ([Anon], 2007), so that the shear can sweep away particles that may accumulate on the membrane. During cross-flow filtration of a non-protein containing solution, increased filtration pressure generally tends to increase the flux across the membrane. However, during the filtration of protein solutions (e.g. whey suspension), increased filtration pressure results in reducing the flux across the membrane owing to the structure and nature of the proteins within the solution and accumulating a more concentrated cake on the membrane surface (Karasu et al, 2009). This pre-conditioning layer will influence the subsequent biofilm formation. Results from Karasu et al. (2009) on a modelling study on UF of whey determined that higher feed flow rate caused a larger volume of particles to be removed from the fouling layer. Therefore, very high cross-flow velocities may be necessary to control fouling (Pearce, 2008).

A spiral-wound configuration is most commonly used in membrane applications today owing to its high membrane surface area to volume ratio and the convenience in replacement and purchase (Bodalo-Santoyo et al., 2004). Feed is separated by membrane layers. Retnetates are collected from the side of the layers. Permeates enter the central tube through permeate collection holes. Other configurations include plate and frame, tubular and hollow fiber (Maubois, 1980). Plate and frame configurations have extreme susceptibility to fouling, owing to the close spacing of the membrane leaves (Cartwright, 2003).

The major materials for spiral-wound membranes in the dairy industry are typically polyethersulphone (PES) and polysulphone (PSF) (D'Souza and Mawson, 2005; Pearce, 2007). PES membranes have good strength and high permeability, and the properties of PES can be modified through a polymer blend (Pearce, 2008). Membranes are usually modified to have a hydrophilic surface because they are easily wetted and resist fouling (Pearce, 2007b). Polyvinylidene fluoride (PVDF) was introduced for membrane concentration in the 1990s (Pearce, 2008), and is now a dominant material for the membrane market, together with PES (Pearce, 2007b). PVDF is stronger and more flexible than PES and excellent in chemical resistance (Boributha et al, 2009).Thus PVDF membrane tends to have longer life (Pearce, 2007b). However, since the hydrophobic surface of PVDF membrane is difficult to modify (Fontananova et al., 2006), it is less resistant and more susceptible to fouling than others (J Lozier et al., 2006; Pearce, 2007).

CONCERNS OVER BIOFILM IN DAIRYMANUFACTURING PLANTS

Generally bacteria prefer to grow on an available surface rather than in the surrounding aqueous phase (KatsikogianniandMissirlis, 2004). Biofilm can develop on any surface exposed to an aqueous environment (Flint et al., 1997a). In dairy and food industries, serious problems caused by biofilms include interfering with heat transfer across the surfaces (Criado et al., 1994), increases in the fluid frictional resistance (Kumar andAnand, 1998) and the corrosion rate at the surface (Liu et al., 2007). In addition, microorganisms growing in biofilms are more difficult to eliminate than free floating bacterial cells (Flint et al., 1997a), and thus cross contamination and post-processing contamination may occur once biofilms have become established in a manufacturing plant (Kumar andAnand, 1998) leading to reduced product shelf life (Zottola, 1994). Such microbial contamination is the major cause of poor quality dairy products (Flint et al., 1997a). The use of membranes has been significantly limited by the problem of fouling, as a small degree of adsorption causes membrane pore blockage (Cheryan, 1986). Biofilm fouling may be favoured by the fouling of the membrane with organic material such as proteins(Kumar andAnand, 1998) that will eventually block the membrane pores preventing further manufacture (Flint et al., 1997a). A mature biofilm on the membrane surface can also change the distribution and surface properties of the filter (Cogan and Chellam, 2008).

MECHANISM OF BIOFILM FORMATION

Biofilm is initiated by the attachment of microorganisms to surfaces and the development of biofilm starts when the attached microorganisms grow (Ivnitsky et al, 2005). The formation of mature biofilms is thought to be the result of early surface colonization by some microorganisms that change the surface properties and facilitate attachment and growth of others (Dang and Lovell, 2000; Jefferson, 2004). Initial adhesion of microorganisms to the surfaces is essential for biofilm formation (Dang and Lovell 1999). Given adequate nutrients, time and suitable temperature, the initial sessile microbial population can eventually form a confluent lawn of bacteria on the membrane surface (Ridgway et al, 1999).

Almost all microorganisms adhered to surfaces secrete exo-polymeric substances (EPS) (Ramsey andWhiteley, 2004) that are mainly carbohydrates (Sutherland and Kennedy, 1996), proteins, lipids,small quantities of nucleic acids and a variety of humic substances (Lee et al., 2010b; Liu and Fang, 2002; Nielsen et al., 1996). EPS are responsible for the membrane fouling (Jacquement et al., 2005) by irreversibly binding to the membranes (Davies et al., 1998), and enhancing the survival and robustness of the biofilm microorganisms by forming a chemically reactive diffusion transport barrier with bacterial cells (Goldman et al., 2009) impeding convective flow and slowing the penetration of biocide into the biofilm (Ivnitsky et al., 2005). The EPS matrix also reinforces cellular bonding to surfaces and stabilizes the biofilm, thereby reducing its susceptibility to sloughing by hydrodynamic shear (Ivnitsky et al., 2005). The bacteria and EPS can even change the surface composition of membranes (Khan et al., 2010) whichprobably results in a shorter membrane life. By using an individual-based model, Kreft and Wimpenny (2001) found that EPS production dramatically changes the biofilm structure. They observed that the density of cells at the bottom of the biofilm was very low when the rate of EPS production was high, due to more energy consumed on EPS synthesis than they could gain at the low oxygen tensions in the depth of the biofilm (KreftandWimpenny, 2001). Pang et al. (2005) found*Sphingomonas* sp. EPS on RO membranes tended to be more closely associated with the single cell or small cell clusters than with larger colonies and the EPS matrix was detected in areas free of biofilm cells, suggesting that the EPS matrix was quite extensive.

MEMBRANE SURFACE CHARACTERISTICSAND BIOFILM FORMATION

The surface properties of membranes are believed to be important in biofilm formation (Pasmore et al., 2001). Bacterial attachment is regulated by the physico-chemical nature of both the bacterial cell and the polymer membrane surface (Ridgway, 1991). The material of construction, surface roughness, hydrophobicity and charge will also affect biofilm formation (Herzberg et al., 2009). These characteristics are examined in more detail below.

Surface Roughness

Membrane roughness refers to the steepness, evenness and topology of peaks and valleys on the membrane surface (Lee et al., 2010b). Membrane surface roughness is an important property affecting biofilm formation (Characklis, 1990; Elimelech et al, 1997; Vrijenhoek et al, 2001). Surface roughness affects the development of younger biofilms more than mature biofilms (Pang et al, 2005). Pasmore et al. (2001) concluded that bacterial attachment was affected by surface roughness through two primary ways. Firstly, the roughness disrupts fluid flow by creating surface areas of low shear where the forces that might remove attached bacteria are significantly reduced. Secondly, the increased roughness increases surface area that makes more room available for cells to attach, since rough surfaces have contours and valleys (Pasmore et al., 2001). They also observed an increase in biofilm with *Pseudomonas aeruginosa* on a rougher UF membrane surface (Pasmore et al., 2001). Similarly, it was found that the degree of roughness had a strong linear relationship with the maximum adhered cell concentration of *Pseudomonas aeruginosa* PAO1 on nanofiltration (NF) membranes (Myint et al., 2010).

Pang et al. (2005) observed that both roughness and depression areas were increased when membranes were in a hydrated form when they used atomic force microscopy (AFM) combined with scanning electron microscopy (SEM) to analyse the surface morphology of dry and hydrated RO membranes made up of cellulose acetate (CA), polyamide (PA), and thin film composites (TFC). They also compared the roughness of those three types of membranes and concluded that the CA membrane had the lowest roughness, while the PA membrane had the largest depression areas. This observation shows the importance of both roughness and areas of depression in permitting biofilm formation. Microorganism entrapment is relatively easy in the depression areas, and therefore, PA membrane is more likely to promote biofilm formation (Pang et al, 2005). Similar observations were also reported by Campbell and co-workers (Campbell et al, 1999), who studied the attachment of *Mycobacterium* sp. onto PA and CA membranes in batch assays.

Surface Hydrophobicity

The hydrophobicity of inanimate substrata influences the strength and kinetics of microbial adhesion and early biofouling (Ridgway et al, 1999). An explanation of hydrophobicity has proved elusive, but it may be a function of hydrogen bonding (Duncan-Hewitt, 1990). Attachment of bacteria to a surface is thermodynamically favourable if the total free energy of adhesion is negative (Teixeira et al., 2005). It has been proposed that a hydrophobic substratum attracts bacteria with a hydrophobic surface and a hydrophilic substratum attracts bacteria with a hydrophilic surface (An and Friedman, 1998; KatsikogianniandMissirlis, 2004). It was found that a NF membrane which is relatively hydrophilic has a higher potential for biofouling by hydrophilic bacteria than a hydrophobic UF membrane (Lee et al., 2010a). Pasmore et al. (2001) found that biofilm initiation by a *Pseudomonas aeruginosa* strain increased as a UF membrane surface became more hydrophobic. Similarly, Lee et al. (2010b) observed that the adhered cell concentration of *Pseudomonas aeruginosa* PAO1 increased proportionally to the RO membrane hydrophobicity.

Surface Charge

Most polymer membranes possess some degree of surface charge due to trace quantities of free carboxylate or sulfonate groups (Ridgway et al., 1999). The charge of the substrate surface can affect the attractive and repulsive forces between the bacterial cells and substrate (Pasmore et al., 2001). Charge attraction was even suggested as having a stronger effect than hydrophobicity on fouling (Koo et al., 2002).Under physiologically relevant pH values (~7), RO membranes tend to be negatively charged (Elimelech et al., 1997; Vrijenhoek et al., 2001). Negative membrane surface charge can reduce fouling by electrostatic repulsion of negatively charged bacterial surfaces (Her et al, 2000). Pasmore et al. (2002) demonstrated that the maximum removal of bacteria from a high-density polyethylene (PE) solid surface was achieved when the solid surface was neutral or had a small negative charge. They also confirmed that as the surface charge increased, either with positive or negative charges, the cell removal decreased (Pasmore et al., 2002).

Other Factors

Biofilm formation is an extremely complicated process that is affected by various factors. In addition to the factors described above, biofilm formation is also influenced by the environmental parameters, such as the flow conditions, the level of nutrients, the concentration of electrolytes and the pH value (Lee et al., 2010b).

Flow rate is considered a dominant factor that strongly influences bacterial adhesion (Isbergand Barnes, 2002) and biofilm structure (Stoodley et al., 1999). Higher shear rates result in higher detachment forces that decrease the number of adhered cells (Katsikogianni and Missirlis, 2004). However, studies show that a high flow rate will not prevent bacterial attachment nor completely remove existing biofilm (Dreeszen, 2003), but it will make the biofilm denser and thinner (Chang et al., 1991).However, biofilm will reach a certain equilibrium thickness depending on both shear force and available nutrient levels (Dreeszen, 2003).Bacteria require certain nutrients for growth and multiplication. Limiting the nutrients will limit bacteria growth. For instance, Ivnitsky et al. (2005) observed a bacterial count of approx. 10^7 CFU/cm^2 in biofilm on a NF membrane surface regardless of the feed applied.

Ionic strength and pH influence bacterial attachment by changing surface characteristics of both the bacteria and the materials, resulting in changing interactions between bacteria and surfaces (Katsikogianni and Missirlis, 2004). Bunt et al. (1993) found that pH and ionic strength influenced the cell surface hydrophobicity and charge. Increasing solution pH results in an increased negative surface charge, and an increased rejection through electrostatic repulsion (Bellona and Drewes, 2005). The highest adhesion to hydrophobic surfaces was found at pH in the range of the isoelectric point when bacteria are uncharged (Bunt et al., 1993). The chemicals adsorbed to the membrane surface are responsible for most of the changes in surface properties (Pasmore et al., 2001).

ISOLATION AND IDENTIFICATION OF BACTERIAFROM MEMBRANE SURFACES

Biofilm microorganisms are normally scraped from a surface using a sterile scalpel or swabbed from the biofilm growing surface, and transferred onto agar plates for multiplication, identification or selection (Dautle et al., 2003; Flemming et al., 2007). Piao et al. (2006) used sonication at 80 W for 2 min in an ice-water bath to dislodge bacteria in biofilms on a membrane surface. In addition to the classic microbiological methods, such as biochemical characterisation using kits such as the BBL CRYSTAL or API identification systems (Dautle et al., 2003; Tang et al., 2009), the identification of microorganisms from biofilm is often based on molecular techniques such as –16S rRNA gene PCR cloning and sequencing (Kwon et al., 2002; Liaqat and Sabri, 2009; Piao et al., 2006). As the cost of sequencing has come down, full genome sequencing has become feasible where pure cultures can be obtained. Where this is not possible, perhaps because members of the biofilm community are not culturable, denaturing gradient gel electrophoresis (DGGE) of amplified DNA, followed by sequencing of fragments, can provide identification.

Whey normally contains predominantly Gram-positive organisms from the starter population (lactic acid bacteria) (Friedrich and Lenke 2006), or thermo-resistant species such as spore-forming *Bacillus* species (Schreiber 2001). However, the predominant isolates recovered from the surfaces of our membrane samples taken from dairy manufacturing plants were Gram-negative bacteria (Tang *et al.* 2009a) Therefore, the high proportion of Gram-negative isolates, especially coliforms, found in this study indicates that the most likely source of contamination may be poor water quality or insufficient plant CIP allowing accumulationof microorganisms on the equipment surfaces, resulting in biofilm formation (Kumar and Anand, 1998). The isolates obtained from the permeate side may be the result of the leakages in the membrane modules resulting from damage to the membrane sheets and permeate collection tubes resulting in opportunities for bacteria contacting the permeate side of membranes. Cultures from the retentate side and permeate side of the ultrafiltration membrane samples are different (Tang et al. 2009a). This may due to the different surface characteristics of the membrane permeate and retentate sides and nutrient levels (Bryers, 1987; Kumar and Anand, 1998; Pasmore et al., 2001; Ridgway, 1991). In our trials, there were no isolates recovered from membranes removed from plants operating hot (55°C) processes (Tang et al. 2009). The bacteria existing in the biofilm in those hot membrane plants were probably non-culturable, as the bacteria in biofilm on the surfaces in dairy environments are subjected to various stresses such as starvation, chemicals, heat, cold and desiccation which injure the cells, rendering them non-culturable (Wong and Cerf, 1995). For our study, the sampling method used had the limitation that it was only able to detect culturable bacteria in the biofilm (Tang et al. (2009).

Cronobactersakazakii is a common environmental contaminant (Lehner and Stephan 2004) and therefore it is not too surprising that it was found together with other Gram-negative micro-organisms (Tang et al. 2009a). The presence of this organism is a concern in infant formula (Lehner and Stephan 2004), but none of the manufacturing plants we studied produced infant formula. Manufacturers of infant formula need to know more about the ecological niche of this micro-organism and how it enters dairy processes.

Previously, *Klebsiellaoxytoca* has been found in milk products in Jordan (El-Sukhon, 2003). Tondo et al. (2004) identified a *K. oxytoca* strain, from raw milk in Brazil producing heat stable protease. Mattila et al. (1990) found *Klebsiellaspp.*in a milk line in a Finland dairy plant. Sharma and Anand (2002) found that *Klebsiella spp.* were predominant Gram-negative isolates in the biofilms from post-pasteurization lines in an experimental dairy plant in India. Both their and our current studies showed the presence of *Klebsiella spp.* after CIP (Sharma and Anand 2002, Mattila et al 1990, Tang *et al.* 2009a). However, this is, so far as we know, the first time that *K. oxytoca* strains have been isolated from dairy UF and RO membrane plants. Therefore, a study on these *K. oxytoca*strains is of importance.

No attempt was made to examine anaerobic bacteria from ultrafiltration membrane surfaces(Tang et al. 2009a) Previous studies showed that contamination of dairy manu-facturing membrane is primarily due to aerobic microflora (Bore andLangsrud, 2005; Flint *et al.*, 1997a), therefore, the isolation of anaerobic microorganisms was not expected to re-present a significant population in the dairy biofilms.

The low levels of protein and carbohydrate on the membrane from one plant possibly reflected the way these membranes were used (Tang et al. 2009a). That membrane module was previously used for processing whey permeate in which there was little protein and most of the lactose would have passed through the membrane, so that the amount remaining on the membrane surface was low. Although, the current CIP had removed much of the organic material from the membrane surface, still some remained. Residual organic material may have contributed to biofilm formation even starting with this low level of organics, by enhancing bacterial attachment and protecting microbial cells from cleaning. We assume that there will be much more organic residues left on the surfaces of membranes used to process milk or whey. The successful isolation of microorganisms from the membranes after CIP indicates that the current CIP procedures were not efficient in terms of biofilm removal, leaving a seed for further biofilm development.

The environment (whey and whey permeate) and microbial interactions are important in the attachment of microbes to membrane surfaces (Tang et al. 2009a).

Trials in our laboratory used the CBR 90 system (BioSurface Technologies, Boseman Montana), to create a similar environment to that experienced in a UF plant processing whey. We were able to replicate the whey composition, temperature and turbulence tobe expected in a whey processing plant, however with theexception that product was not actually passing through the membrane. The results of our study suggested that the whey protein concentration, membrane type including membrane material and age, types of strain and the interactions between different microorganisms are all important factors for biofilm development on UF membrane surfaces (Tang et al. 2009b).

CONTROL OF BIOFILMS ON MEMBRANES

Biofilm on membrane surfaces has been physically, chemically and biologically treated in order to find efficient cleaning strategies. However, membrane materials are sensitive, therefore, control of biofilm on membranes needs particular caution in both the efficiency of the cleaning strategies and the effects on membranes (McDonougand Hargrove, 1972). It was found that preventing the initial attachment of bacteria on a membrane surface was more important than killing bacteria that had already attached (Liu et al., 2010). Therefore, membrane engineering was also used to modify membrane surfaces in terms of reducing or preventing bacterial adhesion (Liu et al., 2010).

Physical Methods

Currently, physical control for membrane biofouling includes reducing the concentration of solids in the feed solution (eg whey), applying a tangential surface shear force and backwashing the membrane module (Chang et al., 2002).However, it was suggested that a high tangential shear force may result in the development of a structurally strong biofilm that could resist further shear force (Percival et al., 1999).

Chemical Methods

Biocides decrease bacterial levels but have less effect on biofilms than on planktonic (free floating) cells and do not affect the availability of nutrients, therefore biofilms may readily reform after biocide treatment. Sanitation of membrane plants should therefore be carried out following a thorough cleaning (D'Souza andMawson, 2005).

Chlorine based sanitisers (e.g. chlorine dioxide and hypochlorites) have been widely used as effective disinfectants (D'Souza and Mawson, 2005). Chlorine dioxide is less effective than many other chlorine based sanitisers (Bohner and Bradley, 1992). Hypochlorites working as membrane-swelling agents assist in flushing out material lodged within the membrane pores

(Cheryan, 1998), however, they often decrease membrane life and should be used with caution (D'Souza andMawson, 2005).

Other sanitisers include peracetic acid, which can pass through RO membranes, enabling sanitation of the permeate side, and has good rinse ability (Krack, 1995). Quaternary ammonium compounds and iodophor based products cannot be used on membranes, as they are often adsorbed onto the membrane surface, causing flux decline and irreversible damage to the membrane (Krack, 1995). Sodium metabisulphite can be used on more sensitive membranes; nevertheless, it requires a long contact time (Krack, 1995). However, extensive chemical cleaning may damage the membrane integrity.

Ozone is believed to be a more powerful sanitiser than chlorine (Flint et al., 1997a). It was observed that although it had an antibacterial effect on planktonic *Enterococcus faecalis* cells, ozone had little effect on its biofilms (Hems et al., 2005). However, ozonation significantly increased the disinfection capacity of a membrane plant in Amsterdam (van der Hoek et al., 2000).

Surfactants and surfactants/biocide combinations have been widely used to treat biofilms. It was found that the combination of sodium dodecyl sulfate with urea was the most effective surfactant combination for cleaning RO membranes (Whittaker et al., 1984). A surfactant (Teepol) has been suggested that can increase the negative charge on the cell wall of *Burkholderia* sp. JS150 and reduce the subsequent attachment to membrane surfaces (Splendiani et al, 2006).Humic substances and surfactants adsorbed to the membrane might also influence membrane surface charge (Childress and Deshmukh, 1998).

The efficacy of CIP currently used in the dairy industry was compared with different cleaners and sanitisers in controlling the biofilm formed by single or dual strains of *K. oxytoca*on PES UF membrane surfaces (Tang et al. 2010). A typical CIP procedure involving alkali, acid and sodium hypochlorite at alkaline pH was chosen as the cleaning control, because this CIP procedure is widely used in the dairy industry. Unfortunately, the CIP control in the CBR 90 did not completely remove the biofilm, perhaps as a result of imperfect cleaning between the membrane sample and the holder in the reactor. There is a crevice between the membrane and the holder around the edges.In some ways, this experimental deficiency mimics the situation in a plant, where rubber seals become cracked and harbour biofilms. The number of remaining culturable cells ($1.9 - 2.19$ log CFU cm^{-2}) after standard CIP on a small membrane surface area (1.27 cm^2) used in our experiments would be a concern when multiplied to reflect the total product contact area of an industrial scale plant. There is evidence elsewhere that biofilms may protect bacterial cells against CIP chemicals and that culturable bacterial cells can remain attached to dairy manufacturing surfaces following a CIP (Austin and Bergeron, 1995; Flintet al., 1999). The cells remaining on the surface will enable rapid regeneration of biofilm once suitable conditions are restored during the processing of dairy liquids.

Biofilm formed by dual strains of *K. oxytoca* was more resistant to cleaning than biofilm formed from single strains (Tang et al. 2010). This might be explained by a difference in the structure of the biofilm formed by a single strain compared with dual strains, or some mutual interaction between the two strains, such as increased polysaccharide production, that resists removal by cleaners. During the sanitation phase, the sanitisers might be expected to kill viable attached cells and thus reduce the viable cell count, rather than removing the biofilms. Also, choosing the right cleaner for biofilm formed by specific strains might loosen or destroy the biofilm structure and would enhance sanitising.

The effectiveness in reducing the number of viable cells in biofilms using mixed enzymes has been reported (Walker et al., 2007). In our studies, cleaning with QuatroZyme®, containing a mixture of enzymes, performed better than other enzyme cleaners. However, more than 17% of the original cells remained culturable after the CIP with QuatroZyme®.

The limitations of using plate counting for assessing cell numbers are that this method may not recover all the viable cells and only culturable cells are countable. Therefore, it is possible that viable but non-culturable cells may persist in the different treatments. The significance of such non-culturable cells in an industrial plant is not known.

Our laboratory trials differed from the industrial scale in the amount of cleaning agent used per unit area of membrane surface, even though the concentrations used for our laboratory experiments were the same as the industrially applied values (Tang et al.2010). The volume of cleaning solution used in dairy membrane plants is $4 - 5$ L m^{-2}(Krack, 1995), while in our laboratory reactor systems the amount of cleaning solution was more than 82 L m^{-2} membrane. This was mainly due to the operating volume of the CBR 90 reactor at 330 mL and a membrane sample with a small surface area (total 30.48 cm^2). Thus the main differences between the laboratory and industrial scale cleaning regime were the volumes of water for flushing, and reagents for cleaning or sanitising. This suggests that using the same cleaners or sanitisers in an industrial scale membrane plant might result in higher residual culturable bacterial counts than those which were achieved in our trials.

Ozonated water appeared to be the weakest sanitiser among those used in this study. This may be because ozonated water application must be strictly controlled, such as being used freshly-made in a completely closed unit; otherwise the ozone will transform into oxygen and lose the disinfectant activity (Guzel-Seydim *et al.*, 2004). Also, the effectiveness of ozone in terms of killing microorganisms is affected by ozone concentration, strains, temperature and pH (Jarroll, 1999).

Biological Methods

Enzymatic cleaning agents can be used to treat fouling on membranes, and they are less aggressive towards the membranes than many chemical cleaners (D'Souza andMawson, 2005). Compared with the traditional cleaning method by alkali, it was found that enzymatic cleaning by protease had a much better performance in terms of removing biofilms from an UF membrane for wastewater treatment, although this is more costly than traditional cleaning (Poeleand van der Graaf, 2005).

Bacteriophage can infect the host bacteria by rapid replication of virions to lyse the host cells or by incorporation into the genome of host cells (Xiongand Liu, 2010). Bacteriophage can reduce microbial attachment to ultrafiltration membrane surfaces by an average of 40% (Goldman et al., 2009). The use of bacteriophage is still relatively new. The advantage is that this is a natural method of control, although the use of bacteriophage as santizers is not widely practiced, probably due to cheaper options being available and a reluctance of plant managers to introduce bacteriophage to a manufacturing environment.

Another natural sanitizer, Vanillin (4-hydroxy-3-methoxybenzaldehyde) extracted from vanilla beans was reported to inhibit the short-and long-chain AHL-mediated quorum sensing system (Xiongand Liu, 2010), and is able to prevent biofouling of RO membrane by *Aeromonashydrophila* (Ponnusamy et al., 2009).

MEMBRANE MODIFICATION

Membranes can be modified to reduce or prevent bacterial adhesion. Techniques include photochemical modification, plasma treatment, the radiation-induced grafting of monomers and the photo-induced polymerization of different monomers (Kochkodan et al., 2006).

Membranes (PSF, PES and regenerated cellulose (RC)) deposited with TiO_2 particles under UV-irradiation at 365 nm had a strong bactericidal effect and resulted in 1.7-2.3 times higher values of water fluxes comparing with those for control membranes (Kochkodan et al., 2008). This reflected the absence of biofilm in the treated membranes and bacterial fouling of control membranes.

To reduce the hydrophobic interaction between bacteria and membranes, PES and PSF membranes were modified with three hydrophilic monomers using UV-assisted graft polymerization (Kaeselev et al., 2001).

PES membrane surfaces can be modified by argon plasma treatment followed by polyacrylic acid (PAA) grafting in a vapour phase, allowing the membrane surfaces to become permanently hydrophilic (Wavhaland Fisher, 2002). This modified membrane is also easier to clean and requires little caustic to recover permeation flux (Wavhaland Fisher, 2002). This is likely to reflect the general premise that hydrophilic surfaces are less prone to bacterial colonisation than hydrophobic surfaces.

Yang et al. (2009) observed good performance of an RO membrane used for seawater desalination, when coated with nanosilver. They treated either membrane surfaces or membrane spacers, and found that almost no multiplication of cells was detected on the membrane when the membrane spacer was nanosilver-coated (Yang et al., 2009). This reflects the long established bacteriocidal property of silver.

CONCLUSION

The main problem with whey processing is controlling the microbiological quality of the final product. Traditionally a waste product from cheese and casein manufacture, whey has been treated as a waste stream that relatively recently has been recognised for some valuable components. The microbiological quality of the raw whey is always a challenge, with thermoduric microorganisms being the greatest concern. However as recent trials have shown, more sensitive Gram negative bacteria are a concern. All microbial contaminants have the potential to grow on the large surface area of the membrane processing plants used in whey manufacture and their construction makes efficient cleaning difficult. Biofilm formation is a major impediment to the use of filtration membranes in cross-flow processes in whey processing plants. The main effects of biofilm on membranes are: (1) reduction of membrane flux and productivity, (2) biodegradation of the membrane material, (3) an increase in power consumption for raising operating pressure, (4) the cost of cleaning and even replacement of membrane modules.

Membrane cleaning strategies require improvements for effective control of biofilms. The dairy industry hasfocussed in general on the control of biofilm formed by *Pseudomonas* species and food borne pathogens and many dairy biofilms are believed to be predominantly single species (Flint et al., 1997). If membranes are predominantly cololonised by mixed species biofilms, this will have an impact on the ability to clean. The biofilm developed by mixed cultures is more complicated than that of pure cultures.

The control of biofilm on membranes in the dairy industry has been dependent on frequent CIP with chemicals, enzymes or disinfectors/sanitizers commonly used in cleaning systems in food manufacturing plants. However, a study of improved control strategies should focus on both the membranes (e.g. selection of membrane materials with modifications) for lowering bacterial attachment, and improvements in membrane cleaning methods for eliminating the biofilm and preventing re-growth.

REFERENCES

An, Y. H. and Friedman, R. J. (1998).Concise review of mechanisms of bacterial adhesion tobiomaterial surfaces.*Journal of Biomedical Materials Research,* 43(3), 338-348.

Anon. (2007).Crossflow filtration: A new approach to wine clarification. *Filtration andSeparation,* 44(2), 36-39.

Araujo, E. A., De Andrade, N. J., Da Silva, L. H. M., De Carvalho, A. F., Silva, C. A. D., andRamos, A. M. (2010). Control of microbial adhesion as a strategy for food and bioprocesstechnology.*Food and Bioprocess Technology,* 3(3), 321-332.

Austin, J. W. and Bergeron, G. (1995).Development of bacterial biofilms in dairy processing lines.*Journal of Dairy Research,* 62(3), 509-519.

Bellona, C. and Drewes, J. E. (2005). The role of membrane surface charge and solute physicochemical properties in the rejection of organic acids by NF membranes. *Journal of Membrane Science,* 249(1-2), 227-234.

Bird, J. (1996).The application of membrane systems in the dairy industry.*Journal of the Society of Dairy Technology,* 49(1), 16-23.

Bodalo-Santoyo, A., Gomez-Carrasco, J. L., Gomez-Gomez, E., Maximo-Martin, M. F., andHidalgo-Montesinos, A. M. (2004). Spiral-wound membrane reverse osmosis and thetreatment of industrial effluents. *Desalination,* 160(2), 151-158.

Bohner, H. F. and Bradley, R. L. (1992).Effective cleaning and sanitizing of polysulfoneultrafiltration membrane systems.*Journal of Dairy Science,* 75(3), 718-724.

Bore, E. and Langsrud, S. (2005). Characterization of micro-organisms isolated from dairyindustry after cleaning and fogging disinfection with alkyl amine and peracetic acid.*Journal of Applied Microbiology,* 98(1), 96-105.

Boributha, S., Chanachaia, A. and Jiraratananon, R. (2009).Modification of PVDF membrane by chitosan solution for reducing protein fouling.*Journal of Membrane Science,* 342(1-2),97-104.

Bryers, J. D. (1987). Biologically-active surfaces - Processes governing the formation andpersistence of biofilms. *Biotechnology Progress,* 3(2), 57-68.

Buckingham-Meyer, K., Goeres, D. M. and Hamilton, M. A. (2007).Comparative evaluation of biofilm disinfectant efficacy tests.*Journal of Microbiological Methods,* 70(2), 236-244.

Bunt, C. R., Jones, D. S. and Tucker, I. G. (1993). The effects of pH, ionic-strength and organicphase on the bacterial adhesion to hydrocarbons (Bath) test. *International Journal ofPharmaceutics,* 99(2-3), 93-98.

Campbell, P., Srinivasan, R., Knoell, T., Phipps, D., Ishida, K., Safarik, J., Cormack, T. et al.(1999). Quantitative structure-activity relationship (QSAR) analysis of surfactantsinfluencing attachment of a Mycobacteriumspto cellulose acetate and aromaticpolyamide reverse osmosis membranes. *Biotechnology and Bioengineering,* 64(5), 527-544.

Cartwright, P. S. (2003). Guides to selecting membrane separation technologies.*Industrial Water World,* 4, 9-13.

Chang, H. T., Rittmann, B. E., Amar, D., Heim, R., Ehlinger, O., and Lesty, Y. (1991).Biofilmdetachment mechanisms in a liquid-fluidized bed.*Biotechnology and Bioengineering,*38(5), 499-506.

Chang, I. S., Le Clech, P., Jefferson, B., and Judd, S. (2002). Membrane fouling in membranebioreactors for wastewater treatment.*Journal of Environmental Engineering-Asce,*128(11), 1018-1029.

Characklis, W. G. (1990). Biofilm processes. In: W. G. Characklis and K. C. Marshall (Eds.),*Biofilms* (1st ed., pp. 195-231). New York, USA: Wiley.

Cheryan, M. (1998).*Ultrafiltration and microfiltration handbook.* Lancaster, UK: TechnomicPublishing Co., Inc.

Cheryan, M. and Mehaia, M. A. (1986).Membrane bioreactors.*Chemtech,* 16(11), 676-681.

Childress, A. E. and Deshmukh, S. S. (1998).Effect of humic substances and anionic surfactants on the surface charge and performance of reverse osmosis membranes.*Desalination,* 118(1-3), 167-174.

Cogan, N. G. and Chellam, S. (2008). Regularized Stokeslets solution for 2-D flow in dead-end microfiltration: Application to bacterial deposition and fouling.*Journal of MembraneScience,* 318(1-2), 379-386.

Criado, M. T., Suarez, B. and Ferreiros, C. M. (1994).The Importance of Bacterial Adhesion in the Dairy-Industry.*Food Technology,* 48(2), 123-126.

D'Souza, N. M. and Mawson, A. J. (2005). Membrane cleaning in the dairy industry: A review.*Critical Reviews in Food Science and Nutrition,* 45(2), 125-134.

Dang, H. Y. and Lovell, C. R. (1999). Bacterial primary colonization and early succession onsurfaces in marine waters as determined by amplified rRNA gene restriction analysis andsequence analysis of 16S rRNA genes. *Applied and Environmental Microbiology,* 66(2),467-475.

Daufin, G., Escudier, J. P., Carrere, H., Berot, S., Fillaudeau, L., and Decloux, M. (2001). Recent and emerging applications of membrane processes in the food and dairy industry.*Food and Bioproducts Processing,* 79(C2), 89-102.

Dautle, M. P., Wilkinson, T. R. and Gauderer, M. W. L. (2003).Isolation and identification ofbiofilm microorganisms from silicone gastrostomy devices.*Journal of Pediatric Surgery,*38(2), 216-220.

Davies, D. G., Parsek, M. R., Pearson, J. P., Iglewski, B. H., Costerton, J. W., and Greenberg, E. P. (1998). The involvement of cell-to-cell signals in the development of a bacterial biofilm.*Science,* 280(5361), 295-298.

Dreeszen, P. H. (2003). *Biofilm: The key to understanding and controlling bacterial growth in automated drinking water systems* (2nd ed.). Waterford, WI, USA: Edstrom Industries Inc.

Duncan-Hewitt, W. C. (1990). Nature of the hydrophobic effect. In: *Microbial Cell Surface Hydrophobicity* (Edited by R. J. Doyle and M. Rosenberg). Pp. 39-73. Washington DC: American Society for Microbiology.

El-Sukhon, S. N. (2003). Identification and. characterization of Klebsiellaeisolated from milk and milk products in Jordan. *Food Microbiology*, 20(2), 225-230.

Elimelech, M., Zhu, X. H., Childress, A. E., and Hong, S. K. (1997). Role of membrane surface morphology in colloidal fouling of cellulose acetate and composite aromatic polyamide reverse osmosis membranes. *Journal of Membrane Science*, 127(1), 101-109.

Flemming, L., Rawlings, D. and Chenia, H. (2007). Phenotypic and molecular characterisation of fish-borne Flavobacteriumjohnsoniae-like isolates from aquaculture systems in South Africa. *Research in Microbiology*, 158(1), 18-30.

Fletcher, M. (1976).Effects of proteins on bacterial attachment to polystyrene.*Journal ofGeneral Microbiology*, 94(Jun.), 400-404.

Flint, S. H., Bremer, P. J. and Brooks, J. D. (1997a). Biofilms in dairy manufacturing plant - Description, current concerns and methods of control.*Biofouling*, 11(1), 81-97.

Flint, S. H., Van den Elzen, H., Brooks, J. D., and Bremer, P. J. (1999). Removal and inactivation of thermo-resistant Streptococcicolonising stainless steel.*International Dairy Journal*, 9(7), 429-436.

Fontananova, E., Jansen, J. C., Cristiano, A., Curcio, E., and Drioli, E. (2006).Effect of additives in the casting solution on the formation of PVDF membranes.*Desalination*, 192(1-3), 190-197.

Friedrich, U. and Lenke, J. (2006).Improved enumeration of lactic acid bacteria in mesophilic dairy starter cultures by using multiplex quantitative real-time PCR and flow cytometryfluorescence in situ hybridization.*Applied and Environmental Microbiology*, 72(6), 4163-4171.

Goldman, G., Starosvetsky, J. and Armon, R. (2009).Inhibition of biofilm formation on UFmembrane by use of specific bacteriophages.*Journal of Membrane Science*, 342(1-2),145-152.

Guzel-Seydim, Z. B., Greene, A. K. and Seydim, A. C. (2004).Use of ozone in the food industry.*Lebensmittel-Wissenschaft Und-Technologie-Food Science and Technology*, 37(4), 453- 460.

Hems, R. S., Gulabivala, K., Ng, Y. L., Ready, D., and Spratt, D. A. (2005).An in vitro evaluation of the ability of ozone to kill a strain of Enterococcusfaecalis.*International Endodontic Journal*, 38(1), 22-29.

Her, N., Amy, G. and Jarusutthirak, C. (2000). Seasonal variations of nanofiltration (NF) foulants: identification and control. *Desalination*, 132(1-3), 143-160.

Herzberg, M., Kang, S. and Elimelech, M. (2009).Role of extracellular polymeric substances(EPS) in biofouling of reverse osmosis membranes.*Environmental Science and Technology*,43(12), 4393-4398.

Hiddink, J., Deboer, R. and Nooy, P. F. C. (1980). Reverse-osmosis of dairy liquids.*Journal of Dairy Science*, 63(2), 204-214.

Hobman, P. G. (1992) Ultrafiltration and Manufacture of WPC IN Zadow, J. G. (1995) *Whey and Lactose Processing*. Chapter 3, pg221, Elsevier, New York.

Isberg, R. R. and Barnes, P. (2002).Dancing with the host: Flow-dependent bacterial adhesion.*Cell*, 110(1), 1-4.

Ivnitsky, H., Katz, I., Minz, D., Shimoni, E., Chen, Y., Tarchitzky, J., Semiat, R., et al. (2005).Characterization of membrane biofouling in nanofiltration processes of wastewatertreatment. *Desalination,* 185(1-3), 255-268.

Jacquement, V., Gaval, G., Rosenberger, S., B., L., and Schrotter, J.-C. (2005). Towards a better characterization and understanding of membrane fouling in water treatment,.*Desalination,* 178, 13-20.

Jarroll, E. L. (1999). Intestinal protozoa. In: A. D. Russell, W. B. Hugo and G. A. J. Ayliffe (Eds.), *Principles and practice of disinfection, preservation and sterilization* (pp. 251-257).Oxford, UK: Blackwell Science Ltd.

Jefferson, K. K. (2004). What drives bacteria to produce a biofilm? *Fems Microbiology Letters,* 236(2), 163-173.

Kaeselev, B., Pieracci, J. and Belfort, G. (2001).Photoinduced grafting of ultrafiltrationmembranes: comparison of poly(ether sulfone) and poly(sulfone). *Journal of MembraneScience,* 194(2), 245-261.

Karasu, K., Yoshikawa, S., Kentish, S. E., and Stevens, G. W. (2009). A model for cross-flowultrafiltration of dairy whey based on the rheology of the compressible cake.*Journal ofMembrane Science,* 341(1-2), 252-260.

Katsikogianni, M., and Missirlis, Y. F. (2004).Concise review of mechanisms of bacterialadhesion to biomaterials and of techniques used in estimating bacteria-materialinteractions.*European Cells and Materials Journal,* 8, 37-57.

Khan, M. M. T., Stewart, P. S., Moll, D. J., Mickols, W. E., Burr, M. D., Nelson, S. E., andCamper, A. K. (2010). Assessing biofouling on polyamide reverse osmosis (RO)membrane surfaces in a laboratory system.*Journal of Membrane Science,* 349(1-2), 429-437.

Kim, S., Lee, S., Hong, S., Oh, Y., Seoul, M., Kweon, J., and Kim, T. (2009). Biofouling ofreverse osmosis membranes: Microbial quorum sensing and fouling propensity.*Desalination,* 247(1-3), 303-315.

Kirtley, S. A. and Mcguire, J. (1989).On differences in surface constitution of dairy productcontact materials.*Journal of Dairy Science,* 72(7), 1748-1753.

Kochkodan, V., Tsarenko, S., Potapchenko, N., Kosinova, V., and Goncharuk, V. (2008).Adhesion of microorganisms to polymer membranes: a photobactericidal effect of surfacetreatment with TiO2. *Desalination,* 220(1-3), 380-385.

Kochkodan, V. M., Hilal, N., Goncharuk, V. V., Al-Khatib, L., and Levadna, T. I. (2006).Effect of the surface modification of polymer membranes on their microbiological fouling.*Colloid Journal,* 68(3), 267-273.

Koo, J. Y., Hong, S. P., Kang, J. W., Kim, J. E., Hyung, H., Kim, Y. H., Yoon, S. et al. (2002). Fouling resistant reverse osmosis membranes, *American Water Works AssociationMembrane Technology Conference* (Vol. 223, pp. 512-522).

Krack, R. (1995). Chemical agents and costs in cleaning and disinfection of membraneequipment, *Fouling and Cleaning in Pressure Driven Membrane Processes* (pp. 151-174).Brussels, Belgium: International Dairy Federation.

Kreft, J. U. and Wimpenny, J. W. T. (2001).Effect of EPS on biofilm structure and function asrevealed by an individual-based model of biofilm growth.*Water Science and Technology,*43(6), 135-141.

Kumar, C. G. and Anand, S. K. (1998). Significance of microbial biofilms in food industry: areview. *International Journal of Food Microbiology,* 42(1-2), 9-27.

Kwon, K. K., Lee, H. S., Jung, S. Y., Yim, J. H., Lee, J. H., and Lee, H. K. (2002). Isolation and identification of biofilm-forming marine bacteria on glass surfaces in Dae-Ho Dike,Korea.*Journal of Microbiology,* 40(4), 260-266.

Lee, E., Shon, H. K. and Cho, J. (2010a). Biofouling characteristics using flow field-flowfractionation: Effect of bacteria and membrane properties. *Bioresource Technology,*101(5), 1487-1493.

Lee, W., Ahn, C. H., Hong, S., Kim, S., Lee, S., Baek, Y., and Yoon, J. (2010b). Evaluation ofsurface properties of reverse osmosis membranes on the initial biofouling stages under nofiltration condition. *Journal of Membrane Science,* 351(1-2), 112-122.

Lehner, A. and Stephan, R. (2004).Microbiological, epidemiological, and food safety aspects of *Enterobactersakazakii.Journal of Food Protection,* 67(12), 2850-2857.

Liaqat, I. and Sabri, A. N. (2009). Isolation and characterization of biocides resistant bacteria from dental unit water line biofilms. *Journal of Basic Microbiology,* 49(3), 275-284.

Liu, H. and Fang, H. H. P. (2002).Extraction of extracellular polymeric substances (EPS) ofsludges.*Journal of Biotechnology,* 95(3), 249-256.

Liu, H., Huang, L., Huang, Z., and Zheng, J. (2007). Specification of sulfate reducing bacteriabiofilms accumulation effects on corrosion initiation. *Materials and Corrosion,* 58(1), 44-48.

Lozier, J., Amy, G., Jacangelo, J., Mysore, C., and Heijmann, B. (2006).Natural organic matter fouling of low-pressure membrane systems, *Proceedings of NWRI Microfiltration 4Conference* (pp. 19-27). Canada.

Mattila, T., Manninen, M. and Kylasiurola, A. L. (1990). Effect of cleaning-in-place disinfectants on wild bacterial strains isolated from a milking line. *Journal of Dairy Research,* 57(1), 33-39.

Maubois, J. L. (1980). Ultrafiltration of whey.*Journal of the Society of Dairy Technology,* 33(2), 55-58.

McDonoug, F. E. and Hargrove, R. E. (1972).Sanitation of reverse osmosis / ultrafiltrationequipment.*Journal of Milk and Food Technology,* 35(2), 102-106.

Meadows, P. S. (1971).Attachment of bacteria to solid surfaces.*Archives of Microbiology,* 75(4), 374-381.

Myint, A. A., Lee, W., Mun, S., Ahn, C. H., Lee, S., and Yoon, J. (2010). Influence of membrane surface properties on the behaviour of initial bacterial adhesion and biofilm development onto nanofiltration membranes. *Biofouling,* 26(3), 313-321.

Nielsen, P. H., Frolund, B. and Keiding, K. (1996). Changes in the composition of extracellular polymeric substances in activated sludge during anaerobic storage. *Applied Microbiology and Biotechnology,* 44(6), 823-830.

O'Toole, G., Kaplan, H. B. and Kolter, R. (2000).Biofilm formation as microbial development.*Annual Review of Microbiology,* 54, 49-79.

Palmer, J., Flint, S. and Brooks, J. (2007).Bacterial cell attachment, the beginning of a biofilm.*Journal of Industrial Microbiology and Biotechnology,* 34(9), 577-588.

Pang, C. M., Hong, P. Y., Guo, H. L., and Liu, W. T. (2005). Biofilm formation characteristics of bacterial isolates retrieved from a reverse osmosis membrane. *Environmental Science andTechnology,* 39(19), 7541-7550.

Pasmore, M., Todd, P., Pfiefer, B., Rhodes, M., and Bowman, C. N. (2002).Effect of polymersurface properties on the reversibility of attachment of Pseudomonas aeruginosain theearly stages of biofilm development.*Biofouling,* 18(1), 65-71.

Pasmore, M., Todd, P., Smith, S., Baker, D., Silverstein, J., Coons, D., and Bowman, C. N. (2001). Effects of ultrafiltration membrane surface properties on *Pseudomonas aeruginosa*biofilm initiation for the purpose of reducing biofouling. *Journal of Membrane Science,*194(1), 15-32.

Pearce, G. (2007a). Introduction to membranes: Manufacturers' comparison: part 2. *Filtration and Separation,* 44(9), 28-31.

Pearce, G. (2007b). Introduction to membranes: Membrane selection. *Filtration and Separation,* 44(3), 35-37.

Pearce, G. (2008). Introduction to membranes-MBRs: Manufacturers' comparison: part 1.*Filtration and Separation,* 45(2), 28-31.

Percival, S. L., Knapp, J. S., Wales, D. S., and Edyvean, R. G. J. (1999). The effect of turbulentflow and surface roughness on biofilm formation in drinking water.*Journal of IndustrialMicrobiology and Biotechnology,* 22(3), 152-159.

Piao, J., Kensuke, F. and Kazuo, Y. (2006). Bacterial community structure on membrane surface and characteristics of strains isolated from membrane surface in submerged membrane bioreactor. *Separation Science and Technology,* 41(7), 1527-1549.

Poele, S. T. and Van der Graaf, J. (2005).Enzymatic cleaning in ultrafiltration of wastewatertreatment plant effluent.*Desalination,* 179(1-3), 73-81.

Ponnusamy, K., Paul, D. and Kweon, J. H. (2009).Inhibition of quorum sensing mechanism and Aeromonashydrophilabiofilm formation by vanillin.*Environmental Engineering Science,* 26(8), 1359-1363.

Ramsey, M. M. and Whiteley, M. (2004).Pseudomonas aeruginosaattachment and biofilmdevelopment in dynamic environments.*Molecular Microbiology,* 53(4), 1075-1087.

Ridgeway, H. F. and Flemming, H. C. (1996). Membrane biofouling, in: Mallevialle, J., Odendaal, P.E. and Wiesner M.R. (Eds.*), Water Treatment Membrane Processes,* McGraw-Hill, New York. 6.1-6.62.

Ridgway, H., Ishida, K., Rodriguez, G., Safarik, J., Knoell, T., and Bold, R. (1999). Biofouling of membranes: Membrane preparation, characterization, and analysis of bacterial adhesion.*Biofilms,* 310, 463-494.

Ridgway, H. F. (1991). Bacteria and membranes - ending a bad relationship.*Desalination,* 83(1-3), 53-53.

Schreiber, R. (2001). Heat-induced modifications in casein dispersions affecting theirrennetability.*International Dairy Journal,* 11(4-7), 553-558.

Sharma, M. and Anand, S. K. (2002).Characterization of constitutive microflora of biofilms indairy processing lines.*Food Microbiology,* 19(6), 627-636.

Speers, J. G. S. and Gilmour, A. (1985).The Influence of milk and milk components on theattachment of bacteria to farm dairy equipment surfaces.*Journal of Applied Bacteriology,*59(4), 325-332.

Splendiani, A., Livingston, A. G. and Nicollella, C. (2006).Control of membrane-attachedbiofilms using surfactants.*Biotechnology and Bioengineering,* 94(1), 15-23.

Stoodley, P., Lewandowski, Z., Boyle, J. D., and Lappin-Scott, H. M. (1999b). Structuraldeformation of bacterial biofilms caused by short-term fluctuations in fluid shear: An insitu investigation of biofilm rheology. *Biotechnology and Bioengineering,* 65(1), 83-92.

Sutherland, I. W. and Kennedy, L. (1996).Polysaccharide lyases from gellan-producing*Sphingomonas spp. Microbiology,* 142, 867-87.

Tang, X., Flint, S. H., Brooks, J. D., and Bennett, R. J. (2009a). Factors affecting the attachment of micro-organisms isolated from ultrafiltration and reverse osmosis membranes in dairy processing plants. *Journal of Applied Microbiology,* 107(2), 443-451.

Tang, X., Flint, S. H., Bennett, R. J., Brooks, J. D., and Morton, R. H. (2009b). Biofilm growth of individual and dual strains of Klebsiellaoxytocafrom the dairy industry on ultrafiltration membranes.*Journal of Industrial Microbiology and Biotechnology,* 36(12), 1491-1497.

Tang, X., Flint, S. H., Bennett, R. J., Brooks, J. D. (2010) The efficacy of different cleaners and sanitisers in cleaning biofilms on UF membranes used in the dairy industry. *Journal of Membrane Science* 352, 71-75.

Tiexeira, P., Lopes, Z., Azweedo, J., Oliveira, R., and Vieira, M. J. (2005).Physico-Chemical surface characterisation of a bacterial population isolated from a milking machine. *Food Microbiology,* 22, 247-251

Tondo, E. C., Lakus, F. R., Oliveira, F. A., and Brandelli, A. (2004). Identification of heat stable protease of Klebsiellaoxytocaisolated from raw milk. *Letters in Applied*

Vadillo-Rodriguez, V., Busscher, H. J., Van der Mei, H. C., De Vries, J., and Norde, W. (2005).Role of Lactobacilluscell surface hydrophobicity as probed by AFM in adhesion tosurfaces at low and high ionic strength.*Colloids and Surfaces B-Biointerfaces,* 41(1), 33-41.

Van der Hoek, J. P., Hofman, J. A. M. H. and Graveland, A. (2000).Benefits of ozone-activated carbon filtration in integrated treatment processes, including membrane systems.*Journal of Water Supply Research and Technology-Aqua,* 49(6), 341-356.

Vejborg, R. M. and Klemm, P. (2008).Blocking of bacterial biofilm formation by a fish protein coating.*Applied and Environmental Microbiology,* 74(11), 3551-3558.

Vrijenhoek, E. M., Hong, S. and Elimelech, M. (2001). Influence of membrane surface properties on initial rate of colloidal fouling of reverse osmosis and nanofiltration membranes. *Journal of Membrane Science,* 188(1), 115-128.

Walker, S. L., Fourgialakis, M., Cerezo, B., and Livens, S. (2007). Removal of microbial biofilms from dispense equipment: The effect of enzymatic pre-digestion and detergent treatment. *Journal of the Institute of Brewing,* 113(1), 61-66.

Wavhal, D. S. and Fisher, E. R. (2002).Hydrophilic modification of polyethersulfone membranes by low temperature plasma-induced graft polymerization.*Journal of Membrane Science,* 209(1), 255-269.

Whittaker, C., Ridgway, H. and Olson, B. H. (1984).Evaluation of cleaning strategies for removal of biofilms from reverse-osmosis membranes.*Applied and Environmental Microbiology,* 48(2), 395-403.

Wong, A. C. L. and Cerf, O. (1995). Biofilms: implications for hygiene monitoring of dairy plant surfaces. *Bulletin - International Dairy Federation,* 302, 40-44.

Xiong, Y. H. and Liu, Y. (2010). Biological control of microbial attachment: a promisingalternative for mitigating membrane biofouling. *Applied Microbiology and Biotechnology,*86(3), 825-837.

Yang, H. L., Lin, J. C. T. and Huang, C. (2009).Application of nanosilver surface modification to RO membrane and spacer for mitigating biofouling in seawater desalination.*Water Research,* 43(15), 3777-3786.

Yasuda, T., Okuno, T. and Yasuda, H. (1994). Contact angle of water on polymer surfaces.*Langmuir,* 10(7), 2435-2439.

Yeon, K. M., Cheong, W. S., Oh, H. S., Lee, W. N., Hwang, B. K., Lee, C. H., Beyenal, H. et al. (2009). Quorum sensing: a new biofouling control paradigm in a membrane bioreactor for advanced wastewater treatment. *Environmental Science and Technology,* 43(2), 380-385.

Zhang, W., Wahlgren, M. and Sivik, B. (1989).Membrane characterization by the contact angle technique .2.Characterization of UF membranes and comparison between the captivebubble and sessile drop as methods to obtain water contact angles.*Desalination,* 72(3),263-273.

Zottola, E. A. (1994). Microbial attachment and biofilm formation - a new problem for the food industry.*Food Technology,* 48(7), 107-114.

Zottola, E. A. and Sasahara, K. C. (1994).Microbial biofilms in the food processing industry - Should they be a concern.*International Journal of Food Microbiology,* 23(2), 125-148

In: Whey: Types, Composition and Health Implications   ISBN: 978-1-61942-862-1
Editors: Rafael M. Benitez and Gustavo M. Ortero   © 2012 Nova Science Publishers, Inc.

Chapter 5

IMMUNE-MODULATING EFFECTS OF WHEY PROTEINS AND PEPTIDES

Kentaro Nakamura [*] *and Taketo Yamaji*

Nutrition Research Department, Food Science Research Laboratory,
Meiji Co. Ltd., Kanagawa, Japan

ABSTRACT

Whey proteins and whey peptides have been known to have physiological as well as nutritional benefits. Until recently, bovine whey proteins and peptides have been mainly studied for their benefits in energy, and muscle performance. Currently, most researches on whey proteins and peptides focus on their benefits for human health. Whey contains various proteins and peptides with physiological functionality. The proteins and peptides found in whey are β-lactoglobulin, α-lactalbumin, immunoglobulins, bovine serum albumin, and lactoferrin, in addition to glycomacropeptide which is made from casein during cheese-making process. Whey proteins and their components have been de-monstrated to have immune-modulating properties, that is, the stimulation of innate and adaptive immunities as well as anti-inflammatory effects. Whey proteins also have other benefits, such as anti-oxidant, anti-hypertensive, anti-bacterial, anti-viral and serum lipid-lowering effects. Peptides derived from whey proteins have also been shown to possess various bioactive properties, such as opioid, anti-hypertensive and immune-modulating effects. This review focuses on the immune-modulating potency of whey proteins and peptides which have been well studied, and the recent progress in our laboratory on the anti-inflammatory potency of whey proteins and peptides.

ABBREVIATIONS

NK: natural killer
Ig: immunoglobulin

[*] Corresponding Author: K. Nakamura. Address: 540 Naruda, Odawara, Kanagawa 250-0862, Japan; Tel.: +81 465 37 3665; Fax: +81 465 37 3624; E-mail address: kentarou.nakamura@meiji.com

β-LG: β-lactoglobulin
α-LA: α-lactalbumin
BSA: bovine serum albumin
LF: lactoferrin
GMP: glycomacropeptide
SRBC: sheep red blood cell
IL: interleukin
PMN: polymorphonuclear cell
ConA: concanavalin A
PHA: phytohemagglutinin
LPS: lipopolysaccharide
GSH: glutathione
TNF: tumor necrosis factor
PFC: plaque forming cell
IFN: interferon
TGF: transforming growth factor
PGE_2:   prostaglandin E2
NF-κB: nuclear factor-kappa B
Stat 3:   signal transducer and activator of transcription 3
SIRS: systemic inflammatory response syndrome
ALT: alanine aminotransferase activity
AST: aspartate aminotransferase activity
ICU: intensive care unit

INTRODUCTION

The immune system plays an important role in the protection against bacterial and viral infections, and also cancers. Deficiencies of the immune system lead to a greater risk of infection and may enhance the severity of diseases. The immune system is composed of two major subdivisions, the innate or non-specific immune system and the adaptive or specific immune system. The innate immune system is our first line of defense against invading organisms while the adaptive immune system acts as a second line of defense and also affords protection against re-exposure to the same pathogen [1-3]. Although these two arms of the immune system have distinct functions, they work closely together. Innate immune system includes physicochemical barriers such as the skin, mucus, lysozyme and complement, as well as natural killer cells (NK cells) and phagocytic cells such as neutrophils and macrophages/monocytes. Adaptive immune responses are mediated by T and B lymphocytes. B lymphocytes produce antibodies (immunoglobulin (Ig)A, IgG, IgM, IgD and IgE) (humoral immunity), while T lymphocytesdifferentiate into T-helper, T-suppressor and cytotoxic lymphocytes (cell mediated immunity).

Milk is one of the most nutritionally complete foods. It is the primary source of food for newborn mammals. The benefit of milk has been recognized for thousands of years, and milk is known to contain several components with physiological functionality. Whey protein is a major component of human milk, and has been well studied on its health benefits. Whey protein comprises almost sixty percent of human milk proteins, and approximately twenty percent of bovine milk proteins. The fractions of whey proteins are β-lactoglobulin (β-LG), α-lactalbumin (α-LA), immunoglobulins (Igs), bovine serum albumin (BSA), and lacto-ferrin (LF), in addition to glycomacropeptide (GMP), which is released from κ-casein during the cheese making process.

β-LG is the most abundant protein found in whey, and represents about half of the total whey protein content in bovine milk, while it is absent from human milk. The structure of βLG is similar to that of retinol binding protein, and β-LG promotes the absorption of retinol to small intestine. α-LA is one of the main proteins in human and bovine milk. This protein contains essential and branched chain amino acids, is readily digestible and has low immunogenenicity. Igs are antibodies present in whey at a rate of approximately 10-15 percent. IgG is the major immunoglobulin found in bovine whey and IgA is the major one in human colostrum. Igs play the role of "passive immunity", the defense against pathogen and viruses. Igs are transferred from mother to child by cord blood or breast-feeding, and are the first line of immune defense of children. LF is an iron-binding glycoprotein with antioxidant properties. Owing to its iron-binding properties, LF has been proposed to play a role in iron uptake by the intestinal mucosa and to manifest a bacteriostatic property by withholding iron from iron-requiring bacteria. This suggests the involvement of LF in the primary defense against pathogenic bacteria. The LF concentration in bovine whey is only 1-2 percent, while in human milk, LF is a major whey protein, with 6-8 g/l in the colostrum and 2-4 g/l in the milk. LF is the most studied of the whey proteins and appears to have a lot of physiological properties. BSA is a source of essential amino acid and is present in whey at the rate of approximately 5-10 percent. There are few studies on the physiological properties of BSA. GMP is a caseinmacropeptide and is found in sweet whey (but not acid whey) at the rate of approximately 10 percent, due to the digestion of casein with chymosin enzyme during the cheese-making process. This is the only casein-derived peptides found in whey.

It is now known that whey components can directly affect cells of the immune system. That is because whey protein has been shown to represent an effective cysteine donor that maintains a concentration of active glutathione (γ-glutamyl-cysteinyl-glycine; GSH) in cells. The GSH antioxidant system is the primary mechanism of cell protection. An adequate supply of GSH is crucial for the maintenance of the immune system [4-6]. The GSH-modulating effects of whey proteins are believed to be the underlying factors for both the immune-enhancing and some antioxidant actions of whey proteins. In animals, whey protein feeding enhanced the immune response and GSH concentrations in the spleen, but these effects were decreased following treatment with an inhibitor of GSH [7-9]. Compared to other protein sources, whey proteins generally contain higher concentration of cysteine, and optimize the immune response. Whey proteins, their components and peptides have been shown to have immune-enhancing/modulating properties [10-12]. In this chapter, we will focus on the immune-enhancing/modulating potency of whey proteins and peptides, and the recent progress in our laboratory on the anti-inflammatory potency of whey proteins and peptides.

IMMUNE-ENHANCING EFFECTS OF WHEY PROTEINS AND PEPTIDES

Stimulation of Innate Immunity

Whey proteins can reduce rotavirus-induced diarrhea and improve the immune system against HIV infection. Certain mechanisms of the protective action of these whey proteins in infections have been suggested, such as increases in NK cells in neonate rats and plasma glutathione concentrations in HIV-infected patients [13,14]. In addition, whey proteins are potent in the prevention and treatment of cancer. Supplementation of whey proteins led an increase in lymphocyte GSH levels and enhancement of NK function in cancer patients [15,16]. *In vitro* and *in vivo* studies have targeted the effects of whey proteins on neutrophils [17,18], granulocytes [18,19] and NK cell activity [20]. Colostral whey proteins from immunized cows activated the phagocytosis of pathogenic microbes by human neutrophils [21].

The effects of some whey components and whey peptides on innate immunity have also been investigated. Bovine whey protein extracts have been shown to reduce apoptosis of human blood neutrophils and to prime normal human blood neutrophils by enhancing their chemotaxis, phagocytosis, oxidative burst, and degranulation [22,23]. The mechanism of action *in vitro* has been proposed to be related mainly to the presence of efficient concentrations of β-LG and α-LA in whey protein extracts [22]. α-LA has been shown to have an immune-enhancing effect in mice [24,25]. The production of interleukin (IL)-1β by macrophages from bronchoalveolar lavage was increased by the presence of this protein [26]. The synthetic tripeptide from α-LA, Gly-Leu-Phe, has been shown to enhance innate immunity [27]. This tripeptide significantly increased the phagocytosis of human and murine macrophages and protected mice against lethal *Klebsiella pneumonia* infections [28]. This peptide also stimulated the adherence of human senescent red blood cells to human monocytes and macrophages, and the phagocytosis of these cells [27,29]. This latter activity is correlated to the presence of specific binding sites on human blood phagocytic cells [27,29]. The properties of this tripeptide in human and rat polymorphonuclear (PMN) cells were also evaluated. This peptide increased the superoxide anion generation by human PMNs through an increase in the oxidative burst response and enhancement of phosphoinositide breakdown with maximal IP3 production in cells [30]. Another peptide (Tyr-Gly-Gly) derived from α-LA has also been shown to stimulate human peripheral blood lymphocytes [31].

Bovine LF also promotes the phagocytosis of human neutrophils [32]. This activation appears to be a result of the specific binding of LF to neutrophils [32]. Following binding, LF is thought to be transported into the nucleus where it activates gene expressions responsible for the activation of the phagocytic mechanism. It was also demonstrated that human and bovine LF stimulated the release of neutrophil-activating IL-8 (a chemokine implicated in the activation of neutrophil activities) from human PMNs [33]. These properties were not abolished by lactoferricin, the main LF derived peptide. LF has also been shown to increase in circulating NK cells as well as CD8$^+$ T cells [34,35]. Recently, a role for CD8$^+$ T cells in the innate immune response has become apparent. Independent of T cell receptor ligation, CD8$^+$ T cells can mount a response against pathogens by secreting cytokines and can defend against tumors by directly killing transformed cells [36]. This innate immune response has been shown to be beneficial in controlling several types of bacterial infections and tumors. LF is thought to play a protective role in the control of tumor metastases through the boost of NK and $CD8^+$ T cells [34,35].

GMP was shown to be a potent immune-enhancer of macrophage proliferation as well as phagocytosis *in vitro*. GMP also induced the production of the IL-1 family of cytokines in murine macrophages and a macrophage cell line [37,38]. Li and Mine demonstrated that proliferation and phagocytic activities of human macrophage like cells (U937) were significantly enhanced in the presence of GMP [39]. Digestion of GMP with pepsin resulted in higher proliferation and phagocytosis, indicating that the enhanced immune-stimulatory effect of GMP was due to pepsin-digested fragments. The authors also showed that both the carbohydrate chain composition and polypeptide portion of GMP were essential for stimulating the effects of GMP.

STIMULATION OF ADAPTIVE IMMUNITY

Lymphocyte Activation and Proliferation

Several studies have focused on the *in vitro* and *in vivo* modulation of lymphocyte proliferation by whey proteins and individual whey protein components. Moreover, a few of them have evaluated the effect of whey hydrolyzed peptides. Mercier and colleagues showed that whey proteins stimulated the *in vitro* proliferation of lymphocytes isolated from murine spleen, but that the effect was reduced following the addition of whey trypsin/chymotrypsin hydrolysates[40]. However, they showed that peptide fractions with basic isoelectric points stimulate cell proliferation at much lower concentrations than the non-fractionated hydrolysates. Another study has showed that the proliferation of spleen cells stimulated by concanavalin A (ConA), phytohemagglutinin (PHA) or lipopolysaccharide (LPS) was no significantly different between whey hydrolysates-fed and casein hydrolysates-fed mice [8]. When the mice were immunized with BCG one week prior to sacrifice, higher mitogen-induced proliferation of splenocytes was, however, observed in the mice fed whey protein hydrolysates than those fed casein hydrolysates[8].

Bounous and Kongshavn have, for the first time, demonstrated an immune-enhancing effect of the individual whey component, β-LG [9]. They showed that the whey proteins (principally β-LG and BSA) increased the number of antibody-forming cells in the spleen of mice immunized with trinitrophenylatedficoll. Moreover, Wong and colleagues demonstrated that β-LG promoted *in vitro* proliferation of murine spleen cells and its stimulatory effects were more intense than those observed with BSA [41]. However, this activity was markedly reduced by tryptic hydrolysis of the protein. The immune effects on murine spleen cells are considered to be due to an increase in glutathione (GSH) production by splenocytes. This has been confirmed by the addition of S-(n-butyl) homocysteinesulfoxamine, an inhibitor of glutamylcysteinesynthetase, which in this case, blocked the stimulatory effect [41].

Conversely, another study disputed that the observed effects of β-LG on spleen cells to pronounce proliferation and produce cytokines were due to endotoxin contamination [42]. This study was conducted using a commercial β-LG product, and a specific isolation technique in the preparation led to the discovery of an endotoxin. Brix and colleagues showed that endotoxin contamination in commercial β-LG preparations, especially LPS contamination, may be responsible for the marked *in vitro* proliferative effect of this protein on murine splenocytes and mesenteric lymph node cells, on the production of cytokines (tumor necrosis factor (TNF)- α, IL-6, IL-1β and IL-10) in spleen cell cultures and murine bone-marrow-derived dendritic cells and on the increased levels of intracellular GSH in splenocytes[42].

However, Wong and colleagues have proven that the effect observed with β-LG was not due to endotoxin contamination by the use of polymixin B, a LPS inhibitor [41]. The use of this LPS inhibitor markedly reduced the effect of LPS, however, it had no effect on β-LG. This study confirms that β-LG actually possesses an immune-enhancing effect. It is important for the reliability of results to measure LPS contamination in commercial whey protein products before studying their immune-modulatory properties [42].

Mahmud and colleagues also found that β-LG induced the proliferation of mouse spleen cells and that mitogenic activity was retained following a reduction in the protein, suggesting that the activity depends on the primary structure [43]. However, in contrast to a previous study [41], they reported that the mitogenic activity of β-LG was stronger following digestion with pepsin, trypsin, chymotrypsin or pancreatin, supporting the view that peptides may be responsible for this activity. In addition, they showed that the most mitogenic pancreatic hydrolysate, which induces significant growth of a human B cell line (U266), did not influence the growth of other cell lines (Ball human B cells, MOLT-4 and Jurkat T cells).

Hydrolyzed α-LA, which contains unidentified peptides, has been demonstrated to modulate B as well as T lymphocyte activity in mice [9], and synthetic peptides from α-LA also enhanced both the *in vitro* proliferation and protein synthesis of ConA-stimulated human peripheral blood lymphocytes [31].

LF and its hydrolysate exhibit both immune-stimulatory and immune-inhibitory potentials. It has been demonstrated that this protein promoted the differentiation of T and B lymphocytes [44,45]. The incubation of immature T lymphocytes in the presence of LF allowed for the differentiation of these cells in CD4+ T cells and the subsequent increase in immune response of sheep red blood cells [44]. In addition, bovine LF hydrolysate promotes cell proliferation, especially in B cells as well as Peyer's patch cells [46]. On the other hand, bovine LF has been showed to inhibit the proliferation of murine splenocytes[46]. It was also shown that the peptic hydrolysates of LF inhibited the blastogenesis induced by mitogens (ConA, PHA, LPS), as observed for intact bovine LF. In addition, the stimulatory effect on splenocyte proliferation was shown not to be due to LPS contamination and that the peptic hydrolysate further digested with trypsin lost its mitogenic activity.

On the other hand, GMP is known to inhibit the LPS- and PHA-induced proliferations of murine splenocytes and rabbit Peyer's patch cells [47-50]. The suppressive effects of various casein digested peptides, containing GMP, were also reported *in vitro*[48,49], suggesting that glycopeptides are responsible for the inhibitory effect. According to Otani and colleagues [49], both the carbohydrate (particularly the N-acetylneuraminic acid residues) and the polypeptide portions are essential for the inhibitory effects on LPS- and PHA-induced proliferative responses of mouse spleen cells. Cross and colleagues showed that a modified whey protein enriched with GMP suppressed the proliferations of T and B lymphocyte and the secretion of IL-4 and interferon (IFN)-□ in a ConA-induced murine splenic lymphocyte culture in a dose-dependent manner, whereas the effect was partly abolished following enzymatic digestion of the extract with pepsin and pancreatin[51].

However, Monnai and colleagues reported that the proliferative response of spleen cells to ConA was enhanced in GMP supplemented mice that were immunized with orally delivered ovalbumin or injected β-LG, whereas there were no significant changes in the LPS and PHA responses [52].Yun and colleagues reported that a glycophosphopeptide fraction isolated from a GMP extract from cheese whey, but without residual GMP, strongly promoted murine splenocyte and Peyer's patch cell proliferation [53]. Furthermore, the carbohydrate of the glycophosphopeptide containing N-linked oligosaccharide chains is an important component in the strong mitogenic activity.

There are several conflicting results with the effects reported for whey proteins and hydrolysates, especially β-LG and GMP, on lymphocyte activation. However, these apparent contradictions can be explained by the different methodological approaches used in these studies, such as the selection of different whey proteins preparations, the origins of the lymphocytes (spleen, Peyer's patch, blood), and the conditions used for the proliferative assays.

Antibody Production

The immune-enhancing effect of whey proteins on the formation of specific antibodies has been well studied [9,54-56]. For example, one study demonstrated that mice fed with whey proteins significantly enhanced humoral immune responses via different routes to a range of heterologous antigens, such as the influenza vaccine, diphtheria and tetanus toxoids, poliomyelitis vaccine, ovalbumin and the cholera toxin sub-unit [57]. The higher levels of antigen-specific antibodies persisted for a long term. The same immune-enhancing effect was observed by Wong and Watson. They reported an elevated level of anti-ovalbumin antibodies in the presence of whey proteins [56]. However, whey protein has also been reported to have no effect on IgA production in murine Peyer's patch cell cultures[58]. Whey protein hydrolysates have been shown to have an impact on the humoral immune system *in vivo*. The effect of an orally administered whey pancreatic hydrolysate on the specific humoral immune response was evaluated in mice using the plaque-forming cell (PFC) assay after a systemic challenge. This dietary treatment produced significantly more PFC to T cell dependent antigens in the spleen than in mice fed a casein hydrolysate[8].

Some whey components have been shown to modulate antibody production. β-LG enhanced the production of IgM in cultures of murine spleen cells, but this effect was abolished by trypsin hydrolysis of this protein [41]. Debbabi and colleagues have investigated the immune responses induced by repeated oral administration of LF in mice. IgA and IgG secretions were enhanced in the Peyer's patches and spleen from LF fed mice [59]. In addition, Wang and colleagues have demonstrated that IgA$^+$ and IgM$^+$ B cells, CD4$^+$ and CD8$^+$ T cells, and NK cells increased in the small intestine of LF fed mice [60]. In this study, LF and lactoferricin enhanced the production of IL-18 and IFN-□, both of which induce stimulation of intestinal immunity. LF hydrolysates containing lactoferricin also significantly enhanced immunoglobulin (IgM, IgG and IgA) production in cultured murine splenocytes and IgA production in Peyer's patch cells [46]. Miyauchi and colleagues also showed that mice supplemented with hydrolyzed bovine LF had significantly greater anti-cholera toxin IgA levels in the intestinal contents than mice fed a control diet after being orally immunized with cholera toxin [46]. These results suggest that LF and LF hydrolysates may be beneficial for enhancing mucosal immunity.

On the other hand, GMP suppresses *in vitro* antibody production to SRBC in murine spleen cell cultures [49]. Monnai and colleagues reported that GMP suppressed the levels of serum IgG specific to dietary ovalbumin and injected β-LG in mice, but had no effect on IgM, IgA and IgE responses [52].

There is some consistency with the effects reported for whey proteins, whey hydrolysates and peptides on antibody production. However, the number of studies and whey components studied are very limited. Consequently, it is too early to form definitive conclusions on the effects of individual whey protein components on antibody production.

IMMUNE-MODULATING EFFECTS OF WHEY PROTEINS AND PEPTIDES

Until now, the only immune-stimulating properties of whey proteins have been discussed. *In vitro* studies show an immunosuppresion of T- and B-lymphocyte proliferation upon stimulation with mitogens [26,51,61]. Whey proteins also show an immunoregulatory effect in spleen cells, since the activation of these cells is downregulated by oral administration of whey proteins [62]. The increase in transforming growth factor (TGF)-β production in cells after whey treatment may explain this regulation.

Allergy, Hypersensitivity and Induction of Oral Tolerance

β-LG is principally responsible for milk allergies in children (2-3% of children suffer from milk allergies). In 80 % of cases, however, allergy symptoms disappear before the age of 3 years [63]. It has been demonstrated that the peptides from β-LG induced oral tolerance and consequently, diminished IgE production specific to β-LG and the allergic reaction to β-LG [64]. This observation suggests that the consumption of peptides from β-LG plays an important protective role against milk allergies. And, many studies have also demonstrated a preventive role against milk allergies from hydrolyzed whey proteins [65-67] .

On the other hand, the consumption of raw milk, but not boiled farm milk, was inversely associated with asthma, atopy, and hay fever in school-aged children [68]. In this study, increased levels of the whey proteins BSA, α-LA, and β-LG were inversely associated with asthma, suggesting that the protective effect of raw milk consumption on asthma might be associated with the whey protein. Another study has also demonstrated that whey supplementation decreased serum IgE levels in children with atopic asthma [69]. Whey proteins have also been demonstrated *in vivo* to decrease allergen-induced airway contraction in a guinea-pig model of asthma [70]. Whey protein did not increase IgG levels after sensitization with ovalbumin, and the ovalbumin-induced anaphylactic response. In addition, it enhanced GSH levels in the liver and decreased prostaglandin E2 (PGE_2) in the effluent fluid. These effects are related to the enhancement of GSH, since allergen-induced early asthmatic reaction is likely to be accompanied by oxidative stress.

In addition, whey hydrolyzed peptides have been shown to have suppressive effects on the development of atopic dermatitis. Shimizu and colleagues showed that in mice induced by the mite *Dermatophagoidespteronyssinus* antigen, those fed on whey hydrolyzed peptides exhibited significantly less atopic dermatitis-like skin lesions than those fed on casein diets [71]. They also showed that serum soluble E-selectin levels, known as a marker of disease activity in atopic dermatitis patients, were significantly lower in the whey peptide-diet group. LF also possesses the capacity to inhibit atopic contact dermatitis induced by oxazolone[72]. In this study, LF applied topically prior to oxazolone sensitization prevents, in a dose dependent manner, the migration of Langerhans cells into the lymph nodes and subsequently activates cytotoxic T cells and the accumulation of dendritic cells in inflamed sites. The mechanism of action seems to be the inhibition of TNF-α production by keratinocytes, which is responsible for delivering the activation signal to Langerhans cells [72].

Anti-Inflammation

LF is well-studied, and well-known as an immune-modulatory agent, which acts both as an immune-suppressive and an immune-stimulatory agent. Various studies have revealed the anti-inflammatory potential of LF in part by inhibiting pro-inflammatory cytokines such as TNF-α, IL-1β and IL-6, which are key inflammatory cytokines [73-75]. Mattsby-Baltzer and colleagues showed that human LF and bovine LF, especially bovine LF, suppressed IL-6 secretion in a LPS-stimulated monocytic cell line (THP-1). Moreover, lactoferricin has also been found to suppress the IL-6 response, suggesting an anti-inflammatory activity for both bovine LF and lactoferricin[75]. Several animal models have demonstrated that LF can protect against inflammatory conditions. A study by Dial and colleagues showed that LF protects against gastritis induced by *Helicobacter felis* bacterium in mice [76]. Moreover, local administration of LF has demonstrated a strong local anti-inflammatory effect in two different arthritis murine models, but this effect was not related to the reduction of the pro-inflammatory cytokine IL-6 [77]. The effect of this protein on arthritis has also been reported in another study, in which LF protected against arthritis in rats induced by adjuvant administration in the right hind paw [78]. In this model, the protective effect against arthritis was due to a downregulation of the pro-inflammatory cytokine TNF-α and an upregulation of the anti-inflammatory cytokine IL-10 [78].

It is also well-known that LF inhibits hepatitis B and C viruses (HCV and HBV) *in vivo* and *in vitro*[79-81]. We have confirmed that LF suppressed TNF-α production and protected against the development of hepatitis caused by LPS sensitization of Kupffer cells [82]. However, the inhibition of cytokine production by LF might be one of the factors that protect against hepatitis. LF has been reported to interact directly with E1 and E2 HCV envelope proteins [83]. It has also been demonstrated that pre-incubation of HCV with bovine LF inhibits viral infection, while cell pretreatment with bovine LF was ineffective [84]. Further studies demonstrated that bovine LF inhibited HCV entry into the cells by interacting with viral particles immediately after mixing the bovine LF and HCV inoculums [85]. But, cell pretreatment with LF was required to inhibit HBV infection, and pre-incubation of HBV with bovine LF had no inhibitory effect on viral infection [79]. These results suggested that bovine LF interaction with susceptible cells was important for its anti-HBV effect.

Whey protein supplementation also showed variable effects in patients infected with the hepatitis B virus [20]. Serum lipid peroxide levels decreased significantly, and IL-2 levels and NK activity increased significantly, while serum alanine aminotransferase activity (ALT) was reduced, and plasma GSH levels increased in 6 and 5 of 8 patients, respectively. However, this effect of whey protein is not thought to be due to the effect of LF, since it contains LF at a concentration of < 0.01 %. As such the hepatoprotective and anti-inflammatory effects of whey protein in hepatitis remain to be clearly identified.

Thus, in our laboratory, we investigated how whey proteins and whey peptides have anti-inflammatory and hepatoprotective potencies. We have demonstrated *in vivo* that whey proteins have anti-inflammatory and hepatoprotective effects on D-galactosamine induced hepatitis and liver fibrosis in rats [86,87]. In this study, whey protein suppressed increases in hepatitis markers such as plasma ALT and aspartate aminotransferase (AST), lactate dehydrogenase and bilirubin. It also suppressed the increase in plasma hyaluronic acid, which is a fibrosis marker, the development of liver fibrosis and bile duct proliferation. In addition, whey proteins also inhibited the production of the inflammatory cytokines TNF-α, IL-1β and IL-6 in plasma that were induced by D-galactosamine injection.

Moreover, whey hydrolyzed peptides also have anti-inflammatory and hepatoprotective effects, and their effects are more intense than those observed with intact whey proteins [87]. The anti-inflammatory and hepatoprotective effects of whey protein and its peptides have also been demonstrated in another hepatitis model induced by ConA, which is understood to represent a model of immune response-mediated hepatitis [87,88]. In this study, whey proteins and peptides suppressed liver injury and increases in AST, ALT and the pro-inflammatory cytokine TNF-α, IL-6 in plasma, which is consistent with the previous study. Analyzed by the DNA microarray method, whey peptides induced alterations of many gene expressions, and the time-dependent profiles of those gene expressions differed from those of casein. In addition, whey protein and whey peptides have been shown to suppress IL-1β and TNF-α mRNA expressions in the liver and IL-6 mRNA expression in the spleen [87]. We speculate that whey protein and whey peptides suppress the activations of NF-κB (nuclear factor-kappa B) and Stat 3 (signal transducer and activator of transcription 3) signal trans-ductions in the liver. However, it is challenging to elucidate how whey peptides modulate inflammatory responses, since a considerable number of genes are affected by whey peptides.

Now, whey peptides and whey-peptide based enteral formulas have been shown to have anti-inflammatory effects in some experimental inflammatory models [89-94] and in a clinical study [95]. It is well known that inflammation is a process that is essential in protecting the host against foreign invasion. However, a variety of clinical conditions, such as trauma, shock, and severe surgical insult, lead to the systemic inflammatory response syndrome (SIRS), which involves uncontrolled and excessive production of pro-inflammatory cytokines [96,97]. SIRS leads to multiple organ failure that increases the risk of impaired functions and mortality in ICU (intensive care unit) patients, and induces sepsis in response to or in combination with an infection. Therefore, whey peptides and whey-peptide based enteral formula could prevent systemic inflammation, thereby avoiding the risk of life threatening conditions triggered by excessive inflammation.

CONCLUSION

The immune system is indispensable for us to eliminate invasive bacterial and viral infections, to rid the body of damaged tissue, and to destroy neoplasms in the body. Various conditions, such as fatigue, aging, some types of diseases, and weakening of the immune system lead to a greater risk of infection and may enhance the severity of disease. On the other hand, excessive or persistent inflammation induces impaired body function that may lead to death. As mentioned above, whey proteins and peptides have two powers to improve immune responses. One is an immune-enhancing property, such as to stimulate NK and phagocytic cells and to activate lymphocytes, and the other is an immune-modulating property, such as to improve allergy symptoms, and to suppress excessive inflammation. Therefore, whey proteins and whey peptides seem to protect the host not only against invasion, but also against aggravation of inflammation.

CONFLICT OF INTEREST

KN and TY are employees of Meiji Co. Ltd.

REFERENCES

Fearon, D. & Locksley, R., (1996). The instructive role of innate immunity in the acquired immune response. *Science. 272*, 50-53.

Ezekowitz, R. & Hoffmann, J., (1996). Innate immunity. *Current Opinion in Immunology. 8*, 1-2.

Greaves, D., (1998). Innate immunity antigen recognition. Web alert. *Current Opinion in Immunology. 10*, 7.

Bounous, G. & Molson, J., (2003). The antioxidant system. *Anticancer Research. 23*, 1411-1415.

Townsend, D.M., Tew, K.D., *et al.*, (2003). The importance of glutathione in human disease. *Biomedicine & Pharmacotherapy. 57*, 145-155.

Wu, G., Fang, Y.Z., *et al.*, (2004). Glutathione Metabolism and Its Implications for Health. *The Journal of Nutrition. 134*, 489-492.

Bounous, G., (2000). Whey protein concentrate (WPC) and glutathione modulation in cancer treatment. *Anticancer Research. 20*, 4785-4792.

Bounous, G. & Kongshavn, P., (1982). Influence of dietary proteins on the immune system of mice. *The Journal of Nutrition. 112*, 1747-1755.

Bounous, G. & Kongshavn, P., (1985). Differential effect of dietary protein type on the B-cell and T-cell immune responses in mice. *The Journal of Nutrition. 115*, 1403-1408.

Beaulieu, J., Dupont, C., *et al.*, (2006). Whey proteins and peptides: beneficial effects on immune health. *Therapy. 3*, 69-78.

Gauthier, S.F., Pouliot, Y., *et al.*, (2006). Immunomodulatory peptides obtained by the enzymatic hydrolysis of whey proteins. *International Dairy Journal. 16*, 1315-1323.

Marshall, K., (2004). Therapeutic applications of whey protein. *Alternative Medicine Review. 9*, 136-156.

Micke, P., Beeh, K.M., *et al.*, (2001). Oral supplementation with whey proteins increases plasma glutathione levels of HIV-infected patients. *European Journal of Clinical Investigation. 31*, 171-178.

Perez-Cano, F.J., Marin-Gallen, S., *et al.*, (2007). Bovine whey protein concentrate supplementation modulates maturation of immune system in suckling rats. *British Journal of Nutrition.* 98, S80-S84.

Kennedy, R., Konok, G., *et al.*, (1995). The use of a whey protein concentrate in the treatment of patients with metastatic carcinoma: a phase I-II clinical study. *Anticancer Research.* 15, 2643-2649.

See, D., Mason, S., *et al.*, (2002). Increased Tumor Necrosis Factor Alpha and Natural Killer Cell (NK) Function using an Integrative Approach in Late Stage Cancers. *Immunological Investigations.* 31, 137-153.

Beaulieu, J., Dubuc, R., *et al.*, (2007). Immunomodulation by a Malleable Matrix Composed of Fermented Whey Proteins and Lactic Acid Bacteria. *Journal of Medicinal Food.* 10, 67-72.

Wong, C.W., Liu, A.H., *et al.*, (1997). Influence of whey and purified whey proteins on neutrophil functions in sheep. *Journal of Dairy Research.* 64, 281-288.

Roth, J.A., Frank, D.E., *et al.*, (2001). Enhancement of Neutrophil Function by Ultrafiltered Bovine Whey. *Journal of Dairy Science.* 84, 824-829.

Watanabe, A., Okada, K., *et al.*, (2000). Nutritional therapy of chronic hepatitis by whey protein (non-heated). *Journal of Medicine.* 31, 283-302.

Loimaranta, V., Nuutila, J., *et al.*, (1999). Colostral proteins from cows immunised with *Streptococcus mutans/S. sobrinus* support the phagocytosis and killing of mutans streptococci by human leucocytes. *Journal of medical Microbiology.* 48, 917-926.

Rusu, D., Drouin, R., *et al.*, (2009). A Bovine Whey Protein Extract Can Enhance Innate Immunity by Priming Normal Human Blood Neutrophils. *The Journal of Nutrition.* 139, 386-393.

Rusu, D., Drouin, R., *et al.*, (2010). A Bovine Whey Protein Extract Stimulates Human Neutrophils to Generate Bioactive IL-1Ra through a NF-kappaB- and MAPK-Dependent Mechanism. *The Journal of Nutrition.* 140, 382-391.

Bounous, G., Stevenson, M.M., *et al.*, (1981). Influence of Dietary Lactalbumin Hydrolysate on the Immune System of Mice and Resistance to Salmonellosis. *Journal of Infectious Diseases.* 144, 281.

Pellegrini, A., Dettling, C., *et al.*, (2001). Isolation and characterization of four bactericidal domains in the bovine beta-lactoglobulin. *Biochimica et Biophysica Acta (BBA) - General Subjects.* 1526, 131-140.

Wong, C.W., Seow, H.F., *et al.*, (1997). Effects of purified bovine whey factors on cellular immune functions in ruminants. *Veterinary Immunology and Immunopathology.* 56, 85-96.

Gattegno, L., Migliore-Samour, D., *et al.*, (1988). Enhancement of phagocytic activity of human monocytic-macrophagic cells by immunostimulating peptides from human casein. *Immunology Letters.* 18, 27-31.

Berthou, J., Migliore-Samour, D., *et al.*, (1987). Immunostimulating properties and three-dimensional structure of two tripeptides from human and cow caseins. *FEBS Letters.* 218, 55-58.

Jaziri, M., Migliore-Samour, D., *et al.*, (1992). Specific binding sites on human phagocytic blood cells for Gly-Leu-Phe and Val-Glu-Pro-Ile-Pro-Tyr, immunostimulating peptides from human milk proteins. *Biochimica et Biophysica Acta (BBA) - Protein Structure and Molecular Enzymology.* 1160, 251-261.

Migliore-Samour, D., Roch-Arveiller, M., *et al.*, (1992). Effects of tripeptides derived from milk proteins on polymorphonuclear oxidative and phosphoinositide metabolisms. *Biochemical Pharmacology. 44*, 673-680.

Kayser, H. & Meisel, H., (1996). Stimulation of human peripheral blood lymphocytes by bioactive peptides derived from bovine milk proteins. *FEBS Letters. 383*, 18-20.

Miyauchi, H., Hashimoto, S., *et al.*, (1998). Bovine Lactoferrin Stimulates the Phagocytic Activity of Human Neutrophils: Identification of Its Active Domain. *Cellular Immunology. 187*, 34-37.

Shinoda, I., Takase, M., *et al.*, (1996). Effects of lactoferrin and lactoferricin on the release of interleukin 8 from human polymorphonuclear leukocytes. *Bioscience, Biotechnology, and Biochemistry. 60*, 521-523.

Iigo, M., Kuhara, T., *et al.*, (1999). Inhibitory effects of bovine lactoferrin on colon carcinoma 26 lung metastasis in mice. *Clinical and Experimental Metastasis. 17*, 43-49.

Sekine, K., Ushida, Y., *et al.*, (1997). Inhibition of initiation and early stage development of aberrant crypt foci and enhanced natural killer activity in male rats administered bovine lactoferrin concomitantly with azoxymethane. *Cancer Letters. 121*, 211-216.

Berg, R.E. & Forman, J., (2006). The role of CD8 T cells in innate immunity and in antigen non-specific protection. *Current Opinion in Immunology. 18*, 338-343.

Monnai, M. & Otani, H., (1997). Effect of bovine kappa-caseinoglycopeptide on secretion of interleukin-1 family cytokines by P388D1 cells, a line derived from mouse monocyte/macrophage. . *Milchwissenschaft. 52*, 192-196.

Otani, H. & Monnai, M., (1995). Induction of an Interleukin-1 Receptor Antagonist-like Component Produced from Mouse Spleen Cells by Bovine kappa-Caseinoglycopeptide. *Bioscience, Biotechnology, and Biochemistry 59*, 1166-1168.

Li, E.W.Y. & Mine, Y., (2004). Immunoenhancing Effects of Bovine Glycomacropeptide and Its Derivatives on the Proliferative Response and Phagocytic Activities of Human Macrophagelike Cells, U937. *Journal of Agricultural and Food Chemistry. 52*, 2704-2708.

Mercier, A., Gauthier, S.F., *et al.*, (2004). Immunomodulating effects of whey proteins and their enzymatic digests. *International Dairy Journal. 14*, 175-183.

Wong, K.F., Middleton, N., *et al.*, (1998). Immunostimulation of Murine Spleen Cells by Materials Associated with Bovine Milk Protein Fractions. *Journal of Dairy Science. 81*, 1825-1832.

Brix, S., Bovetto, L., *et al.*, (2003). Immunostimulatory potential of beta-lactoglobulin preparations: Effects caused by endotoxin contamination. *The Journal of allergy and clinical immunology. 112*, 1216-1222.

Mahmud, R., Matin, M.A., *et al.*, (2004). Mitogenic Effect of Bovine β-lactoglobulin and its Proteolytic Digests on Mouse Spleen Resting Cells. *Pakistan Journal of Biological Sciences. 7*, 2045-2050.

Zimecki, M., Mazurier, J., *et al.*, (1991). Immunostimulatory activity of lactotransferrin and maturation of CD4- CD8- murine thymocytes. *Immunology Letters. 30*, 119-123.

Zimecki, M., Mazurier, J., *et al.*, (1995). Human lactoferrin induces phenotypic and functional changes in murine splenic B cells. *Immunology. 86*, 122-127.

Miyauchi, H., Kaino, A., *et al.*, (1997). Immunomodulatory Effect of Bovine Lactoferrin Pepsin Hydrolysate on Murine Splenocytes and Peyer's Patch Cells. *Journal of Dairy Science. 80*, 2330-2339.

Otani, H., Monnai, M., *et al.*, (1992). Bovine kappa-casein as inhibitor of the proliferation of mouse splenocytes induced by lipopolysaccharide stimulation. *Milchwissenschaft. 47*, 512-515.

Otani, H. & Monnai, M., (1993). Inhibition of proliferative responses of mouse spleen lymphocytes by bovine milk kappa-casein digests. *Food and Agricultural Immunology. 5*, 219-229.

Otani, H., Monnai, M., *et al.*, (1995). Inhibition of mitogen-induced proliferative responses of lymphocytes by bovine kappa-caseinoglycopeptides having different carbohydrate chains. *Journal of Dairy Research. 62*, 349-357.

Otani, H. & Hata, I., (1995). Inhibition of proliferative responses of mouse spleen lymphocytes and rabbit Peyer's patch cells by bovine milk caseins and their digests. *Journal of Dairy Research. 62*, 339-348.

Cross, M.L. & Gill, H.S., (1999). Modulation of immune function by a modified bovine whey protein concentrate. *Immunology and Cell Biology. 77*, 345-350.

Monnai, M., Horimoto, Y., *et al.*, (1998). Immunomodificatory effect of dietary bovine kappa-caseinoglycopeptide on serum antibody levels and proliferative responses of lymphocytes in mice. *Milchwissenschaft. 53*, 129-131.

Yun, S., Sugita-Konishi, Y., *et al.*, (1996). Isolation of mitogenic glycophosphopeptides from cheese whey protein concentrate. *Bioscience, Biotechnology, and Biochemistry. 60*, 429-433.

Bounous, G., Kongshavn, P., *et al.*, (1988). The immunoenhancing property of dietary whey protein concentrate. *Clinical and Investigative Medicine. 11*, 271-278.

Bounous, G., Shenouda, N., *et al.*, (1985). Mechanism of altered B-cell response induced by changes in dietary protein type in mice. *The Journal of Nutrition. 115*, 1409-1417.

Wong, C.W. & Watson, D.L., (1995). Immunomodulatory effects of dietary whey proteins in mice. *Journal of Dairy Research. 62*, 359-368.

Low, P.P.L., Rutherfurd, K.J., *et al.*, (2003). Effect of dietary whey protein concentrate on primary and secondary antibody responses in immunized BALB/c mice. *International Immunopharmacology. 3*, 393-401.

Shida, K., Nagami, K., *et al.*, (1992). Effect of Milk Components on IgA Production in Peyer's Patch Cell Cultures from Mouse. *Bioscience, Biotechnology, and Biochemistry. 56*, 1874-1875.

Debbabi, H., Dubarry, M., *et al.*, (1998). Bovine lactoferrin induces both mucosal and systemic immune response in mice. *Journal of Dairy Research. 65*, 283-293.

Wang, W.P., Iigo, M., *et al.*, (2000). Activation of Intestinal Mucosal Immunity in Tumor-bearing Mice by Lactoferrin. *Cancer Science. 91*, 1022-1027.

Otani, H. & Odashima, M., (1997). Inhibition of proliferative responses of mouse spleen lymphocytes by lacto- and ovotransferrins. *Food and Agricultural Immunology 9*, 193-201.

Penttila, I.A., Zhang, M.F., *et al.*, (2001). Immune modulation in suckling rat pups by a growth factor extract derived from milk whey. *Journal of Dairy Research. 68*, 587-599.

Host, A., (2002). Frequency of cow's milk allergy in childhood. *Annals of allergy, asthma & immunology : official publication of the American College of Allergy, Asthma, & Immunology. 89*, 33-37.

Pecquet, S., Bovetto, L., *et al.*, (2000). Peptides obtained by tryptic hydrolysis of bovine beta-lactoglobulin induce specific oral tolerance in mice. *Journal of Allergy and Clinical Immunology. 105*, 514-521.

Han, Y.S., Park, H.Y., *et al.*, (2003). Short-term Effect of Partially Hydrolyzed Formula on the Prevention of Development of Atopic Dermatitis in Infants at High Risk. *Journal ofKorean Medical Science. 18*, 547-551.

Tanabe, S., Tesaki, S., *et al.*, (2003). Isolation and Structural Elucidation of a Peptide Derived from Edam Cheese that Inhibits beta-Lactoglobulin Transport. *Journal of Dairy Science. 86*, 464-468.

Peng, H.J., Su, S.N., *et al.*, (2004). Effect of ingestion of cow's milk hydrolysed formulas on whey protein-specific Th2 immune responses in naïve and sensitized mice. *Clinical & Experimental Allergy. 34*, 663-670.

Loss, G., Apprich, S., *et al.*, (2011). The protective effect of farm milk consumption on childhood asthma and atopy: The GABRIELA study. *The Journal of allergy and clinical immunology. 128*, 766-773.e764.

Lothian, J., Grey, V., *et al.*, (2006). Effect of whey protein to modulate immune response in children with atopic asthma. *International Journal of Food Sciences and Nutrition. 57*, 204-211.

Kloek, J., Mortaz, E., *et al.*, (2011). A whey-based glutathione-enhancing diet decreases allergen-induced airway contraction in a guinea-pig model of asthma. *British Journal of Nutrition. 105*, 1465-1470.

Shimizu, N., Dairiki, K., *et al.*, (2006). Dietary whey protein hydrolysate suppresses development of atopic dermatitis-like skin lesions induced by mite antigen in NC/Nga mice. *Allergology International. 55*, 185-189.

Kimber, I., Cumberbatch, M., *et al.*, (2002). Lactoferrin: influences on Langerhans cells, epidermal cytokines, and cutaneous inflammation. *Biochemistry and Cell Biology. 80*, 103-107.

Haversen, L., Ohlsson, B.G., *et al.*, (2002). Lactoferrin down-regulates the LPS-induced cytokine production in monocytic cells via NF-kappaB. *Cellular Immunology. 220*, 83-95.

Machnicki, M., Zimecki, M., *et al.*, (1993). Lactoferrin regulates the release of tumour necrosis factor alpha and interleukin 6 in vivo. *International Journal of Experimental Pathology. 74*, 433-439.

Mattsby-Baltzer, I., Roseanu, A., *et al.*, (1996). Lactoferrin or a Fragment Thereof Inhibits the Endotoxin-Induced Interleukin-6 Response in Human Monocytic Cells. *Pediatric Research. 40*, 257-262.

Dial, E.J., Romero, J.J., *et al.*, (2000). Recombinant Human Lactoferrin is Effective in the Treatment of *Helicobacter felis*-infected Mice. *Journal of Pharmacy and Pharmacology. 52*, 1541-1546.

Guillen, C., McInnes, I.B., *et al.*, (2000). The effects of local administration of lactoferrin on inflammation in murine autoimmune and infectious arthritis. *Arthritis & Rheumatism. 43*, 2073-2080.

Hayashida, K., Kaneko, T., *et al.*, (2004). al administration of lactoferrin inhibits inflammation and nociception in rat adjuvant-induced arthritis. *Journal of Veterinary Medical Science. 66*, 149-154.

Hara, K., Ikeda, M., *et al.*, (2002). Lactoferrin inhibits hepatitis B virus infection in cultured human hepatocytes. *Hepatology research. 24*, 228.

Ikeda, M., Sugiyama, K., *et al.*, (1998). Lactoferrin markedly inhibits hepatitis C virus infection in cultured human hepatocytes. *Biochemical and Biophysical Research Communications. 245*, 549-553.

Tanaka, K., Ikeda, M., *et al.*, (1999). Lactoferrin Inhibits Hepatitis C Virus Viremia in Patients with Chronic Hepatitis C: A Pilot Study. *Cancer Science. 90*, 367-371.

Yamaguchi, M., Matsuura, M., *et al.*, (2001). Lactoferrin protects against development of hepatitis caused by sensitization of Kupffer cells by lipopolysaccharide. *Clinical and Diagnostic Laboratory Immunology 8*, 1234-1239.

Yi, M., Kaneko, S., *et al.*, (1997). Hepatitis C virus envelope proteins bind lactoferrin. *Journal of Virology. 71*, 5997-6002.

Ikeda, M., Sugiyama, K., *et al.*, (1998). Lactoferrin Markedly Inhibits Hepatitis C Virus Infection in Cultured Human Hepatocytes. *Biochemical and Biophysical Research Communications. 245*, 549-553.

Ikeda, M., Nozaki, A., *et al.*, (2000). Characterization of antiviral activity of lactoferrin against hepatitis C virus infection in human cultured cells. *Virus Research. 66*, 51-63.

Kume, H., Okazaki, K., *et al.*, (2006). Hepatoprotective effects of whey protein on D-galactosamine-induced hepatitis and liver fibrosis in rats. *Biosci Biotechnol Biochem. . 70*, 1281-1285.

Yamaji, T. & Kume, H., (2008). Hepatoprotective Effects of Whey Protein and Whey Peptides on Hepatitis. *Milk Science. 56*, 115-118.

Sasaki, H. & Kume, H., (2007). Milk whey proteins/peptides, natural beneficial modulators of inflammation. *Bulletin of the international Dairy Federation. 417*, 43-50.

Nakamura, K., Ogawa, S., *et al.*, (2011). A new immune-modulating diet enriched with whey-hydrolyzed peptide, fermented milk, and isomaltulose attenuates gut ischemia-reperfusion injury in mice. *Clinical Nutrition. 30*, 513-516.

Takayanagi, T., Sasaki, H., *et al.*, (2011). A New Enteral Diet, MHN-02, Which Contains Abundant Antioxidants and Whey Peptide, Protects Against Carbon Tetrachloride-induced Hepatitis. *Journal of Parenteral and Enteral Nutrition. 35*, 516-522.

Yamaguchi, M., (2005). Feature and anti-inflammatory effect of whey proteins and their peptides. *Milk Science. 54*, 123-127.

Yamaguchi, M. & Uchida, M., (2008). MHN-02, liquid food combined with whey peptides, suppresses interleukin-6 release after intestinal ischemia/reperfusion in rats. *Milk Science. 57*, 87-90.

Oz, H., Chen, T., *et al.*, (2009). Nutrition intervention: a strategy against systemic inflammatory syndrome. *Journal of Parenteral and Enteral Nutrition. 33*, 380-389.

Kume, H., Okazaki, K., *et al.*, A newly designed enteral formula containing whey peptides and fermented milk product protects mice against concanavalin A-induced hepatitis by suppressing overproduction of inflammatory cytokines. *Clinical Nutrition. in press*,

Kaido, T., Mori, A., *et al.*, (2010). Impact of enteral nutrition using a new immuno-modulating diet after liver transplantation. *Hepatogastroenterology. 57*, 1522-1525.

Hassoun, H.T., Kone, B.C., *et al.*, (2001). Post-Injury Multiple Organ Failure: the Role of the Gut. *Shock. 15*, 1-10.

Beale, R.J., Bryg, D.J., *et al.*, (1999). Immunonutrition in the critically ill: A systematic review of clinical outcome. *Critical Care Medicine. 27*, 2799-2805.

In: Whey: Types, Composition and Health Implications   ISBN: 978-1-61942-862-1
Editors: Rafael M. Benitez and Gustavo M. Ortero   © 2012 Nova Science Publishers, Inc.

Chapter 6

BIOACTIVE PEPTIDES WITH HEALTH BENEFIT AND THEIR DIFFERENTIAL CONTENT IN WHEY OF DIFFERENT ORIGIN

Palmiro Poltronieri[1], Maria Stella Cappello[1] and Oscar Fernando D'Urso[2]

[1] Author affiliation: CNR-ISPA, Institute of Sciences of Food Productions, Agrofood Department, National Research Council of Italy, Lecce, Italy
[2] University of Salento, Department of Biological and Environmental Sciences and Technologies, Lecce, Italy

ABSTRACT

The type and composition of whey at dairy plants mainly depends upon the processing techniques resulting from caseins removal during cheese-making. The content and composition of whey proteins from goat, sheep camel, mare and donkey differ consistently from whey protein content in cow milk. Whey proteins proteolysis generates smaller peptides some of which possess beneficial biological activities, and their total content is influenced by whey origin and composition. The industrial exploitation of whey proteins may follow two approaches. From one side, following the principle of sustainable economy and waste recycling the industry could exploit the high amounts of whey by-products as source of valuable peptides. On the other side, a different approach has been pursued through extraction of individual proteins from milk or whey consisting in chitosan addition to milk, acidification, centrifugation and chromatographic separation using anionic resins added in bulk that exploit different Isoelectric points of each whey protein. Whey bioactives are a valuable source of functional proteins that can be exploited in novel formulations, to be assumed through food ingestion. This chapter discusses the beneficial effects and potential applications of different whey isolates originating from different mammal milks, and the approaches to exploitation of whey protein fractions of different whey types.

INTRODUCTION

Whey, the serum or liquid part of milk remaining after separation of the curd, results from the coagulation of milk by acid or proteolytic enzymes. Whey proteins have a relevant nutritional value, and several commercial uses have been developed by the industry associated to the dairy. The composition and characteristics of whey depend on the production technology, the end product and the quality of milk used. Liquid whey consists of 93% water and contains 50% of the total solids present in milk, of which lactose is the main constituent.

A high nutritional value of bovine milk proteins and in particular to the whey proteins is widely recognized. Also, the multiple functional properties of major milk proteins are well characterized and exploited by various industries. Milk proteins have attracted growing scientific and commercial interest as a source of biologically active molecules having distinct characteristics. The nutritional and techno-functional properties of whey is studied and advances in whey research have shown that whey is a valuable source for highly prized nutraceutical ingredients.

Whey proteins after ingestion are cleaved by the gut proteases and made available through the uptake by oligopeptide pumps and transporters. Thus, short peptide sequences contained within whey proteins are the supposed effectors of the bioactivity of individual whey proteins.

Availability and stability: longer peptides must enter the gut barrier and show some degree of resistance to proteolysis. Many studies on whey peptides have been made using parenteral injection in animals. In fact, an in vitro study indicated a β-lactoglobulin fragment to be a potent inhibitor of Angiotensin Converting Enzyme (ACE) activity in vitro. However it is probably not sufficiently stable to gastrointestinal and serum proteinases and peptidases to act as an hypotensive agent in humans following oral ingestion (Walsh et al. 2004). In addition the tetra-peptide, α-lactalbumin f (50–53), a-lactorphin (Tyr-Gly-Leu-Phe) which is known to produce an antihypertensive effect in vivo when administered subcutaneously to normotensive Wistar Kyoto strain and spontaneously hypertensive rats (SHR), elicited no effect typical of active opioids in behavioural tests in mice after intraperitoneal administration (Nurminen et al. 2002, Ijaes et al. 2004).

Functional peptides have been studied in milk, whey, enzymatic protein hydrolysates and fermented dairy products (Meisel 2005; Korhonen and Pihlanto 2007; Gobbetti et al., 2002; Gobbetti et al., 2007; Hartmann and Meisel 2007; Korhonen 2009; Korhonen 2010).

Whey peptides have been studied for anti-clotting, anti-thrombotic and hypotensive activity (Gobbetti et al., 2007), mood regulation and opioid-like activity, antibacterial activity (Clare et al., 2003), immunomodulation, anti-inflammatory activity, anti-carie properties (Martinez et al., 2009), prebiotic activity, mineral binding properties, gastrointestinal health effect, hypocholesterolemic effects, insulinotropic effects, memory and stress effects (Korhonen, 2010).

The amino acid composition of whey proteins gives them a special role in physiology and functionality. Whey proteins contain a high amount of sulphured amino acids, which contributes to their great nutritional quality. Sulfured amino acids seem to enhance the immune function of the organism, due to regulation of glutathione, a sulphured tripeptide which protects the cell and is a substrate for enzymes that reduce oxidised substrates.

Whey proteins are rich in branched amino acids isoleucine, leucine and valine, necessary in the muscle cells to promote protein synthesis. These amino acids are metabolized to generate energy in muscles rather than in the liver. Many mass and body-building drinks and snack are enriched in whey proteins and branched chain peptides.

Whey proteins have a high content in sialic acid (N-acetyl-neuraminic acid, NANA). In addition to be assimilated for the synthesis of neuronal membranes and glycosylated antigens, sialic acid forms glycans with highly restricted expression on human leukocytes, modulating their immune responses (Drake et al., 2008).

Several nutraceutical products are marketed today from whey proteins, with specific health claims (Faryabi et al., 22008). Among other products, there are: Cysteine Peptide, produced by DMV International, NL, (whey hydrolysate), claimed to aid to raise energy level and sleep, and Vivinal Alpha, produced by Borculo Domo Ingredients (BDI), NL, (whey hydrolysate), containing a peptide claimed to aid relaxation and sleep.

WHEY TYPES: SOURCES, CONTENT AND COMPOSITION

Whey proteins are concentrated from whey to produce two different ingredients with different sensory properties (Evans et al., 2010). The best known products are the Whey Proteins Concentrate (WPC), with a protein content of 25-80%, rich in lactose, and the Whey Protein Isolate (WPI), a dried powder resulting in more than 90% proteins obtained after lactose separation. Whey proteins are highly used in food industry, as WPI, Sweet whey solids (SWS), WPC and freeze-dried WPC (containing 35 and 75% protein, and varying amounts of residual lipids and phospholipids) (Vaghela and Kilara 1996). Whey proteins have been used as texturising WPI in snacks (Onwulata et al., 2001), meat analogs, candies, cranberry snacks and jellies, and as WPC in the baked products industry (Smithers et al., 1996). Finally, whey proteins provide nutraceuticals through different types of peptides (Yalcin 2006) with health-promoting and/or specific use claims (i.e. muscle mass implementation). For instance, lactoferrin enriched infant milk powders are produced and marketed by Morinaga Milk Industry, Japan (Tomita et al., 2009).

It is estimated that 90% of the bovine milk used for cheese production results in whey. Hundreds of million tonnes of whey are produced only in Europe. In Turkey this sums up to 2.7 million tonnes/year, while in Italy only the production of Parmesan-type cheese reaches an amount of 200 tonnes of cheese/year corresponding to 3 million tonnes of whey produced. Even in the presence of a tight regulation on whey disposal, about 30% percent of whey is currently discarded as a waste.

In renneted curd, k-caseins are cleaved by chymosin to release the 106-169 C-terminal peptide containing several phosphorylated serines and glycosylated threonines, the Caseinomacropeptide (CMP). The release of calcium bridges between the phosphorylated k-caseins allows the transition from the calcium-linked soluble casein micelle nets into the casein coagulum, resulting in casein separation from the serum and formation of the cheese curd. In milk, whey proteins are stabilised by caseins, that act as chaperones protecting proteins from unfolding, aggregation and precipitation. Thus, whey proteins devoid of the casein fraction are more sensitive to thermal treatment, as in the manufacture of "ricotta" cream, obtained by heating the whey and separation of coagulated proteins floating on the surface of the serum. The major whey proteins undergo denaturation upon heating to a temperature above 60° C, forming inter- and intra-molecular bonds that are either physical (hydrophobic, electrostatic, etc.) or chemical (disulfide bonds). The presence of protein variants differing in amino acid substitutions codified by alleles in different varieties or in different species add to the variability in heat stability of each whey protein.

The most abundant type of whey originates from the manufacture of cheese products, in which coagulation of casein is achieved by addition of chymosin, or other κ-casein cleaving proteases. Since the rennet-induced coagulation of caseins occurs at approximately pH 6.5, this type of whey is referred to as sweet whey. A second type of whey, acid whey (pH 5), results from the fermentation of sweet whey by the Lactic Acid Bacteria starters. In a third type of whey, the rennet coagulum is obtained by acidification with citric acid, or mineral acids, that coagulate the caseins. It is applied in the manufacture of fresh cheeses such as cottage and quark cheese, and a type of low-moisture mozzarella produced without starters through the combined action of rennet and citric acid. These acid wheys are either containing whole length proteins (the first type does not contain proteases) or casein-originated peptides, but do not contain fermenting bacteria, thus are stabilized.

The water-soluble components of sweet and acid wheys are lactose (70–72% of total solids), whey proteins (8 – 10%) and minerals (12–15%). The main differences (shown in the table 1) between the two whey types are mineral content (higher content of calcium in acid whey), the pH and a partial proteolysis of the proteins by chymosin and the proteases of the starter strains.

Table 1. Typical composition of sweet and acid whey

Components	Sweet whey (g/L)	Acid whey (g/L)
Total solids	63.0 – 70.0	63.0 – 70.0
Lactose	46.0 – 52.0	44.0 – 46.0
Protein	6.0 – 10.0	6.0 – 8.0
Calcium	0.4 – 0.6	1.2 – 1.6
Phosphate	1.0 – 3.0	2.0 – 4.5
Lactate	2	6.4
Chloride	1.1	1.1

Dairy-based whey drinks rely on the fermentation of liquid whey protein concentrate or the enrichment of milk and milk products with dry whey protein concentrate (WPC) and whey protein isolate (WPI) (Morr and Ha 1993; Peter et al., 1996).

The major technological challenge of the production of beverages based on liquid WPC is the sedimentation of insolubilised proteins. Heat treatment at low pHs causes protein sedimentation. This is relatively less important in unfermented whey beverages as long as they are heat treated at neutral pHs. Therefore, the use of sweet whey is more suitable for the beverage industry than acid cheese whey (Ozer and Kirmaci 2010), and the total whey protein content is higher than in the acid cheese whey.

Finally, whey permeate resulting from the separation of whey proteins is used in the production of carbonated soft drinks, such as Rivella drinks made in Switzerland.

Whey has been used for long times as a substrate for preparation of whey–agar, a culture medium able to support the growth of *Lactobacillus* species.

N-acetyl-neuraminic acid (NANA)-containing whey proteins promote the growth of the *Bifidobacterium* genus. Whey proteins are beneficial for the gut microflora, and rich in probiotic peptides thus facilitating well-being and the intestinal balance between bacteria, favouring the probiotic ones, and the maintenance of reduction-oxidation potential between gut bacteria.

WHEY PROTEINS CONTENT IN DIFFERENT ANIMAL SPECIES

Whey proteins composition differs in milks of different mammal species, so that it may range from 6 to 10 g/L of proteins. Even the casein/whey protein ratio differs consistently between mammalian species. It ranges from 3.2:1 up to 4.7:1 in goat, sheep and cow, respectively, while it is 0.4:1 in human, 1.1:1 in horse and 1.3:1 in donkey milk (Uniacke-Lowe et al., 2010). Sheep milk (Wendorff 2005; Park et al., 2007) has the highest content of total proteins, 5.2% (weight/volume) while it is 3.2% in cow and goat milk. On the other side, horse and equine milks contain a low quantity of proteins, 2.7% (weight/volume), and the composition and protein content resemble those in human milk. Seasonal variation in protein content in sheep and goat whey was reported (Casper et al., 1998).

PURIFICATION METHODS FOR WHEY PROTEINS

Several methods have been described producing at high yield purified whey proteins, making use of sweet whey as cheap material, or starting directly from milk, as milk serum protein concentrates (SPC) (Evans et al., 2010). These methods rely on physical-chemical differences (Bonnaillie and Tomasula 2008), such as protein fractionation at different pH. While the isoelectric point of β-LG, α-LA, CMP and serum albumin ranges between 4 and 6, Lf is charged positively until pH 8. Thus anion and cation exchange resins exploited the differences in isoelectric points at different pH for purification of individual whey proteins (Ye et al, 2000; Plate et al., 2006; Mehra and O'Kennedy 2008). These methods combine ultrafiltration on membranes with different cut-offs (Cheanga and Zydney 2004) applied also to protein separation from ovine and goat whey (Diaz et al., 2004), electrodialysis (Bazinet et al., 2004), differential acidification, electroacidification (achieving the delipidation of WPC), acidification through supercritical carbon dioxide (Poulin et al., 2006; Tomasula and Boswell 1999).

Bipolar membrane electroacidification (BMEA) technology allows acidification and de-mineralization of solutions without any salt addition (Shee at el., 2007) obtaining a WPC devoid of lipids with optimum emulsifying properties.

In a work on Lactoferrin purification (De Lorenzis et al. 2008) we used defatted milk, that was acidified to pH 4.5 with a food grade acid. Caseins were centrifuged on the bottom of 300 ml tubes. The whey supernatant was alkalinised to pH 5.6. After addition of carboxymethylsepharose, the batch solution was kept under stirring for 2 h and then centrifuged or decanted. The supernatant was removed, and the resin collected in an open column to perform cation exchange chromatography. This method showed short times of processing and high yield of Lf recovery. A similar process is suitable to be applied to sweet and acid whey.

BIOACTIVITY OF WHEY PROTEINS AND PEPTIDES

Whey proteins, most of which have been claimed to have some function and bioactivity, are described, from the most abundant one to the low abundant one, as well as the properties of homologue proteins from different animal species.

β-Lactoglobulin (β-LG), not present in human and camel milk, is the most abundant protein in whey of other mammal species: it sum up to 3,7 g/L in sheep, 74% of whey proteins, from 3 to 3.2 g/L in goat and cow' whey respectively, 58 to 65% of total whey proteins, and 2.5 g/L in equine wheys. Its sequence (bovine, ovine and equine β-LGs) contain several amino acid substitutions most of which conserve the overall charge and isoelectric points, and in some case (equine β-LG) introduces a glycine producing a longer protein. Bovine β-LG is quite resistant to digestion by pepsin. This resistance may contribute to the allergy to cow milk in sensible individuals that develop atopic dermatitis, urticaria, or even anaphylactic reactions. Resistance to digestion is not uniform among species, with ovine β-LG g being highly sensible to pepsin proteolysis (El-Zahar et al., 2005). Some individual show cross-reactivity to milks of related species (sheep, goat), that is less frequent with equine milk. Patients with negative Skin Prick Tests (SPT) tolerate well camel, donkey and (to a lesser extent) goat milk (Ehlayel et al., 2012).

The peptide YLLF, β-lactophorin/ β-lactorphin, corresponding to the fragment β-LG(102-105), has non-opioid, stimulatory effect on ileum. *β*-LG trypsin-originated peptide *f*(142-148), ALPMHIR, may show anti-hypertensive activity.

Proteolytic digestion of bovine β-LG by trypsin yields four peptide fragments with bactericidal activity. These peptides correspond to β-LG *f*(15–20), *f*(25–40), *f*(78–83) and *f*(92–100), (Pellegrini et al. 2001; Haque and Chand 2008). These peptides, negatively charged, inhibit only Gram-positive bacteria.

β-LG originates other opioid-like peptides such as YVPFPPF and HIRL *f*(146-149) (β-lactotensin).β-LG exhibits prebiotic effects on *Bifidobacterium* and *Lactobacillus* species.

α-lactalbumin (α-LA) is the second most abundant whey protein. Its content is 2 g/L in goat, 27% of whey proteins, 1.2 g/L in sheep and cow, 15% of total whey proteins, and 2.4 g/L in equine whey. It binds and transports retinol and fatty acids, and calcium ions. α-LA is rich in branched amino acids isoleucine, leucine and valine, necessary in the muscle cells to promote protein synthesis.

It contains several cysteines, forming four intra-molecular disulphide bonds, linking Cys6 to Cys120, Cys28 to Cys111, Cys61 to Cys77 and Cys73 to Cys93, according to the human α-LA enumeration. Its variants show conserved isoelectric points, ranging between 4.8 and 5.11.

α-LA originates peptides with antimicrobial (Pellegrini et al. 1999; Haque and Chand 2008) and anti-stress properties, partly mediated by a high tryptofan content used in serotonin synthesis.

α-LA originates α-lactophorin/ α-lactorphin, α-LA(50-53), with sequence YGLF, similar to the opioid peptides YGGF, which act on opioid receptors (Ijaes et al.2004). α-LA(50-53) is an Opioid agonist and Angiotensin Converting enzyme (ACE) inhibitor. α-lactophorin has been shown to exert a weak opioid activity to smooth muscles. When injected into the bloodstream, these peptides induce an analgesic and sedative effect on the nervous system. When α -lactophorin was given subcutaneously to conscious, unrestrained spontaneously hypertensive (SHR) and normotensive rats, blood pressure decreased in the SHR rats. This response was blocked by opioid receptor antagonist naloxone, suggesting the opioid receptors were mediating the effect. Positive neurocognitive effects have been associated with bioactive peptides originating from α-LA and other whey components (Camfield et al., 2011).

Caseinomacropeptide (CMP or GMP), comprises from 10 to15% of whey proteins, thus is the third most abundant peptide in rennet-based cheese whey. It corresponds to the 106-169 C-terminal peptide from κ-casein, containing several phosphorylated serines and glycosylated threonines, and contains sialic acid, *N*-acetylgalactosamine and other mucin-like glucans (Thomä-Worringer et al. 2006). The level of phosphorylation and glycosylation is highly heterogeneous, with CMP variants present in different glycosylated forms (disaccharide, trisaccharide and tetrasaccharide chains). The goat CMP contains 25 μg sialic acid per mg of dry weight, 2-fold less than in bovine CMP (Moreno et al., 2001). CMP was found glycosylated up to 36% in goat, and to a lesser extent, approximately 30% of total CMP, in ovine milk (Moreno et al., 2000). CMP is a hydrophilic, thermostable peptide, with a net negative charge even at low pH. CMP content is higher in cow, sheep, and goat whey, reflecting the higher caseins content. CMP is very low in equine milk, either due to a low caseins/whey proteins ratio, and to the low content of κ-casein (since other caseins support the precipitation of casein coagulum), but contains 68 amino acids, compared to 63 amino acids in bovine CMP and 65 in human CMP. Phenylalanine does not occur in goat CMP and its content is negligible in CMP of other origins.

CMP exhibits prebiotic effects on Bifidobacteria and Lactobacilli. CMP, and other phosphorylated peptides derived from casein, have been shown to increase the solubility of calcium and enhance the absorption of calcium (Martinez et al., 2009).

CMP can be used as an antimicrobial peptide to fight caries and displaces *Streptococcus mutans* and *Porphyromonas gingivalis*, two oral opportunistic pathogens (Malkoski et al. 2001; Aimutis 2004), while it favors the growth of Lactobacilli in the oral cavity.

GMP showed to possess intestinal anti-inflammatory activity on monocytes (Requena et al., 2009). Bovine GMP enhances the secretion of tumour necrosis factor (TNF), interleukin (IL)-1β and IL-8, with the involvement of the NF-κB, ERK and MAP kinase signalling pathways. GMP may exert an indirect intestinal anti-inflammatory effect through potentiation of host defences against invading microorganisms.

Bovine, ovine, and caprine CMP have been shown to inhibit platelet aggregation and, therefore, the formation of thrombi. Casomorphins are peptides of different length, included between the 106-116 region of the GMP molecule, containing a tetrapeptide sequence similar to the fragment 400–411 of fibrinogen γ-chain, shown to inhibit both aggregation and fibrinogen binding to ADP-treated platelets (Phelan and Kerins 2011). Several fragments have been shown to have anti-thrombotic activity: these include fragments f(108-110), f(106-112), and f(113-116). The pentapeptide f(112–116) was reported to strongly inhibit adenosine diphosphate (ADP)-induced platelet aggregation (Martinez et al., 2009).

Anti-ACE peptides with antihypertensive activity are contained within CMP sequence. GMP trypsin hydrolysate originates two peptides, MAIPPK and MAIPPKK, f(106-112) containing in the inside the sequence IPP, with strong anti-ACE activity (Gobbetti et al., 2007).

Lactoferrin (Lf) content in whey varies according to the species of origin: 1.6 g/L in human milk, up to 600 mg/L in equine whey, but only 100 - 200 mg/L in bovine, goat and sheep whey. Cow, buffalo, goat and sheep Lfs share over 90 % sequence identity with each other and form an extremely closely related group. Lf binds iron ions on a wide range of pH (10% of Lf is saturated with Fe^{2+}) and also other essential elements (vanadium, manganese, molybdenum, and zinc ions). Lf structure is bi-lobular, each lobe binding and retaining one Fe^{2+}, even at low pH (except the C-terminal lobe of camel Lf), the crystallographic and three dimensional analysis showed a highly conserved three-dimensional structure in Lfs of different origin (Baker et al., 2000). The lobes are connected by an alpha-helical linker peptide that is cleaved by pepsin in two symmetric lobes (Baker and Baker 2005). A comparison of native and deglycosylated Lf have shown that Lf binding properties for iron are unaffected, but the loss of carbohydrate increased its sensitivity to proteolysis. Most of the glycosylation sites are highly exposed, on the protein surface, but there are glycosylation sites, such as Asn545, in cow, buffalo, sheep and goat Lfs, in a surface cleft between the two domains of the C-lobe; providing additional interactions with both domains, that may help to stabilize the closed state.

The N-terminal lobe includes the lactoferricin (Lfcin) sequence, shown to possess antibacterial properties (Bellamy et al. 1992; Lopez Exposito and Recio 2006). Lfcin H (human) differs slightly from Lfcin B (bovine) in length and in amino acid composition: hLfcin is a 47 amino acid peptide, while bLfcin is a 25 peptide, forming a loop of similar length containing positively charged amino acids, by bLfcin is devoid of the Cysteine-Cysteine intra-chain bond and has a shorter C-terminal (Tomita et al., 2009). The four Arginine residues at the human Lf N-terminus are highly atypical of lactoferrins generally, suggesting that some of the Lf properties could be species-specific (Baker and Baker 2005).

Lf and its derived peptides inhibit the attachment of cariogenic *Streptococcus mutans* to hydroxyapatite coated with saliva or purified saliva host ligands (Johansson and Holgerson 2011). A use of LF-derivatives in oral care and as food preservative has been proposed (Martinez et al., 2009).

Lfcin B, obtained by hydrolysis of lactoferrin by pepsin, was found to promote phagocytic activity of human neutrophils (Miyauchi et al., 1997; Miyauchi et al., 1998; Shinoda et al., 1996). Lf-derived peptides can affect cytokine production from leucocytes (Mattsby Baltzer et al., 1996; Requena et al., 2009)

LACTOFERRICIN AND OTHER BACTERICIDAL PEPTIDES

Antimicrobial effect of LF is considered to rely on two characteristics, one is the ability to determine pores on membranes, or through deprivation of iron by iron chelation. Antimicrobial peptides derived from bovine LF f(17–41) and human LF f(1–47) inhibited a number of pathogens (Gobbetti et al., 2007; Yamauchi et al., 1993).

The discovery of these Lfcin fragments as antimicrobial peptides derived from whey protein gave rise to a proposed mechanism of membrane lysis of LF, independent of its iron-binding properties. It is recognised that the antibacterial activity of lactoferricin starts with the electrostatic interaction with the negatively charged membranes of bacteria. In this initial binding, lipopolysaccharide and the teichoic acid have been identified as binding site in Gram-negative and Gram-positive bacteria, respectively. The structure–activity of Lfcin has been studied during last decade. It has been suggested that antimicrobial, antifungal, antitumor, and antiviral properties of Lfcin can be related to tryptophan/ arginine-rich proportion of the peptide. Bovine and human LFcin were initially released from the precursor protein by enzymatic hydrolysis with porcine pepsin (Bellamy et al., 1992), although other proteolytic enzymes, such as chymosin, can produce analogous fragments (Hoek et al., 1997; Recio and Visser 1999). When hydrolysing bovine LF with pepsin, in addition to LFcin and longer peptides containing LFcin within their sequences (various heterodimers), other cationic peptides corresponding to a region of the N-lobe and in spatial proximity to LFcin are released. These peptides corresponded to LF f(277–288), LF f(267–285), and LF f(267–288). Bovine Lfcin has shown more potent antimicrobial activity than the human equivalent. The motif RRWQWR in the bovine Lf-derived peptides is highly homologous to motif RRWCFR, identified in one antimicrobial peptide in horseshoe crab hemolimph.

Comparing the antibacterial activity of bovine, ovine and goat Lfcins, all the peptides were active in the apo form, free of Fe^{2+}. It was found that goat LF peptides showed good anti-*E. coli* activity without displacement of a bovine LF binding to bacteria (Recio and Visser 2000). Recently, a peptide internal to the sequence of LF, f(268–284), and designated lactoferrampin (LFampin), has been chemically synthesised and has demonstrated anti-bacterial activity against *B. subtilis*, *E. coli*, and *P. aeruginosa* (van der Kraan et al., 2004; Sanchez-Gomez et al., 2011). LFampin 265-284 (and LFampin 265-280) peptides in bio-physical studies showed the highest ability to form an α-helix and the strongest interaction with model membranes and inhibiting the tested microorganisms (*E. coli*, *S. sanguinis*) (Adao et al., 2011).

Fragments obtained by chemical synthesis of residues 17–41 of murine and caprine LF have demonstrated antibacterial activity although to a lesser extent than bovine LFcin (Vorland et al., 1999). Hydrolysis of caprine and ovine LF by pepsin resulted in antibacterial hydrolysates and a homologous peptide to LFcin, corresponding to fragment 14–42, was identified in the caprine LF hydrolysate. Caprine LFcin showed lower antibacterial activity than bovine LFcin against *E. coli* but comparable activity against *Micrococcus flavus*. The region corresponding to LFcin within the sequence of ovine LF was hydrolysed by the action of pepsin, and hence, the activity observed in the ovine LF hydrolysate could be caused by other LF fragments (Recio and Visser, 2000; Vorland et al., 1999).

Serum albumin: its content ranges between 0,3 and 0,4 g/l, summoning 6-8% of total whey proteins in cow milk, and 4% of goat and sheep whey proteins. Bovine serum albumin is produced at industrial scale for laboratory use, as osmolyte, highly soluble protein on a wide pH range, and blocking reagent in immunological analyses.

The Serum Albumin peptide 399-404, YGFQDA, called Serophorin, has opioid-like activity.

ALKAWSVAR is an ACE-inhibitory peptide with inhibition in the micromolar range (IC50 3 μmol/L).

Immunoglobulins (IgA, IgG, IgM) (from 500-700 g/L in goat/cow' whey to 1100 g/L in human milk and 1600 g/l in equine serum). These proteins are soluble in their native forms, independent of pH. Immunoglobulins are highly soluble proteins that do not tolerate oxidation and reducing agents, or thermal stress.

Lysozyme (Lyz) is a lysosomal enzyme that confers antibacterial property to saliva and bodily fluids. The enzyme is a muramidase (peptidoglucan-N-acetylmuranoyl hydrolase) that cleaves β-1-4 bonds between N-acetylmuramic acid and N-acetyl-D-glucosamine residues in bacterial cell walls. Its content in mammalian milks varies from less than 1 mg/L in bovine milk (similar to the content of ovine milk and half the content of caprine) to 300 g/L in human milk and 790 mg/L in equine milk. (Chandan et al 1968, Fox and Kelly 2006). Its structure and amino acid sequence resembles that of α-La (Moatsou 2010). Lysozyme is effective in treatment of periodentitis and prevention of tooth decay.

Folate-binding protein is a glycoprotein with about 22% carbohydrates (Rubinoff et al., 1977; Hansen et al, 1979), and binds 9.2 mg folic acid/g of protein. Its concentrations in goat milk (12 mg/l) are higher than in cow and other types of milk.

A **Proline rich polypeptide** [PRP] was studied for variety of immunotropic functions, including promotion of T cell activation and inhibition of autoimmune disorders such as multiple sclerosis (Camfield et al., 2011).

Proteoso-peptone fraction (PP3) is a minor peptide fraction in bovine and goat whey. This fraction has been characterized as a mixture of heat-stable acid-soluble (at pH 4.6) 135 amino-acid phosphorylated glycoprotein that does not derive from caseins. PP3 contains two distinct domains. The first one covers the N-terminal part (residues 1–97) and is negatively charged. The second domain in the C-terminal, named lactophoricin, is positively charged. Lactophoricin, with its amphipathic character adopting an a-helical structure, is able to permeabilize planar lipid bilayers (Campagna et al., 2001; Campagna et al., 2004) with bacteriostatic activity against Gram-positive and Gram-negative bacteria.

CONCLUSION

Whey proteins and their internal peptides are adsorbed and assimilated in the gut during digestion and proteolytic processing. Then the active fragments are made available to exert their effect and circulate in the body. Wheys from different origin contain different protein fractions. GMP can be extracted and obtained in appreciable amounts in some whey protein isolates. On the other side, equine wheys, almost devoid of GMP fraction, could be exploited for production of lysozyme, lactoferrin and immunoglobulins. Horse and donkey β-LG are well tolerated and digested, while being less cross-reactive in β-LG-allergic patients, and the same was found for camel β-LG.

Goat whey can be applied for the separation of α-LA, since it is present in high amounts, making use of non denatured whey. Concerning the use of acid whey, since it may contain proteolysis products from whey proteins, there is a need to solve problems on how to optimally separate the peptides maintaining high yield of protein recovery. Thus, in the next years it may be envisaged an increase in production of WPIs from goat, sheep, equine or camel wheys as rich sources of beneficial peptides with claims on human health.

REFERENCES

Adao R., Nazmi K., Bolscher J.G., Bastos M. C- and N-truncated antimicrobial peptides from LFampin 265-284: Biophysical versus microbiology results. *Journal Pharmacy Bioallied Science*, 2011, 3(1):60-69.

Aimutis W.R. Bioactive properties of milk proteins with particular focus on anticariogenesis. *Journal of Nutrition*, 2004, 134(4):989S-95S.

Baker H.M., Anderson B.F., Kidd R.D., Shewry S.C., Baker E.N. Lactoferrin three-dimensional structure: a framework for interpreting function. Pp. 3–15. In: Shimazaki K., Tomita M., Tsuda H. (Eds.) Lactoferrin: Structure, Function and Applications. Elsevier Science, Amsterdam, 2000.

Baker E.N., Baker H.M. Molecular structure, binding properties and dynamics of lactoferrin. *Cellular Molecular Life Science*, 2005, 62:2531–2539.

Bazinet L., Ippersiel D., Mahdavi B. Effect of conductivity control on the separation of whey proteins by bipolar membrane electroacidification. *Journal Agriculture Food Chemistry*, 2004, 52(7):1980-1984.

Bellamy W., Takase M., Yamauchi K., Wakabayashi H., Kawase K., Tomita M. Identification of the bactericidal domain of lactoferrin. *Biochimica Biophysica Acta*, 1992, 1121:130-136.

Bonnaillie L.M., Tomasula P.M. Whey processing and fractionation. Pp.15-38. In: Onwulata C.I., Huth P. (Eds) Whey Processing, Functionality and Health Benefits. Wiley-Blackwell, 2008.

Camfield D.A., Owen L., Scholey A.B., Pipingas A., Stough C. Dairy constituents and neurocognitive health in ageing. *British Journal of Nutrition,* 2011, 22:1-17.

Campagna S., Cosette P., Molle G., Gaillard J.L. Evidence for membrane affinity of the C-terminal domain of bovine milk PP3 component. *Biochimica Biophysica Acta*, 2001, 1513:217–222.

Campagna S., Mathot A. G., Fleury Y., Girardet J.M., Gaillard J.L. Antibacterial activity of Lactophoricin, a synthetic 23-residues peptide derived from the sequence of bovine milk component-3 of protease peptone. *Journal of Dairy Science*, 2004, 87:1621–1626.

Casper J.L.; Wendorff W.L.; Thomas D.L. Seasonal changes in protein composition of whey from commercial manufacture of caprine and ovine specialty cheeses. *Journal of Dairy Science*, 1998, 81(12):3117–3122.

Chandan R.C., Parry R.M. Jr, Shahani K.M. Lysozyme, lipase and ribonuclease in milk of various species. *Journal of Dairy Science*, 1968, 51:606–607.

Cheanga B., Zydney A.L. A two-stage ultrafiltration process for fractionation of whey protein isolate. *Journal Membrane Science,* 2004, 231(1-2):159-167.

Clare D.A., Catignani G.L., Swaisgood H.E. Biodefense properties of milk: the role of antimicrobial proteins and peptides. *Current Pharmaceutical Design,* 2003; 9:1239-1255.

De Lorenzis E., Semeraro C., De Blasi M.D., Mita G., Poltronieri P. Emulsions based on the interactions between lactoferrin and chitosans. *Food Biophysics*, 2008, 3:169-173.

Diaz O., Pereira C.D., Cobos A. Functional properties of ovine whey protein concentrates produced by membrane technology after clarification of cheese manufacture by-products. *Food Hydrocolloids,* 2004, 18:601–610.

Drake P.M., Nathan J.K., Stock C.M., Chang P.V., Muench M.O., Nakata D., Reader J.R., Gip P., Golden K.P.K., Weinhold B., Gerardy-Schahn R., Troy F.A. II, Bertozzi C.R.. Polysialic acid, a glycan with highly restricted expression, is found on human and murine leukocytes and modulates immune responses. Journal Immunology, 2008, 181:6850-6858.

Ehlayel M., Bener A., Abu Hazeima K., Al-Mesaifri F. Camel Milk Is a Safer Choice than Goat Milk for Feeding Children with Cow Milk Allergy. *ISRN Allergy*, 2011, in press. doi:10.5402/2011/391641.

El-Zahar K., Sitohy M., Choiset Y., Métro F., Haertlé T., Chobert J.-M. Peptic hydrolysis of ovine b-lactoglobulin and a-lactalbumin. Exceptional susceptibility of native ovine b-lactoglobulin to pepsinolysis. *International Dairy Journal*, 2005, 15:17-27.

Evans J., Zulewska J., Newbold M., Drake M.A., Barbano D.M. Comparison of composition and sensory properties of 80% whey protein and milk serum protein concentrates. *Journal Dairy Science* 2010, 93(5):1824-1843.

Faryabi B., Mohr S., Onwulata C.I., Mulvaney S.J. Functional Foods Containing Whey Proteins. Pp. 213-226. In: Onwulata C.I., Huth P. (Eds) Whey Processing, Functionality and Health Benefits. Wiley-Blackwell, 2008. ISBN: 978-0-8138-0903-8.

Fox P.F. and Kelly A.L. Indigenous enzymes in milk: overview and historical aspects – Part 2. *International Dairy Journal*, 2006, 16:517–532.

Gobbetti M., Stepaniak L., De Angelis M., Corsetti A., Di Cagno R. Latent bioactive peptides in milk proteins: Proteolytic activation and significance in dairy processing. *Critical Reviews in Food Science and Nutrition*, 2002, 42:223–239.

Gobbetti M., Minervini F., Rizzello C.G. Bioactive peptides in dairy products. Pp. 489–517. In: Hui Y.H., Chandan R., Clark S., Cross N.A. (Eds.) Handbook of Food Products Manufacturing: Health, Meat, Milk, Poultry, Seafood, and Vegetables. John Wiley & Sons. Hoboken, NJ, 2007.

Hansen S.I., Holm J., Lyngbye J. Change in binding properties of folate-binding protein in cow's whey due to removal of a cofactor during affinity chromatographic purification. *Biochimica Biophysica Acta*, 1979; 579(2):479–482.

Haque E., Chand R. Antihypertensive and antimicrobial bioactive peptides from milk proteins. *European Food Research Technology*, 2008, 227:7–15.

Hartmann R., Meisel H. Food-derived peptides with biological activity: From research to food applications . *Current Opinion in Biotechnology*, 2007, 18(2):163–169.

Hoek K.S., Milne J.M., Grieve P.A., Dionysius D.A., Smith R. Antibacterial activity of bovine lactoferrin derived peptides. *Antimicrobial Agents Chemotherapy* 1997, 41:54-59.

Ijäes H., Collin M., Finckenberg P., Pihlanto-Leppälä A., Korhonen H., Korpela R. Antihypertensive opioid-like milk peptide a-lactorphin: lack of effect on behavioral tests in mice. *International Dairy Journal*, 2004, 14:201–205.

Johansson I., Holgerson L.P. Milk and oral health. *Nestle Nutrition Workshop Series Pediatric Programme,* 2011;67:55-66.

Korhonen H., Pihlanto A. Technological options for the production of health - promoting proteins and peptides derived from milk and colostrum . *Current Pharmaceutical Design*, 2007, 13(8):829–843.

Korhonen H.J. Milk-derived bioactive peptides: From science to applications. *Journal Functional Foods*, 2009, 1:177–187.

Korhonen H.J. Health-Promoting Proteins and Peptides in Colostrum and Whey. Pp. 151-168. In: Mine Y., Li-Chan E., Jiang B. (Eds) Bioactive Proteins and Peptides as Functional Foods and Nutraceuticals. Wiley-Blackwell, 2010. ISBN: 978-0-8138-1311-0.

Lopez Exposito I., Recio I. Antibacterial activity of peptides and folding variants from milk proteins. *International Dairy Journal*, 2006, 16:1294–1305.

Malkoski M., Dashper S.G., O'Brien-Simpson N.M., Talbo G.H., Macris M., Cross K.J., Reynolds E.C. Kappacin, a novel antimicrobial peptide from bovine milk. *Antimicrobial Agents Chemotherapeutics,* 2001, 45:2309–2315.

Martinez M.J., Carrera Sánchez C., Rodríguez Patino J.M., Pilosof A.M.R. Bulk and interfacial behaviour of caseinoglycomacropeptide (GMP). *Colloids and Surfaces B: Biointerfaces,* 2009, 71(2):230-237.

Mattsby Baltzer I., Roseanu A., Motas C., Elverfors J., Engberg I., Hanson L.A. Lactoferrin or a fragment thereof inhibits the endotoxin-induced interleukin-6 response in human monocytic cells. *Pediatric Research,* 1996; 40:257-262.

Mehra R., O'Kennedy B.T. Separation of β-lactoglobulin from whey. Pp. 39-61. In: Onwulata C.I., Huth P. (Eds). Whey Processing, Functionality and Health Benefits. Wiley-Blackwell, 2008. ISBN-13: 978-0-8138-0903-8.

Meisel H. Biochemical properties of peptides encrypted in bovine milk proteins. *Current Medicinal Chemistry,* 2005, 12:1905–1919.

Miyauchi H., Kaino A., Shinoda I., Fukuwatari Y., Hayasawa H. Immunomodulatory effect of bovine lactoferrin pepsin hydrolysate on murine splenocytes and Peyer's patch cells. *Journal Dairy Science,* 1997; 80:2330-2339.

Miyauchi H., Hashimoto S., Nakajima M., Shinoda I., Fukuwatari Y., Hayasawa H. Bovine lactoferrin stimulates the phagocytic activity of human neutrophils: identification of its active domain. *Cell Immunology,* 1998; 187:34-37.

Moatsou G. Indigenous enzymatic activities in ovine and caprine milks. *International Journal Dairy Technology*, 2010, 63:16-31.

Moreno J.F., Recio I., Olano A., Lopez-Fandino R. Chromatographic characterization of ovine κ-casein macropeptide. *Journal Dairy Research,* 2000, 67:349-359

Moreno J.F., Recio I., Olano A., Lopez-Fandino R. Heterogeneity of caprine κ-casein macropeptide. *Journal Dairy Research*, 2001, 68: 197-208.

Morr C.V., Ha E.Y. Whey protein concentrates and isolates. Processing and functional properties. *Critical Reviews Food Science Nutrition*, 1993, 33(6):431-476.

Nurminen M.L., Sipola M., Kaarto H., Pihlanto-Leppälä A., Piilola K., Korpela R. a-lactorphin lowers blood pressure measured by radiotelemetry in normotensive and spontaneously hypertensive rats. *Life Science*, 2000, 66:1535–1543.

Onwulata C.I., Smith P.W., Konstance R.P., Holsinger V.H. Incorporation of whey products in extruded corn, potato or rice snacks. *Food Research International,* 2001, 34(8):679-687.

Ozer B.H., Kirmaci A.H. Functional milks and dairy beverages. *International Journal Dairy Technology*, 2010, 63:1-15.

Park Y.W., Juarez M., Ramos M., Haenlein G.F.W. Physicochemical characteristics of goat and sheep milk. *Small Ruminant Research*, 2007, 68:88–113.

Pellegrini A., Dettling C., Thomas U., Hunziker P. Isolation and characterization of four bactericidal domains in the bovine b-lactoglobulin. *Biochimica Biophysica Acta*, 2001, 1526:131–140.

Pellegrini A., Thomas U., Bramaz N., Hunziker P., von Fellenberg, R. Isolation and identification of three bactericidal domains in the bovine a-lactalbumin molecule. *Biochimica Biophysica Acta*, 1999, 1426,439–448.

Peter S., Rattray W., Jelen P. Heat stability and sensory quality of protein- standardized 2% fat milk. *Milchwissenschaft*, 1996, 51: 611–615.

Phelan M., Kerins D. The potential role of milk-derived peptides in cardiovascular disease. *Food Function*, 2011, 2(3-4):153-67.

Plate K., Beutel S., Buchholz H., Demmer W., Fischer-Frühholz S., Reif O., Ulber R., Scheper T. Isolation of bovine lactoferrin, lactoperoxidase and enzymatically prepared lactoferricin from proteolytic digestion of bovine lactoferrin using adsorptive membrane chromatography. *Journal Chromatography A*, 2006, 1117(1):81-86.

Poulin J.F., Amiot J., Bazinet L. Simultaneous separation of acid and basic bioactive peptides by electrodialysis with ultrafiltration membrane. *Journal Biotechnology* 2006, 123:314-328.

Recio I., Visser S. Two ion-exchange chromatographic methods for the isolation of antibacterial peptides from lactoferrin. In situ enzymatic hydrolysis on an ion-exchange membrane. *Journal Chromatography A*, 1999, 831:191-201.

Recio I., Visser S. Antibacterial and binding characteristics of bovine, ovine and caprine lactoferrins: A comparative study. *International Dairy Journal*, 2000, 10:597–605.

Requena P., Daddaoua A., Guadix E., Zarzuelo A., Suárez M.D., Sánchez de Medina F., Martínez-Augustin O. Bovine glycomacropeptide induces cytokine production in human monocytes through the stimulation of the MAPK and the NF-kappaB signal transduction pathways. *British Journal Pharmacology*, 2009, 157(7):1232-1240.

Rubinoff M., Schreiber C., Waxman S. The isolation and characterization of the folate binding protein from goat milk. *FEBS Letters*, 1977, 75(1):244–248.

Sanchez-Gomez S., Japelj B., Jerala R., Moriyon I., Fernandez Alonso M., Leiva J., Blondelle S. E., Andra J., Brandenburg K., Lohner K., Martinez de Tejada G. Structural Features Governing the Activity of Lactoferricin-Derived Peptides That Act in Synergy with Antibiotics against *Pseudomonas aeruginosa* In Vitro and In Vivo. Antimicrobial Agents Chemotherapy, 2011, 55:218-228.

Shee F.L., Angers P., Bazinet L. Delipidation of a whey protein concentrate by electroacidification with bipolar membranes. *Journal Agriculture Food Chemistry*, 2007, 55(10):3985-3989.

Shinoda I., Takase M., Fukuwatari Y., Shimamura S., Koller M., Konig W. Effects of lactoferrin and lactoferricin(R) on the release of interleukin 8 from human polymorphonuclear leukocytes. *Bioscience Biotechnology Biochemistry*, 1996; 60:521-523.

Smithers G.W., Ballard F.J., Copeland A.D., de Silva K.J., Dionysius D.A., Francis G.L., Goddard C., Grieve P.A., Mcintosh G.H., Mitchell I.R., Pearce R.J., Regester G.O. New opportunities from the isolation and utilization of whey proteins. *Journal of Dairy Science*, 1996, 79:1454-1459.

Thomä-Worringer C., Sørensen J., López-Fandiño R. Health effects and technological features of caseinomacropeptide. *International Dairy Journal*, 2006, 16:1324-1333.

Tomasula P.M., Boswell R.T. Measurement of the solubility of carbon dioxide in milk at high pressures. *Journal Supercritical Fluids*, 1999, 16:21-26.

Tomita M., Wakabayashi H., Shin K., Yamauchi K., Yaeshima T., Iwatsuki K. Twenty-five years of research on bovine lactoferrin applications. *Biochimie*, 2009, 91:52-57.

Uniacke-Lowe T., Huppertz T., Fox P.F. Equine milk proteins: chemistry, structure and nutritional significance. *International Daily Journal*, 2010, 20:609-629.

van der Kraan M.I., Groenink J., Nazmi K., Veerman E.C., Bolscher J.G., Nieuw Amerongen A.V. Lactoferrampin: a novel antimicrobial peptide in the N1-domain of bovine lactoferrin. *Peptides*, 2004, 25(2):177-183.

Vaghela M., Kilara A. Lipid Composition of Whey Protein Concentrates Manufactured Commercially and in the Laboratory. *Journal Dairy Science*, 1996, 79(7):1172-1183.

Vorland L.H., Ulvatne H., Rekdal Ø., Svendsen J.S. Initial binding sites of antimicrobial peptides in *Staphylococcus aureus* and *E. coli*. *Scandinavian Journal Infectious Diseases*, 1999, 31:467–473.

Walsh D.J., Bernard H., Murray B.A., MacDonald J., Pentzien A.K., Wright G.A. In vitro generation and stability of the lactokinin beta-lactoglobulin fragment (142-148). *Journal Dairy Science*, 2004, 87:3845–3857.

Wendorff W.L. Sheep Milk and Milk Products: Composition. Pp. 797-799. In: Ullrey D.E., Baer K.C., Pond W.G. Eds. Encyclopedia of Animal Science. Marcel Dekker, 2005.

Yalcin AS. Emerging therapeutic potential of whey proteins and peptides. *Current Pharmaceutical Design*, 2006, 12:1637–1643.

Yamauchi K., Tomita M., Giehl T.J., Ellison R.T. Antibacterial activity of lactoferrin and a pepsin-derived lactoferrin peptide fragment. *Infection and Immunity*, 1993, 61:719–728.

Ye X., Yoshida S., Ng T.B. Isolation of lactoperoxidase, lactoferrin, alpha-lactalbumin, beta-lactoglobulin B and beta-lactoglobulin A from bovine rennet whey using ion exchange chromatography. *International Journal Biochemistry Cell Biology*, 2000, 32:1143-1150.

In: Whey: Types, Composition and Health Implications   ISBN: 978-1-61942-862-1
Editors: Rafael M. Benitez and Gustavo M. Ortero   © 2012 Nova Science Publishers, Inc.

Chapter 7

EFFECTS OF STRUCTURAL CHANGES IN β-LACTOGLOBULIN ON ITS ALLERGENICITY

Néstor J. Delorenzi[a], Andrea Moro[a], Pablo A. Busti[a], Germán D. Báez[a] and Griselda A. Ballerini[a,b]

[a]Área Fisicoquímica, Departamento de Química-Física, Facultad de Ciencias Bioquímicas y Farmacéuticas, Universidad Nacional de Rosario, Rosario, Argentina
[b]Centro de Investigaciones y Desarrollo en Tecnología de los Alimentos, Universidad Tecnológica Nacional, Facultad Regional Rosario, Rosario, Argentina

ABSTRACT

Among identified food allergens, milk exhibits a relevant allergenic potential related to the multiplicity and diversity of the involved proteins. The main whey protein, beta-lactoglobulin, is usually considered to be the major cow's milk allergen. This protein, absent in human milk, is resistant to gastric acid and to proteolytic action, and it has the ability to cross the intestinal mucosa. Food processing can alter the allergenic properties of proteins by hiding, destroying or exposing allergic epitopes through protein structural changes. Some researches have been carried out on the thermal stability of the β-lactoglobulin allergen structure, and a significant reduction in its allergenecity was observed depending on the assayed thermal treatment. The use of microbial trans-glutaminase can also modify the immunogenicity of food proteins. Recently, it was suggested that the polymerization of β-lactoglobulin catalyzed by transglutaminase might decrease the antigenic response by hiding antigenic sites due to molecular rearrange-ments. In our recent experiences, β-lactoglobulin aggregates were formed by two different treatments, thermal and enzymatic. In the first one, 55 mg mL^{-1} β-lactoglobulin solutions in 20 mM sodium phosphate buffer pH 6.8, were heated at 85 °C from different periods of time: 1, 3, 5, 7, 10 and 15 min. In the enzymatic method, 25 mg mL^{-1} β-lactoglobulin solutions in 20 mM sodium phosphate buffer pH 8.0, in the presence of 0.07 M cysteine, were incubated with transglutaminase (at a level of 1 U g^{-1} substrate), for different times: 30, 60, 120 and 180 min. Protein structural characterization was analyzed based on electrophoresis, fluorescence, circular dichroism and viscosity studies. Comparing both treatments, it was observed that heating produces a higher degree of unfolding and therefore, a higher index of surface hydrophobicity; less compact and more asymmetrical aggregates, with higher flexibility. These conformational changes can be related to the lesser degree of allergenicity observed, either by the major accessibility to a proteolytic attack, in the case of the unfolding, or by hiding epitopes, in the case of formation of more compact protein aggregates.

INTRODUCTION

The dairy components of many infant food formulas are modified by adding bovine whey in order to enrich them nutritionally and/or to modify their aspect through changes in their functional properties. The dominant whey protein, β-lactoglobulin (β-LG), is largely responsible for the physicochemical properties and functional behaviour of whey protein products used as food ingredients [1]. Adding bovine whey proteins might result unsuitable, due to human milk does not contain β-LG, the major soluble protein in bovine milk, and its presence in food could lead to allergic phenomena. In fact, β-LG is considered to be one of the main allergens in bovine milk [2,3,4,5], and cow's milk allergic is the most common food allergy in young children. These food allergies generally correspond to an immediate type of IgE-mediated immune response. Moreover, β-LG seems to be resistant to gastric digestion and apparently remains intact having also the ability to cross the intestinal mucosa [6,7,8]. Therefore, its amino acid composition may be nutritionally unavailable for infants.

Food processing can alter the allergenic properties of proteins by hiding, destroying or disclosing allergic epitopes through conformational changes of the proteins [9,10]. However, the denaturation of β-LG *per se* does not appear to be sufficient to reduce its allergenicity [11,12]. Enzimatic proteolysis and heat treatment [10] are frequently used in the production of partially or extensively hydrolysed formulas to lower the proportion of native β-LG in order to reduce the antigenicity of milk proteins. However, residual allergenicity has been reported in several of these commercial preparations [13,14,15], which may be due to inaccessibility of some sequential epitopes to proteases, even in the denatured protein.

There are several methods to treat β-LG leading to its denaturation and to changes in its allergenic properties: heat treatment; high pressure treatments; enzymatic hydrolysis, which increases the accessibility and cleavage of immunogenic hydrophobic regions into the molecule; food irradiation, in which milk protein epitopes could be structurally modified by gamma radiation; the use of transglutaminase (TG) [16,17,18,19,20], an enzyme that catalyses the formation of inter and intramolecular bonds between glutamine and lysine residues, which decreases the allergenicity of the proteins by masking IgE antibody binding sites due to cross-linking [19], making them less immunogenic after polimerization with TG.

Recently, our group has researched [21,22] the effects that β-LG suffers after different treatments, heating or TG enzymatic one. The results allowed us the characterization of structural changes, showing that both assayed treatments led to denaturation and aggregation of the protein, in different degrees and features of the products obtained, which were studied in terms of structural and functional characteristics. All these results might be coherent with the results that involve allergenicity quoted by other authors.

β-LG ALLERGENICITY MODIFIED BY HEAT TREATMENT OR BY ENZYMATIC TREATMENT WITH TRANSGLUTAMINASE

Among identified food allergens, milk exhibits a relevant allergenic potential related to the multiplicity and diversity of the involved proteins. β-LG is usually considered to be the major cow's milk allergen, that is, the protein most frequently recognized by human IgE [23]. Several epitopes are spread along the 162 amino-acids of the molecule of β-LG, either as short linear sequences or large fragments. These epitopes structures and their integrity in the β-LG molecule are responsible for the immunogenicity of the molecule [24], and therefore, for the allergenic potential of milk products.

Considering the technological treatments performed in the dairy industry, product formulation and heating processes can be considered to be the most significant factors suspected to induce severe structural modifications on β-LG. Many investigations have been performed about the thermal stability of the β-LG allergen structures, and significant reduction in β-LG allergenicity was observed, according to thermal procedure that has been used [25,26].

In particular, the IgE binding capacities of β-LG are decreased by heating at 80-100 °C for 15 min, but residual allergenicity remains even after severe heating [27,28]. Depending on the heating treatment (blanching, baking, cooking, grilling, roasting), possible structures and chemical changes of proteins are denaturation/aggregation, side-chain amino acid alteration, and Maillard reaction with other molecules such as sugars [26,29].

Heat treatments between 80-100 °C led to significant proteolysis of β-LG on subsequent incubation with pepsin due to measurable changes in the conformational structure of the protein. It was proved that heating over 80 °C causes a dissociation of dimeric β-LG and a following partial unfolding of β-LG backbone. The possible exposure of cleavage sites resulting from the thermal denaturation could explain the increase on the susceptibility to proteolysis by pepsin. Therefore, heat treatment induces a loss of β-LG antigenicity, which could be explained by the increase of its digestibility [10]. Moreover, these authors found also that heat denaturation improved significantly the susceptibility of β-LG against the trypsin/chymotrypsin as another method of protein digestion.

According to the results obtained by other authors [18], the polymerization of β-LG using either heat treatment or Cys to promote the TG reaction, led to high molecular weight structures. With respect to the protein antigenicity, Cys-TG polymerization could have hidden antigenic sites due to a new molecular rearrangement, decreasing the allergenic properties.

In other works, digestibility of milk proteins, studied by the effect of pancreatic enzymes *in vitro*, was impaired by TG treatment. Highly cross-linked proteins may be the cause of impaired *in vitro* digestibility of TG-treated milk proteins by a mechanism which could involve sterically shielding of peptide bonds [30].

To sum up, heat treatment of milk proteins produces an increment of digestibility as a consequence of denaturation, which produces a disruption of the epitopes structures and a consequent decay of allergenicity. On the other hand, TG treatment produces a decreasing of allergenicity of milk proteins by hiding antigenic sites as a consequence of the formation of aggregates, but with a decreased digestibility.

Structural Changes in β-LG Subjected to Heat Treatment

Our group has studied β-LG solutions (55 mg mL^{-1} in 20 mM sodium phosphate buffer, pH 6.8) heated for 0, 1, 3, 5, 7, 10 and 15 min at 85 °C, and then, analyzed them by electrophoresis in SDS-PAGE (non reduced) [21]. The loss of monomeric β-LG and the appearance of other species were quantified by gel densitometry (Figure 1). Heating at 85 °C, the quantities of dimers and trimers decreased, whereas the amount of aggregates larger than trimers increased abruptly. The largest amount of dimers and trimers was found at 3 min of heating, whereas at 10 min of heating, oligomers and polymers represented more than 80% of the species in solution.

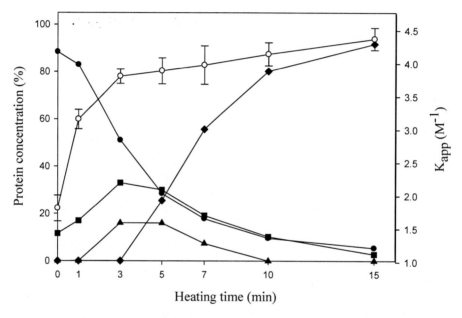

Figure 1. Protein concentrations (%) of different species formed by heating β-LG at 85 °C and for different periods of time (0, 1, 3, 5, 7, 10 and 15 min): monomers (●), dimers (■), trimers (▲) and aggregates larger than trimers (oligomers and polymers) (♦). (○) K_{app} (M^{-1}) from the Stern-Volmer graphs at different times of incubation with TG.

Fluorescence quenching of proteins by acrylamide is an accepted method for determining surface hydrophobicity [31]. Fluorescence intensity (F_0) of a sample of β-LG 10 μM, placed in the cell of a Jasco FP-770 spectrofluorometer, was measured at 337 nm, using excitation at 295 nm. Aliquots of 7 M acrylamide, used as fluorescence quencher, were sequentially added in the cell content, and each new fluorescence intensity (F) was measured. Acrylamide concentrations ranged from 0 to 0.2 M. The F_0/F ratio was plotted versus the quencher concentration (Stern-Volmer plot). In the used range, this plot was linear and the Stern-Volmer equation can be expressed as:

$$\frac{F_0}{F} = 1 + K_{app}\left[acrylamide\right] \tag{1}$$

K_{app} is an apparent constant because β-LG has more than one tryptophanyl (Trp) residue that can be quenched by acrylamide. The initial slope of Stern-Volmer plots, K_{app}, is an index of surface hydrophobicity of the protein [31].

The more flexible the protein structure and/or the higher the unfolded species concentration, the more pronounced the slope in the Stern-Volmer plot and then, greater K_{app} is. Besides, during the unfolding process, the protein surface becomes more and more hydrophobic due to the appearance of non-polar amino acids, which were previously hidden inside the protein structure. In the Figure 1, it can be seen the effectiveness of the quenching process, measured trough the K_{app} values, which increased with the length of heating treatment, verifying the minimum value for the unheated protein and the maximum, after 3 min of heating time, which corresponds to the main conformational and surface hydrophobicity changes. The K_{app} increment can be ascribed to the presence of a percentage of non-native monomers and aggregates of low molecular weight of denatured molecules, irreversibly formed during heat treatment. The fluorescence quenching of β-LG in urea 8 M without any heating treatment was also studied, in order to compare chemically and thermally denatured structures [21].

The analysis of near UV (250-320 nm) CD spectra was used to characterize the tertiary structure of proteins. There were found two negative peaks of the ellipticity in the CD spectra of native β-LG, which were mainly due to Trp19 absorbance, diminished their intensities and being particularly pronounced between 3 min and 5 min of heating, with smaller changes for subsequent heating times [21]. The far UV (190-250 nm) CD spectra largely reflect the secondary structure of proteins. The effects of heating β-LG solutions at 85 °C on the far UV CD spectra showed a shift to shorter wavelengths in the spectra, being particularly pronounced between 3 min and 5 min of heating, with smaller changes for subsequent heating times. Thus, in the assayed conditions, all tested methods (electrophoresis in non reduced SDS-PAGE, fluorescence quenching by acrylamide and circular dichroic spectra measurements) pointed at 3 min of heating as a critical time, in terms of conformational changes and aggregation processes. At this time, the more significant conformational changes take place: non-native monomers are present and the greatest amount of dimers and trimers is produced, and the proportion among the β-LG species was: monomer 51%, dimer 33% and trimer 16% (Figure 1).

STRUCTURAL CHANGES IN β-LG SUBJECTED TO ENZYMATIC TREATMENT WITH TRANSGLUTAMINASE

In another work of our group [22], it was noted that the β-LG molecule is a poor substrate for TG and that it must be partially or completely denatured to undergo enzymatic cross-linking. Thus, in several works, enzymatic treatment was assayed in presence of reducing agents such as dithiothreitol (DTT), beta-mercaptoethanol or Cysteine (Cys), but since DTT and beta-mercaptoethanol are not allowed for using in food application [33], Cys was the chosen reducing agent. It produces conformational changes on proteins and the subsequent exposure of the enzyme-targeted sites, because of the disruption of disulfide bonds in the substrate molecule. Solutions containing 25 mg mL^{-1} of β-LG, 0.07 M Cys and microbial TG (Activa®) at a level of 1 U g^{-1} substrate were prepared in 20 mM sodium phosphate buffer pH

8.0. The aggregation reaction was carried out at 40 °C for different periods of time (30, 60, 120 and 180 min). Enzyme reaction was stopped at 60 °C for 15 min. β-LG solutions non-treated and treated with TG were analyzed by SDS-PAGE (reducing conditions) and the different β-LG species were quantified by gel densitometry (Figure 2). With increasing incubation time with TG, the amount of monomeric β-LG decreased and aggregates of several sizes were formed: dimers, trimers, oligomers and polymers. For longer periods of incubation time, the quantities of dimers and trimers decreased, whereas the amount of aggregates larger than trimers increased abruptly. At 60 min of incubation time with TG, the largest amount of dimers and trimers was found, and oligomers and polymers appeared, representing approximately 50% of the species in solution at 180 min.

In our studies of fluorescence quenching by acrylamide for β-LG cross-linked by TG in the presence of Cys [22], it was observed that initial K_{app} value from Stern-Volmer plots is higher than that obtained for β-LG without any treatment and in the absence of Cys, as the presence of this reducing agent breaks disulfide bonds, making the opening of the protein structure easier. The effectiveness of the quenching process, measured through the K_{app} values, increased with the length of enzymatic treatment, verifying a minimum value for the initial time, and a maximum after 60 min of incubation time with TG. The K_{app} increment during the TG treatment can be ascribed to the presence of a percentage of non-native monomers and an increasing percentage of irreversibly formed aggregates of low molecular weight of unfolded molecules. The slight decrease in K_{app} value for 180 min of incubation time with TG is coherent with the presence of aggregates of high molecular weight whose compact structure could reduce Trp accessibility (Figure 2).

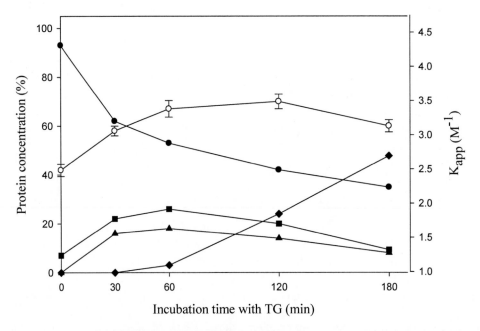

Figure 2. Protein concentrations (%) of different species formed incubating β-LG solutions with TG in the presence of Cys for different periods of time (0, 30, 60, 120 and 180 min): monomers (●), dimers (■), trimers (▲) and aggregates larger than trimers (oligomers and polymers) (♦). (○) K_{app} (M^{-1}) from the Stern-Volmer graphs at different times of incubation with TG.

It has been noted that the most significant conformational change was verified and the greatest amount of dimers and trimers was produced at 60 min of incubation with TG, pointing out this time as the critical one for this enzymatic treatment. Moreover, at this time, a proportion of different species of β-LG was: monomer 53%, dimer 26%, trimer 18% and larger aggregates 3%, which is very similar to the species proportion that was found in the critical time identified for heat treatment. Since two different critical times were identified for each treatment, 3 min for heat treatment and 60 min for the enzymatic one, from now on, the protein sample heated during 3 min is calling HT-β-LG and the sample enzymatically treated for 60 min, is calling TG-CL-β-LG [22].

COMPLEMENTARY STUDIES

Complementary studies (urea unfolding profiles and intrinsic viscosity studies) were carried out specifically for the following selected samples: β-LG (without any treatment), β-LG-Cys (treated with 0.07 M Cys), TG-CL-β-LG, HT-β-LG.

UREA UNFOLDING PROFILES

Equilibrium unfolding curves using urea is a convenient method to estimate the conformation stability of a protein [34]. Chemical unfolding profiles on the previously mentioned β-LG samples, in the presence of urea, were performed following previous works developed for our group [31,35]. A series of urea solutions, from 0 to 8 M, in 20 mM sodium phosphate buffer at pH 6.8, were assayed. The mixtures of each pre-treated β-LG solution with urea solutions were made in order to obtain a final protein concentration of 0.13 mg mL^{-1}. With the aim to determine the λ_{max} for each sample, fluorescence emission spectra were carried out, using an excitation wavelength of 295 nm.

Assuming a two-state model [36,37,38], in which a species of a protein possesses only two different conformational states with different values of an observed property (Y), the fraction of protein with a conformational change (F_U), at any given urea concentration, can be determined from the following equation:

$$F_U = \frac{Y - Y_{MIN}}{Y_{MAX} - Y_{MIN}} \tag{2}$$

where Y_{MIN} and Y_{MAX} are the observed property values in 0 and 8 M urea, respectively. In the present work, λ_{max} values were used as the observed property Y. The parameter used in this assay is $[urea]_{1/2}$, the urea concentration capable of changing the conformation of the 50% of protein molecules, which corresponds to F_U value of 0.5.

Urea promotes unfolding by both indirect and direct mechanisms. Direct urea interactions consist of hydrogen bonding to the polar moieties of the protein, particularly peptide groups, leading to screening of intramolecular hydrogen bonds. Solvation of the hydrophobic core proceeds via the influx of water and urea molecules. Urea also promotes protein unfolding in an indirect way by altering water structure and dynamics, as also occurs on the introduction of nonpolar groups to water, thereby diminishing the hydrophobic effect and facilitating the exposure of the hydrophobic core residues. Overall, urea-induced effects on water indirectly contribute to unfolding by encouraging hydrophobic solvation, whereas direct interactions provide the pathway [39, 40].

INTRINSIC VISCOSITY

Intrinsic viscosity is a measure of the hydrodynamic volume a molecule occupies. Intrinsic viscosity was measured with an Ostwald capillary viscometer in a controlled temperature water bath (25 ± 0.1 °C). The water draining time was 89.44 s. To determine intrinsic viscosity of each sample, draining times of β-LG solutions of five different concentrations, between 10 and 60 mg mL^{-1}, were measured. Two measurements for each concentration were performed [22]. On the basis of the well-known Huggins equation:

$$\frac{\eta_i}{C} = [\eta] + k \cdot [\eta]^2 \cdot C \tag{3}$$

where η_i is the viscosity increment, C is the concentration of protein (g mL^{-1}) and [η], the intrinsic viscosity, was determined from the extrapolation of the plot of η_i / C versus C [41].

STRUCTURAL CHANGES IN THE β-LG AS AN EXPLANATION OF THE CHANGES IN ITS ALLERGENICITY: COMPARISON BETWEEN HEATING AND ENZYMATIC TREATMENTS

The differences between K_{app} for β-LG without any treatment and values of K_{app} for treated β-LG, which are directly related to unfolding degree, are shown in Table 1 [22]. The minimum K_{app} value is verified for native β-LG and the maximum, for β-LG chemically denatured with the highest concentration of urea, when the protein reaches its greater de-naturation state. Between these extremes, it can be observed that K_{app} decreased in the following order: HT-β-LG > TG-CL-β-LG > β-LG-Cys. These results point at the presence of a residual structure that hinders the full Trp residues accessibility to the acrylamide in these species.

The obtained [urea]$_{1/2}$ values incremented in the following order: HT-β-LG < TG-CL-β-LG < β-LG-Cys < β-LG , as it is shown in Table 1. The higher the value of [urea]$_{1/2}$, the more difficult the disruption on protein structure. In the case of β-LG-Cys, the observed conformational changes demonstrated that the rupture of disulfide bonds by the Cys as reducing agent, did not involve extensive unfolding of β-LG molecules. On the other hand, native β-LG presented an intrinsic viscosity value of 3.7 mL g^{-1} (Table 2) [22], which corresponds to a compact and globular spherical protein, regardless of their molecular weight [42].

A value 19% higher than this was presented by β-LG-Cys. This increment can be due to an increase of the molecular hydrodynamic volume of the protein, because of the loss of native structure caused by disruption of disulfide bonds [38]. Besides, this moderate increment is coherent with the moderate conformational changes found in fluorescence studies.

Table 1. Fluorescence studies for the selected β-LG samples: Kapp and [urea]$_{1/2}$

Treatment	K_{app} (M^{-1})	$[urea]_{1/2}$ (M)
β-LG [a]	1.97 ± 0.18	4.88 ± 0.10
β-LG-Cys [b]	2.48 ± 0.15	4.66 ± 0.15
TG-CL-β-LG	3.35 ± 0.12	4.30 ± 0.05
HT-β-LG	3.74 ± 0.10	4.09 ± 0.08
β-LG + urea[c]	12.05 ± 0.10	-

Table 2. Intrinsic viscosity for the selected β-LG samples

Sample	$[\eta]$ $(mL\ g^{-1})$
β-LG	3.7 ± 0.2
β-LG-Cys	4.4 ± 1.3
TG-CL-β-LG	6.0 ± 0.9
HT-β-LG	9.2 ± 1.0

The highest value of intrinsic viscosity was obtained for HT-β-LG, followed by a lower value for TG-CL-β-LG (Table 2). These results are consistent with the effects produced by heating [43]: the formation of larger species, with larger effective volume fraction than native molecules and, more important in terms of viscosity, aggregates that are more asymmetric in shape. On the other hand, TG-CL-β-LG generates a more compact structure [44,45] and then, less asymmetric aggregates which lead to a lower intrinsic viscosity value.

De la Fuente, Singh and Hemar [46] have reviewed several different mechanisms that have been developed for the thermal denaturation/aggregation of β-LG. Regardless of the proposed mechanism, some events must be considered during the heating process. Firstly, a critical conformational change in the β-LG monomer exposes the free sulfhydryl group (Cys 121). This reactive group in the modified molecule can induce thiol/disulfide exchange reactions, leading to the formation of disulfide-linked aggregates. The disulfide linkage involved in the intermolecular interchange reaction would most likely be the Cys66-Cys160, which is found in one of the external loops of β-LG. The other disulfide is buried in the inner parts of the protein and is less available for reaction [47,48]. In addition to this aggregation by covalent intermolecular disulfide bonds, non-covalent interactions (ionic, van der Waals, hydrophobic) may also be involved. The contribution of non-covalent interactions will become of increasing importance with pH values closer to the isoelectric point and/or with higher salt concentrations, but these were not the environmental conditions assayed in the present work. Therefore, in the first stage of heat-induced denaturation/aggregation of β-LG, in the absence of added salt and near neutral pH, denatured monomers were linearly linked to form intermediate oligomers (di-, tri- and tetramers) via intermolecular disulfide-bond reactions [49,50].

The secondary structure of native β-LG consists of nine β-strands (~ 50%), a single α-helix (~15%), several turns (~20%), and random arrangements (~15%) [51]. During thermal treatment, the hydrogen bonds which stabilized the native structure of β-LG are broken, causing a loss of α-helix and β-sheets structures, creating new intermolecular β-sheets arrangements and enhancing the exposition of hydrophobic residues to the solvent [21,52, 53].

The treatment with TG promotes ε-(γ-glutamyl)lysine bonds and causes aggregation of the protein, leading to high molecular weight species. In the case of subsequently applying both treatments, heating and then enzymatic TG cross-linking, Eissa et al. [52] suggested that a low number of bonds had been created, in spite of the potential number of bonds which could be formed according to the glutamine and lysine residues present in the backbone of β-LG (glutamine and lysine residues per β-LG molecule are 9 and 15, respectively).

On one hand, large aggregates formed by heating β-LG at low ionic strength, the condition assayed, seem to be open in contrast to structures formed at salt concentrations larger than 0.1 M that appear much denser [49,54]. On the other hand, Tanimoto et al. (1988) [45] have shown that aggregates produced by TG treatment of β-LG in the presence of another denaturant, like dithiothreitol, contains intramolecular bonds that impede unfolding of the molecules upon heating, hence suggesting a compact nature of the polymerized β-LG molecules.

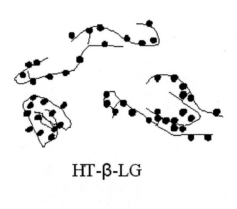

HT-β-LG

TG-CL-β-LG

Figure 3. Possible structures of different species of β-LG produced by heating treatment (HT-β-LG) and TG treatment (TG-CL-β-LG). Hydrophobic residue (●).

As it shown in Figure 3, the different spatial rearrangement of the molecules of β-LG is very different according to the employed treatment. As consequence of heat treatment, HT-β-LG presents a higher degree of unfolding with a greater exposition of hydrophobic residues to the solvent, leading to a higher index of surface hydrophobicity, a less compact structure and a more asymmetrical form of the aggregates formed. This particular higher exposition of amino acid residues can explain the observed increment of digestibility, since it leads to a major accessibility of the epitopes structures to be damaged and consequently, the decay of the allergenicity is more likely.

As it also can be seen in Figure 3, the TG treatment leads to the formation of aggregates of β-LG, and then TG-CL-β-LG presents a less degree of unfolding, with a lesser exposition of hydrophobic residues to the solvent, a minor index of surface hydrophobicity, a more compact structure and a more symmetrical form of the aggregates formed. All these structural changes hide the antigenic sites, diminishing their exposition and then, a decay of allergenicity is verified. Besides, these changes also make the digestibility of the milk protein was less important.

To sum up, the specific results about allergenicity of the main milk protein, β-LG, can be satisfactorily explained by the results obtained when protein structural changes that were studied [21,22].

REFERENCES

[1]   Foegeding, E.A., Davis, J.P., Doucet, D., and Mc Guffey, M.K. (2002). Advances in modifying and understanding whey protein functionality. *Trends in Food Science and Technology*, 13, 151-159.

[2]   Huang, Q., Coleman, J.W.,and Stanworth, D.R. (1985). Investigation of the allergenicity of β-lactoglobulin and its cleavage fragments. *International Archives of Allergy and Applied Immunology*, 78, 337-344.

[3]   Otani, H. (1987). Antigenically reactive regions of bovine milk proteins. *Agriculture Research Quarterly*, 21, 135-142.

[4]   Okamoto, M., Hayashi, R., Enomoto, A., Kaminogawa, S., and Yamauchi, K. (1991). High pressure proteolytic digestión of food proteins: Selective elimination of β-lactoglobulin in bovine milk whey concentrate. *Agricultural and Biological Chemistry*, 55, 1253-1257.

[5]   Sélo, I., Negroni, L., Creminon, C., Yvon, M., Peltre, G., and Wal, J.M. (1998). Allergy to bovine β-lactoglobulin specificity of human IgE using cyanogen bromide-derived peptides. *International Archives of Allergy and Applied Immunology*, 117, 20-28.

[6]   Reddy, I.M., Kella, N.K.D., and Kinsella, J.E. (1988). Structural and conformational basis of the resistance of β-lactoglobulin to pectic and chymotryptic digestion. *Journal of Agricultural and Food Chemistry*, 36, 737-741.

[7]   Sorva, R., Makinen-Kiljunen, S., and Juntunen-Backman, K. (1994). Beta-lactoglobulin secretion in human milk varies widely after cow's milk ingestion in mothers of infants with cow's milk allergy. *Journal of Allergy and Clinical Immunology*, 93, 787-792.

[8] Yvon, M., Van Hille, I., Pelissier, J.P., Guilloteau, P., and Toullec, R. (1984). In vivo milk digestión in the calf abomasum. *Reproduction, Nutrition, Development*, 24, 835-843.

[9] Guo, M.R., Fox, P.F., Flynn, A.,and Kindstedt, P.S. (1995). Susceptibility of β-lactoglobulin and sodium caseinate to proteolysis by pepsin and trypsin. *Journal of Dairy Science*, 78, 2336-2344.

[10] Peyron, S., Mouecoucou, J., Fremont, S., Sanchez, C., and Gontard, N. (2006). Effects of heat treatment and pectin addition on β-lactoglobulin allergenicity. *Journal of Agricultural and Food Chemistry*, 54, 5643-5650.

[11] Kleber, N., Krause, S., Illgner, S., and Hinrichs, J. (2004). The antigenic response of β-lactoglobulin is modulated by thermally induced aggregation. *European Food Research and Technology*, 219, 105-110.

[12] Vegarud, G.E, Langsrud, T., and Svenning, C. (2000). Mineral-binding milk proteins and peptides; occurrence, biochemical and technological characteristics. *Journal of Nutrition,* 84(1), 91-98.

[13] Restani, P., Veloná, T., Plebani, A., Ugazio, A.G., Poiesi, C., Murano, A., and Galli, C.L. (1995). Evaluation by SDS-PAGE and immunoblotting of residual antigenicity in hydrolysed protein formulas. *Clinical and Experimental Allergy: Journal of the British Society for Allergy and Clinical Immunology*, 25, 651-658.

[14] Van Berensteijn, E.C.H., Meijer, R.J.G.M., and Schmidt, D.G. (1995). Residual antigenicity of hypoallergenic infant formulae and the occurrence of milk specific IgE antibodies I patients with clinical allergy. *Journal of Allergy and Clinical Immunology*, 96, 365-374.

[15] Calvo, M.M., and Gómez, R. (2002). Peptidic profile, molecular mass distribution and immunological properties of comercial hypoallergenic infant formulas. *Milchwissenschaft*, 57, 187-190.

[16] Babiker, E.F., Hiroyuki, A., Matsudomi, N., Iwata, H., Ogawa, T., and Bando, N. (1998). Effect of polysaccharide conjugation or transglutaminase treatment on the allergenicity and functional properties of soy protein. *Journal of Agricultural and Food Chemistry*, 46, 866-871.

[17] Clare, D.A., Gharst, G., and Sanders, T.H. (2007). Transglutaminase polymerization of peanut proteins. *Journal of Agricultural and Food Chemistry*, 55, 432-438.

[18] Battaglin Villas-Boas, M., Viera, K.P., Trevizan, G., de Lima Zollner, R., and Netto, F.M. (2010). The effect of transglutaminase-induced polymerization in the presence of cysteine on β-lactoglobulin antigenicity. *International Dairy Journal*, 20, 386-392.

[19] Watanabe, J., Tanabe, S., Watanabe, M., Shinmoto, H., and Sonoyama, K. (2004). The production of hypoallergenic wheat flour and the analysis of its allergy suppressive effects. *Biofactors*, 22, 295-297.

[20] Wróblewska, B., Jedrychowski, L., Hajós, G., and Szabó, E. (2008). Influence of alcalase and transglutaminase on immunoreactivity of cow milk whey proteins. *Czech Journal of Food Science*, 26, 15-23.

[21] Moro, A., Báez, G.D., Busti, P.A., Ballerini, G.A, and Delorenzi, N.J. (2011). Effects of heat-treated β-lactoglobulin and its aggregates on foaming properties. *Food Hydrocolloids*, 25 (5),1009-1015.

[22] Báez, G.D.; Moro, A.; Ballerini, G.A.; Busti, P.A.; Delorenzi, N.J. (2011). Comparison between structural changes of heat-treated and transglutaminase cross-linked beta-lactoglobulin and their effects on foaming properties. *Food Hydrocolloids*, 25 (7), 1758-1765.

[23] Wal, J.M. (2002). Cow's milk proteins/allergens. *Annals of Allergy, Asthma and Immunology*, 89, 3-10.

[24] Wal, J.M. (2001). Structure and function of milk allergens. *Allergy*, 56, 35-38.

[25] Taylor, S.L., and Lehrer, S.B. (1996). Principles and characteristics of food allergens. *Critical Reviews in Food Science and Nutrition*, 36, 91-118.

[26] Paschke, A., and Besler, M. (2002). Stability of bovine allergens during food processing. *Annals of Allergy, Asthma and Immunology*, 89, 16-20.

[27] Baldo, B.A. (1984). Milk allergies. *Australian Journal of Dairy Technology*, 39, 120-128.

[28] Lee, Y.H. (1992). Food processing to altering allergenic potential of milk based formula. *Journal of Pediatrics*, 121, 47.

[29] Hoffmann, M.A.M., Roefs, S.P.F.M., Verheul, M., Van Mil, P.J.J.M., and Kruif, K.G. (1996). Aggregation of β-lactoglobulin studied by in situ light scattering. *Journal of Dairy Research*, 63, 423-440.

[30] Roos, N., Lorenzen, P.C., Sick, H., Schrezenmeir, J., and Schlime, E. (2003). Cross-linking by transglutaminase changes neither the in vitro proteolysis nor in vivo digestibility of caseinate. *Kieler Milchwirtschaftliche Forschungsberichte*, 55, 261-276.

[31] Moro, A., Gatti, C. A., and Delorenzi, N. J. (2001). Hydrophobicity of whey protein concentrates measured by fluorescence quenching and its relation with surface functional properties. *Journal of Agricultural and Food Chemistry*, 49(10), 4784-4789.

[32] Eissa, A.S., Bisram, S., and Khan, S.A. (2004). Polymerization and gelation of whey protein isolates at low pH using transglutaminase enzyme. *Journal of Agricultural and Food Chemistry*, 52(14), 4456-4464.

[33] Faergemand, M., Otte, J., and Qvist, K.B. (1997). Enzymatic cross-linking of whey protein by Ca $^{+2}$-independent microbial transglutaminase from Streptomyces lydicus. *Food Hydrocolloids*, 11, 19-25.

[34] Shirley, B.A. Urea and guanidine hydrochloride denaturation curves. In B.A. Shirley, *Protein stability and folding, theory and practice*. New Jersey: Humana Press Inc., 1995, pp. 177-190.

[35] Busti, P. A., Scarpeci, S., Gatti, C. A., and Delorenzi, N. J. (2005). Binding of alkylsulfonate ligands to bovine β-lactoglobulin: effects on protein denaturation by urea. *Food Hydrocolloids*, 19(2), 249-255.

[36] Pace, N.C. (1986). Determination and analysis of urea guanidine hydrochloride denaturation curves. *Methods in Enzymology*, 131, 266-280.

[37] Pace, N.C. (1990). Conformational stability of globular proteins. *Trends in Biochemical Sciences*, 15 (1), 14-17.

[38] Tanford, C. (1968). Protein denaturation. *Advances in Protein Chemistry*, 23, 121-282.

[39] Bennion, B.J., and Daggett, V. (2003). The molecular basis for the chemical denaturation of proteins by urea. *Proceedings of the National Academy of Sciences of the United States of America*, 100(9), 5142-5147.

[40] Rossky, P.J. (2008). Protein denaturation by urea. *Proceedings of the National Academy of Sciences of the United States of America*, 105(44), 16825-16826.

[41] Tanford, C. (1961). Transport processes, viscosity. In C. Tanford, *Physical Chemistry of Macromolecules* (pp. 318-338). New York: John Wiley and Sons, INC.

[42] Ross-Murphy, S.B. (1994). Rheological methods. In S.B. Ross-Murphy, *Physical Techniques for the Study of Biopolymers* (pp. 343-392). Glasgow: Blackie Academic and Professional.

[43] Vardhanabhuti, B., and Foegeding, E.A. (1999). Rheological properties and characterization of polymerized whey protein isolates. *Journal of Agricultural and Food Chemistry*, 47(9), 3649-3655.

[44] Matsumura, Y., Lee, D-S., and Mori, T. (2000). Molecular weight distributions of α-lactalbumin polymers formed by mammalian and microbial tranglutaminases. *Food Hydrocolloids*, 14(1), 49-59.

[45] Tanimoto, S-Y., and Kinsella, J.E. (1988). Enzymatic modification of proteins: effects of transglutaminase cross-linking on some physical properties of β-lactoglobulin. *Journal of Agricultural and Food Chemistry*, 36(2), 281-285.

[46] De la Fuente, M.A., Singh, H., and Hemar, Y. (2002). Recent advances in the characterization of heat-induced aggregates and intermediates of whey proteins. *Trends in Food Science and Technology*, 13(8), 262-274.

[47] McKenzie, H.A., Ralston, G.B., and Shaw, D.C. (1972). Location of sulhydryl and disulfide groups in bovine β-lactoglobulins and effects of urea. *Biochemistry*, 11(24), 4539-4547.

[48] Papiz, M.Z., Sawyer, L., Eliopoulos, E. E., North, A. C., Findlay, J. B., Sivaprasadarao, R., Jones, T. A., Newcomer, M. E., and Kraulis, P.J. (1986). The structure of beta-lactoglobulin and its similarity to plasma retinol-binding protein. *Nature*, 324(6095), 383-385.

[49] Bauer, R., Carrotta, R., Rischel, C., and Ogendal, L. (2000). Characterization and isolation of intermediates in β-lactoglobulin heat aggregation at high pH. *Biophysical Journal*, 79(2), 1030-1038.

[50] Croguennec, T., O'Kennedy, B. T., and Mehra, R.(2004). Heat-induced denaturation/aggregation of β-lactoglobulin A and B: kinetics of the first intermediates formed. *International Dairy Journal*, 14(5), 399-409.

[51] Boye, J.I., Ismail, A.A., and Alli, I. (1996). Effect of physico-chemical factors on the secondary structure of beta-Lactoglobulin. *Journal of Dairy Research*, 63(1), 97-109.

[52] Eissa, A.S., Puhl, C., Kadla, J.F., and Khan, S.A. (2006). Enzymatic cross-linking of β-lactoglobulin: conformational properties using FTIR spectroscopy. *Biomacromolecules*, 7 (6), 1707-1713.

[53] Kim, D.A., Cornec, M., and Narsimhan, G. (2005). Effect of thermal treatment on interfacial properties of beta-lactoglobulin. *Journal of Colloid and Interface Science*, 285(1), 100-109.

[54] Foegeding, E.A., Bowland, E.L., and Hardin, C.C. (1995). Factors that determine the fracture properties and microstructures of globular protein gels. *Food Hydrocolloids*, 9(4), 237-249.

In: Whey: Types, Composition and Health Implications   ISBN: 978-1-61942-862-1
Editors: Rafael M. Benitez and Gustavo M. Ortero   © 2012 Nova Science Publishers, Inc.

Chapter 8

BEHAVIOUR OF WHEY PROTEINS AS FAT REPLACERS IN LOW-FAT FOOD PRODUCTS

Bárbara E. Meza[1], Roxana A. Verdini[1, 2] and Amelia C. Rubiolo[1]

[1]Instituto de Desarrollo Tecnológico para la Industria Química, Consejo Nacional de Investigaciones Científicas y Técnicas, Universidad Nacional del Litoral, Santa Fe, República Argentina

[2]Departamento de Química Analítica, Facultad de Ciencias Bioquímicas y Farmacéuticas, Universidad Nacional de Rosario e Instituto de Química Rosario, Rosario, República Argentina

ABSTRACT

Whey proteins are used as fat mimetics in low-fat food manufacture in order to improve sensorial quality of the final product. The success of whey proteins as fat replacers lies in the potential capacity of these proteins to imitate the human sensory perception of fat. For example, whey proteins can be incorporated in foods as micro-particles. Microparticulated whey proteins have a mean particle size in the order of homogenized fat globules. As a result, the use of whey proteins as fat replacers in low-fat foods (for example cheeses, ice creams, and yogurts) has made it possible to achieve sensory characteristics similar to full-fat products with a reduction in the fat content and beneficial health implications. The present chapter is a brief review about the use of whey proteins as fat replacers in low-fat food products concerning the physicochemical, rheological, and functional properties.

INTRODUCTION

Available evidence suggest that high dietary fat intake (specially saturated fat) has been implicated in the etiology of obesity, that is associated with cardiovascular diseases, type 2 diabetes, hypertension, and certain types of cancers (Poirier et al., 2006). Therefore, a tendency to consume low-fat foods is growing around the world to achieve health benefits.

The development of low-fat products is being a priority for a large number of food companies.

However, the reduction of the lipid content can cause negative effects on food sensory characteristics considering that fat imparts desirable appearance, flavour, mouthfeel, and texture in traditional foods (Lucca and Tepper, 1994). Some strategies were implemented by food industries in order to improve the sensory characteristics of low-fat food products. For instance, the use of fat mimetics (a type of fat replacer that imitates the organoleptic and physical properties of fat molecules in food systems but with considerably less calories) was reported (Jones, 1996). Fat mimetics are ingredients of carbohydrate or protein origin, being whey proteins one example of protein-based fat mimetic.

Whey proteins are the nitrogenous compounds that remain soluble in whey after the isoelectric precipitation of caseins at pH 4.6 (de Wit, 1981), which are generally recognized as safe (GRAS) products by the Food and Drug Administration (FDA, 2011). In general, depending on the total protein content, whey proteins are commercialized as isolates (WPI) and concentrates (WPC). For example, WPC have protein contents between 30 to 85%.

It is known that whey proteins have specific functional properties, like gelling, water-holding, emulsifying, and foaming capacity apart from good solubility in a high pH range (de Wit et al., 1988; Ennis and Mulvihill, 2000). Some of those functional properties have been proven attractive for the use of whey proteins as fat replacers. However, additional processing conditions, like controlled heat treatment and microparticulation, need to be incorporated in order to improve their potential use as fat mimetics. Modified whey proteins or microparticles have the potential capacity for imitating the human sensory perception of fat, because they have a mean particle size (1 to 3 μm) in the range of homogenized fat globules (Singer, 1996). Whey proteins are suitable for low-fat dairy products (like yogurts and cheeses), salad dressings, and frozen desserts (Lobato-Calleros et al., 2004; McMahon et al., 1996; Liu et al., 2007; Ruger et al., 2002). Also, whey proteins can be used in foods that undergo cooking and baking (El-Magoli et al., 1996; Zoulias et al., 2002).

The present chapter is a brief review about the use of whey proteins as fat replacers in low-fat food products concerning the physicochemical, rheological, and functional properties.

EFFECT OF WHEY PROTEINS IN FOOD TEXTURE

Textural properties of foods are a group of physical characteristics that derive from their structural elements. These properties are related to the deformation, disintegration, and flow of the food under a force, and they are measured objectively by functions of mass, time, and distance (Bourne, 2002). This way, textural properties are related to the mechanical and the rheological properties.

Textural and rheological properties of low-fat foods can be improved by the addition of whey proteins (Rubiolo and Carrara, 2010). As it was discussed before, whey proteins have good water and fat-binding capacities and they have the potential ability for imitating the human sensory perception of fat. In many low-fat food products that are cooked or heated for further consumption, like ground beef patties and cookies, a good moisture and fat entrap-ment is desirable (El-Magoli et al., 1996; Zoulias et al., 2002). On the other hand, in low-fat ready-to-eat products, like frozen desserts and cheeses, it is important to maintain the mouthfeel and creaminess that is characteristic of the full-fat food version (Sahan et al., 2008; Prindiville et al., 2000). Examples of commercial whey protein-based fat replacers are shown in Table 1.

The water-binding capacity of whey proteins is associated with their gelling properties. It is known that whey proteins partially unfold and aggregate at temperatures over 70 °C (de Wit et al., 1988). Protein content, pH, salt concentration, and heating conditions (like time and temperature) play an important role in determining whether this reaction will yield the formation of soluble aggregates or a gel structure. For instance, low concentrations (< 10%) and moderate temperatures (60 to 90 °C) support the formation of small soluble aggregates that bind water and increase the viscosity of the food. Nevertheless, protein concentrations between 10 to 12% and heat treatments in the range of 70 to 90 °C, favour the formation of gels (Lucca and Tepper, 1994). An illustration representing the denaturation and aggregation process of heat-treated whey proteins is shown in Figure 1.

Moreover, considering that foods that contain whey proteins as fat replacers can be frozen, Meza et al. (2010a) characterized the viscoelastic behaviour of whey protein suspensions containing small and soluble aggregates that underwent the freezing process. In this case, a decrease in the range of viscous behaviour of heat-treated suspensions was observed, possibly because freeze-concentration and ice crystal formation could produce the modifycation or disruption of the structure of the small soluble protein aggregates. On the other hand, freezing produced an increase in the range of viscous behaviour of unheated suspensions, probably due to protein aggregation that occurred during freezing.

The fat-binding capacity of whey proteins is related to their emulsifying properties. The amphiphilic nature of whey proteins confers increased water solubility, good surface-active and emulsion-stabilizing properties (Sullivan et al., 2008). During emulsion formation, whey proteins diffuse to the oil-water interface and the hydrophobic groups expand into the oil phase, allowing the hydrophilic groups to extend into the aqueous phase. This phenomenon reduces the interfacial tension and stabilizes the emulsion, increasing the opportunities for fat-protein interactions (Lucca and Tepper, 1994).

In order to improve the whey protein functionality, like the ability for imitating the human sensory perception of fat, aggregation under controllable denaturing conditions (time and temperature) and microparticulation process were developed. A flow diagram with the principal steps of the microparticulation process is presented in Figure 2. Basically, this process involves the heating of proteins to produce a gel structure. However, protein aggregates produces large particles, which are perceived as rough in the mouth. Instead, if a high shearing force is applied during the heating of proteins, small and spherical (0.1-2.0 μm diameter) protein gel particles are produced. These microparticles are similar to fat with a creamy and smooth texture (O'Connor and O'Brien, 2011). In addition to textural benefits, micoparticulated whey proteins (MWP) inhibit syneresis and increase the water-binding capacity of low-fat foods.

**Table 1. Examples of commercial whey protein-based fat replacers
(adapted and extended from Jones, 1996)**

Whey protein-based fat replacer	Trade mark	Manufacturer	Possible applications
Microparticulated whey protein	Simplesse®	NutraSweet Kelco Company (San Diego, California, USA)	Dairy products (ice cream, cheese, yogurt), salad dressings, spreads, sauces, toppings, frostings, baked goods
	LeanCreme®	APV SPX Corporation (Silkeborg, Denmark)	
Partially denatured whey protein concentrate	Dairy-Lo®	Pfizer Food Science Group (New York, USA)	Milk/dairy products (cheese, yogurt, sour cream, ice cream), spreads

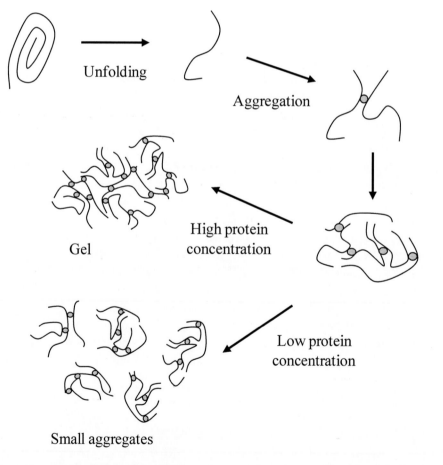

Figure 1. Illustration representing the denaturation and aggregation process of heat-treated whey proteins (adapted and extended from Aguilera, 1995).

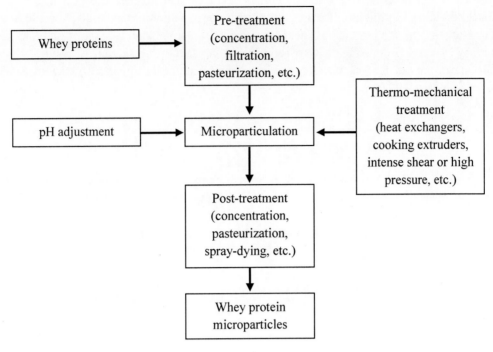

Figure 2. Flow diagram of microparticulated whey proteins manufacture process (adapted and extended from Sanchez and Paquin, 1997).

A number of commercial products have been developed based on the microparticulation process. The first patent was created by NutraSweet Co. with the trade mark Simplesse[®] (NutraSweet Co., Deerfield, IL, USA). Simplesse[®] is obtained from WPC, which is thermo-coagulated at pH 3.7-4.2 and then neutralized in a shear apparatus designed by Singer et al. (1988). However, other operation conditions for obtaining MWP where found in literature. For example, Sanchez and Paquin (1997) obtained MWP using high pressure homogenization of a pre-heated WPC. Microfluidization carried out immediately after heat aggregation of proteins under quiescent conditions yielded MWP. Another device suitable for the micro-particulation process is a scraped surface heat exchanger, where the heating of WPC at 80 °C with subsequently cooling under a high shearing load was carried out in order to produce protein aggregates of about 10 µm (Spiegel, 1999).

Other process has been developed by APV SPX Corporation in Silkeborg (Denmark), involving ultra-filtration of whey followed by a combination of heat treatment and special mechanical treatment of the concentrate (Mounsey et al., 2009). This process enables the production of LeanCreme[TM]. In addition, aggregation under controlled denaturing conditions (time and temperature) allowed to develop a fat replacer called Dairy-Lo[®] (Pfizer Food Sc. Group, New York, USA). Dairy-Lo[®] is a WPC that was heat treated until a considerable de-naturation of proteins is achieved (60-80%).

Concerning on the structural implications, whey protein microparticles can act as active or inert fillers in food systems, although this hypothesis has not been completely elucidated (Torres et al, 2011). The remaining native protein that is present in MWP product could interact with caseins, as well as other native proteins, and thus be integrated into the protein network as active filler. In addition, MWP maintain good solubility although they are denatured whey proteins. This phenomenon can be attributed to the following factors: (1) optimal defolding of protein molecules during thermal denaturation under acidic conditions, because any disulphide interaction is excluded, and (2) thermal stabilization of the defolded status by lactose. Both effects were considered to favour non-covalent bonds, which contribute to the outstanding physicochemical, functional and nutritive properties of MWP (Lieske and Gerd, 1994).

APPLICATION IN LOW-FAT FOODS

Whey proteins are a suitable ingredient in the manufacture of a large variety of low-fat foods. Examples of this kind of products found in literature are shown in Table 2.

**Table 2. Examples of low-fat food products elaborated
with whey protein-based fat replacers found in literature**

Low-fat food product	Whey protein-based fat mimetic	Reference
Yogurts	Microparticulated whey proteins (Simplesse®) and whey protein concentrate	Lobato-Calleros et al. (2004); Sandoval-Castilla et al. (2004)
	Microparticulated whey proteins (Simplesse®) and partially denatured whey protein concentrate (Dairy Lo®)	Yazici and Akgun (2004)
	Microparticulated whey proteins	Torres et al. (2011)
Ice-creams	Partially denatured whey protein concentrate (Dairy Lo®)	Prindiville et al. (2000); Ruger et al. (2002)
	Whey protein isolate	Akalln et al. (2008)
Cheeses	Microparticulated whey proteins (Simplesse®)	Romeith et al. (2002); Sahan et al. (2008); Meza et al. (2010b, 2011)
	Partially denatured whey protein concentrate (Dairy Lo®)	Zalazar et al. (2002)
	Microparticulated whey proteins (Simplesse®) and partially denatured whey protein concentrated (Dairy Lo®)	McMahon et al. (1996)
Beef hamburgers	Whey protein concentrate	El-Magoli et al. (1996); Desmond et al. (1998)
Meatballs	Whey powder (13% protein)	Serdaroğlu (2006)
Cookies	Microparticulated whey proteins (Simplesse®)	Zoulias et al. (2002)

Yogurt

Low-fat yogurts, as traditional full-fat yogurts, are dairy products obtained from the lactic fermentation of milk (Lucey et al., 1998) whose structure can be described as an acidic gel network of aggregated caseins enclosing fat globules and serum. According to Walstra et al. (2006), the rheological behaviour of yogurt is similar to a viscoelastic solid. However, if the gel structure is broken, like for example in the stirred yogurt making process, a viscous non-Newtonian fluid can be formed.

Changes in yoghurt fat content can modify the textural and rheological properties. Therefore, the use of whey proteins as ingredient in the manufacture process of different types of low-fat yogurts has been reported. In order to study the effect of several whey protein-based fat replacers (like Simplesse® and whey protein concentrate powder) in the microstructure and texture of low-fat yogurts, Sandoval-Castilla et al. (2004) performed instrumental texture profile analysis. From scanning electron micrographs, those authors observed that casein micelles were predominantly linked by particle-particle interactions in yogurts made with WPC. However, yogurts made with Simplesse® showed a spatial dis-tribution of casein micelles similar to regular full-fat yogurt, in which MWP formed part of the protein matrix. On the other hand, yogurts made with WPC and blends of WPC and MWP generated samples with similar textural characteristics of full-fat yogurts. In addition, yogurts made with MWP showed lower tension and firmness but higher cohesiveness than control full-fat yogurts. In the same way, Lobato-Calleros et al., (2004) evaluated the effect of WPC and MWP in the flow and the creep compliance properties of low-fat yoghurts. Results obtained by those authors indicated that different fat replacers provided diverse effects in improving the protein network of low-fat yoghurt. For example, the addition of WPC pro-duced a protein network structure with flow and viscoelastic properties similar to the full-fat version. However, the incorporation of MWP alone or combined with WPC did not improve the rheological properties of low-fat yoghurt.

Another kind of low-fat yoghurt, strained yoghurt (a semisolid product made from yoghurt by removing some part of its serum) has been studied taking into account the effect of whey proteins addition. Yazici and Akgun (2004) analyzed the use of Simplesse® and Dairy Lo® in this type of yoghurts, comparing their physical, chemical, and sensory pro-perties during storage. According to the textural and rheological parameters obtained in the study, samples made with Dairy-Lo® presented higher viscosity than samples made with Simplesse®. On the other hand, Torres et al. (2011) investigated the effect of several types of MWP products as fat replacers (with different particle sizes and denaturation degree) on the rheological and sensory characteristics of stirred yoghurts. Those authors published that yogurts made with MWP had high creaminess and viscosity (with high yield stress and elastic modulus), a slow meltdown in the mouth, as well as creamy flavour and low syneresis than control yogurts. These results emphasized that the degree of denaturation of the whey protein included in the MWP powders that were used as fat replacer is important for the sensory and rheological properties of yoghurts.

Ice Cream

Low-fat dairy ice creams are a type of complex colloidal food system consisting of edible ice, mixtures of water, flavour ingredients, and other components which are partly frozen and beaten to form a rigid foam. Components like sugar, milk, and fat present in the traditional full-fat product have importance in the ice cream quality. Specially, fat content has importance in the ice cream flavour, in the formation of a solid structure during freezing, and therefore in the consistency, appearance, and melting resistance (Walstra et al., 2006).

The use of whey proteins as ingredient in the elaboration process of different types of low-fat ice creams has been reported. Ruger et al. (2002) studied the effect of double homogenization and the incorporation of WPC (substituted for 1% non-fat dry milk) on ice crystal size in different ice creams. In this study, the icy texture defect was evident as ice crystals grow throughout storage, indicating that 1% WPC replaced by 1% non-fat dry milk in ice creams mix did not improve the texture of these products by sensory evaluation. In the same way, Prindiville et al. (2000) determined the effect of cocoa butter and whey protein-based fat replacers (Simplesse® and Dairy-Lo®) on the sensory properties of low-fat and non-fat chocolate ice creams. Hardness, viscosity, and melting rate were measured by physical methods. Simplesse® acted less similar to milk fat than Dairy Lo® in fresh ice cream in terms of thickness and mouthcoating. Also, during 12 weak of storage, Simplesse® was more successful in reducing the development of icy texture than Dairy-Lo®. In addition, Akalln et al. (2008) evaluated the rheological properties of regular, reduced, and low-fat ice creams preparing reduced-fat and low-fat ice creams with WPI and inulin as fat replacers. The apparent viscosity, consistency coefficient, flow behaviour index, hardness, and melting characteristics were measured. The results obtained in this work indicated that WPI affected the rheological properties of reduced-fat and low-fat ice creams, resulting in significantly higher apparent viscosities, consistency indexes, and greater deviations from a Newtonian flow. In addition, both hardness and melting resistance increased in reduced-fat and low-fat ice creams by using WPI.

Cheese

Traditional or full-fat cheeses of all varieties are characterized by a protein matrix interspersed with fat globules. Caseins are the main constituent that builds cheese structure, while fat content affects the microstructure of cheese (Gunasekaran and Ak, 2003). Low-fat cheeses have less and smaller fat globules within the protein network. As consequence, the structure of the low-fat cheeses is dominated by proteins, having firm and rubbery body and texture (Mistry, 2001).

Numerous studies related to the use of whey protein-based fat replacers in several low-fat cheese varieties have been found in literature. Romeith et al. (2002) evaluated the changes in composition, proteolysis, texture, and sensory properties of low-fat White-Brined cheese made with a carbohydrate-based and a protein-based (Simplesse®) fat replacers. Textural parameters (for instance hardness, gumminess, and chewiness) were obtained from texture profile analysis (TPA). The authors observed that the mean values of TPA parameters and the maximum stress (at 80% deformation on uniaxial compression) of low-fat cheeses were significantly lower than those obtained in full-fat cheeses used as control samples, suggesting a great improvement in cheese texture when fat replacers were included in low-fat formulas. Sahan et al. (2008) evaluated the quality of low-fat Kashar cheese made with fat replacers of carbohydrate and whey protein (Simplesse®) origin. Cheeses made with fat replacers were compared with full-fat cheeses used as control samples during 90 days of ripening. The results obtained in this work indicated that the use of fat replacers in the manufacture of low-fat Kashar cheese increased water binding capacity, improved overall quality of the cheeses, and enhanced cheese proteolysis. In addition, texture attributes and meltability increased significantly with addition of fat replacers. Zalazar et al. (2002) evaluated the sensory and rheological properties of Cremoso Argentino low-fat soft cheese containing Dairy-Lo® as fat replacer. In this study oscillatory measurements, like frequency sweeps, were performed. Those authors indicated that the high moisture content of cheeses made with Dairy-Lo® was a problem for the shelf life of this product, as a consequence of the extensive softening observed after 30 days of ripening. In relation to cheese microstructure, McMahon et al. (1996) studied a low-fat Mozzarella cheese made with whey protein-based fat replacers (Simplesse® and Dairy Lo®) and evaluated the location of the fat replacer in the cheese matrix, using scanning electron microscopy. According to the results obtained by those authors, the distribution of the fat replacers within the cheese was influenced by the extent of microparticulation, size of the fat replacer particles and processing steps that caused an interaction between the fat replacer and the caseins in milk. Apparent viscosity of cheeses at 80°C was not significantly affected by addition of fat replacers. Cheeses made with Simplesse® had higher overall meltability than cheeses made with Dairy-Lo®. Also, no discrete Dairy-Lo® particles were observed in the protein matrix, indicating a low level of microparticulation (particles < 0.2 pm) of the proteins in Dairy-Lo®.

In order to study the effect of the freezing process (freezing at -25 °C, frozen storage at -25 °C during 33 days, and thawing at 6 °C) on the viscoelastic behaviour during the ripening of a commercial low-fat soft cheese made with Simplesse® as fat replacer, Meza et al. (2011) performed frequency sweeps in the linear viscoelastic region. The obtained results were compared with refrigerated low-fat cheeses used as control samples (Meza et al., 2010b). In this case, frequency dependency of viscoelastic data was evaluated using power-law equations ($G'=a\omega^x, G''=b\omega^y$). The freezing process produced an increase the viscous behaviour and a decrease in values of coefficient a of power-law equation. However, the decay rate of coefficient a during the studied ripening period was not influenced by this process. In addition, the freezing process produced an increase in the maturation index (MI) of cheeses. In this case, MI values increased from 3.6 to 10.24% in control cheeses and from 4.09 to 12.97% in frozen cheeses during 76 days of ripening, being MI values of frozen cheeses higher than refrigerated cheeses.

Other Foods

Meat-based foods are other type of products where fat can be replaced by whey protein-based fat mimetics. For instance, low-fat ground beef patties formulated with WPC powder as fat replacer were studied, evaluating the cooking characteristics in comparison with control samples with higher fat content (El-Magoli et al., 1996). Those authors indicated that WPC powder at the 4% level can be effectively used as a functional ingredient in low-fat beef patties due to its heat gelation and emulsification properties, which enhance moisture and fat entrapment. These phenomena resulted in an increased ground beef patties cooked yield, fat and moisture retention, and resistance to shrinkage. In addition, Desmond et al (1998) analyzed the effects of varying levels of WPC powder (with tapioca starch and oat fibre) on the physical, texture, and sensory characteristics of low-fat beef burgers. In this study, response surface methodology was used to characterize the simultaneous effects of the three ingredients. Significant models of regression were checked for cooking properties (yield and water holding capacity), sensory attributes (tenderness and juiciness), and mechanical texture attributes. The obtained results indicated that both whey protein and oat fibre had a limited influence in those parameters. Serdaroğlu (2006) evaluated the effect of whey powder as fat replacer in Turkish type meatballs prepared with different levels of beef fat (5%, 10%, and 20%). In this study, cooking characteristics, juiciness, colour parameters, and sensory properties were evaluated. The authors observed that the addition of whey powder as fat replacer (2% or 4%) significantly increased cooking yield (regardless of the fat level) and increased fat and moisture retention of meatballs. In addition, whey powder had no detrimental effect on sensory properties.

Cookies are other type of products where fat can be replaced by whey protein-based fat mimetics. Texture, flavour, and appearance are the main quality attributes of cookies and fat is an important ingredient in the cookie making-process, because it contributes with the texture and mouthfeel. The effect of carbohydrate or protein-based fat mimetics (Simplesse®) on rheological and textural properties of cookies has been reported (Zoulias et al., 2002).The effect of the type of fat mimetic and the percentage of fat replacement on the textural behaviour of this kind of products was studied by compression tests. In this case, the obtained stress-strain curves were fitted by an exponential equation containing parameters as the maximum stress, the maximum strain, and a viscoelastic exponent. As a result, simple mathematical model for maximum stress and the ratio of maximum stress/maximum stress (indicative of hardness and brittleness of the cookies), was developed. The published results indicated that hardness and brittleness of cookies generally increased with fat replacement.

CONCLUSION

The growing tendency to consume low-fat food products, due to the possible benefits for human health, implicates a challenge for the food industries. In those companies, the developing of low-fat products with similar sensory characteristics of the original full-fat food version is a priority. This way, the use of fat replacers is considered an alternative. The success of whey proteins used as fat replacers is related to their specific functional properties, like water and fat binding capacity. Also, in order to improve the whey protein functionality, like the ability for imitating the human sensory perception of fat, aggregation under controlled denaturing conditions (time and temperature) and microparticulation process were improved. Those treatments facilitate the addition of whey proteins in the elaboration process of foods. Consequently, the use of whey proteins as fat replacers in low-fat food products has made it possible to achieve similar sensory quality of the full-fat food version, but with beneficial healthy implications, like less calories.

ACKNOWLEDGMENT

This chapter was griten with the financial support of Universidad Nacional del Litoral, Consejo Nacional de Investigaciones Científicas y Técnicas and the Agencia Nacional de Promoción Científica y Tecnológica of Argentina.

REFERENCES

Aguilera, J. M. (1995). Gelation of whey proteins. *Food Technology*, 49, 83-89.

Akalln, A. S.; Karagözlü, C.; Ünal, G. (2008). Rheological properties of reduced-fat and low-fat ice cream containing whey protein isolate and inulin. *European Food Research and Technology*, 227, 889-895.

Bourne, M. C. (2002). *Food texture and viscosity: concept and measurement*. Academic Press, San Diego, California, USA.

de Wit, J. N. (1981). Structure and functional behaviour of whey proteins. *Netherlands Milk and Dairy Journal*, 35, 47-64.

de Wit, J. N.; Hontelez-Backx, E.; Adamse, M. (1988). Evaluation of functional properties of whey protein concentrates and whey protein isolates. 3. Functional properties in aqueous solution. *Netherlands Milk and Dairy Journal*, 42, 155-172.

Desmond E. M.; Troy D. J.; Buckley, D. J. (1998). The effects of tapioca starch, oat fibre and whey protein on the physical and sensory properties of low-fat beef Burgers. *Lebensmittel-Wissenschaft und-Technologie*, 31, 653- 657.

El-Magoli, S. B.; Laroia, S.;Hanse, P. M. T. (1996). Flavor and texture characteristics of low fat ground beef patties formulated with whey protein concentrate. *Meat Science*, 42, 179-193.

Ennis, M. P.; Mulvihill, D. M. (2000). *Milk proteins. In Handbook of Hydrocolloids*. G. O. Phillips and P.A. Williams (Editors). CRC Press LLC., Cambridge, UK.

FDA Whey protein concentrate 21 CFR 184.1979C. (2011). U.S. Government Printing Office, Washington, D.C., USA.

Gunasekaran, S.; Ak, M. M. (2003). *Cheese rheology and texture*. CRC Press LLC., Florida, USA.

Jones, S. (1996). Classified list of fat replacers and their applications. In *Handbook of Fat Replacers*. S. Roller and S. A. Jones (Editors). CRC Press LLC., New York, USA.

Jones, S. (1996). Issues in fat replacement. In *Handbook of Fat Replacers*. S. Roller andS. A. Jones (Editors). CRC Press LLC., New York, USA.

Lieske, B.; Gerd, K. (1994). Microparticulation of whey protein: related factors affecting the solubility. *Z LebensmUntersForsch*, 199, 289-293.

Liu H.; Xu, X. M.; Guo, S. D. (2007). Rheological, texture and sensory properties of low-fat mayonnaise with different fat mimetics. *Lebensmittel-Wissenschaft und-Technologie,*40, 946-954.

Lobato-Calleros, C.; Martínez-Torrijos, O.; Sandoval-Castilla, O.; Perez-Orozco, J. P.; Vernon-Carter, E. J. (2004). Flow and creep compliance properties of reduced-fat yoghurts containing protein-based fat replacers. *International Dairy Journal*, 14, 777-782.

Lucca, P. A.; Tepper, B. J. (1994). Fat replacers and the functionality of fat in foods. *Trends in Food Science & Technology*, 51, 12-19.

Lucey, J. A.; Singh, H. (1998). Formation and physical properties of acid milk gels: a review. *Food Research International*, 30, 529-542.

McMahon, D. J.; Alleyne, M. C.; Fife, R. L.; Oberg, C. J. (1996). Use of fat replacers in low fat Mozzarella cheese. *Journal of Dairy Science*, 79, 1911-1921.

Meza, B. E.; Verdini R. A.; Rubiolo, A. C. (2011). Effect of freezing on the viscoelastic behaviour during the ripening of a commercial low-fat soft cheese. *International Dairy Journal*, 21, 346-351.

Meza, B. E.; Verdini, R. A.; Rubiolo, A. C. (2010a). Effect of freezing on the viscoelastic behaviour of whey protein concentrate suspensions. *Food Hydrocolloids*,24, 414-423.

Meza, B. E.; Verdini, R. A.; Rubiolo, A. C. (2010b). Viscoelastic behavior during the ripening of a commercial low-fat soft cheese. *Dairy Science and Technology*, 90, 589-599.

Mistry, V. V. (2001). Low fat cheese technology. *International Dairy Journal*, 11, 413-422.

Mounsey, J. S.; O'Kennedy, B. T.; Corrigan, B.; Kelly, P. M.; O'Callaghan, D. J. (2009). Effect of microparticulated whey protein addition on the heat stability and rennet/acid gelling properties in model milk systems. *Milchwissenschaft*, 64, 14-17.

O'Connor, T. P.; O'Brien, N. M. (2011). *Fat replacers. In Encyclopedia of Dairy Sciences*. J. W. Fuquay, P. F. Fox and P. L. H. McSweeney (Editors). Academic Press, Oxford, UK.

Poirier, P.; Giles, T. D.; Bray, G. A.; Hong, Y.; Stern, J. F.; Pi-Sunyer, X.; Eckel, R. H. (2006). Obesity and cardiovascular disease: pathophysiology, evaluation, and effect of weight loss. *Circulation*, 113, 898-918.

Prindiville, E. A.; Marshall, R. T.; Heymann, H. (2000). Effect of milk fat, cocoa butter, and whey protein fat replacers on the sensory properties of low-fat and non-fat chocolate ice cream. *Journal of Dairy Science*, 83, 2216-2223.

Romeih, E.A.; Michaelidou, A.; Biliaderis, C. G.; Zerfiridis, G. K. (2002). Low-fat white-brined cheese made from bovine milk and two commercial fat mimetics: chemical, physical and sensory attributes. *International Dairy Journal*, 12, 525-540.

Rubiolo A. C; Carrara C. R. (2010). Estrategias para utilizar proteínas del lactosuero para mejorar aspectos de la alimentación y el rendimiento en la cadena de productos lácteos de la región pampeana argentina. In *Strumenti per la Garanzia Della Qualitádei Prodottu Agroalimentari:* Analisi Tecnico-Economica per le Filiere Lattiero-Caseare, dell´Olio d´Oliva e del Vino. A. Frascareli (Editor). Universitá degli Studi di Perugia, Perugia, Italy.

Ruger, P. R.; Baer, R. J.; and Kasperson, K. M. (2002). Effect of double homogenization and whey protein concentrate on the texture of ice cream. *Journal of Dairy Science*, 85, 684-692.

Sahan, N.; Yasar, K.; Hayaloglu, A. A; Karaca, O. B.; Kaya, A. (2008). Influence of fat replacers on chemical composition, proteolysis, texture profiles, meltability and sensory properties of low-fat Kashar cheese, *Journal of Dairy Research*, 75, 1-7.

Sanchez, C.; Paquin, P. (1997). Protein and protein-polysaccharide microparticles. In *Food Proteins and their Applications*. S. Damodaran and A. Paraf (Editors). Marcel Dekker Inc., New York, USA.

Sandoval-Castilla, O.; Lobato-Calleros, C.; Aguirre-Mandujano, E.; Vernon-Carter, E. J. (2004). Microstructure and texture of yogurt as influenced by fat replacers. *International Dairy Journal,* 14, 151-159.

Serdaroğlu, M. (2006). Improving low-fat meatball characteristics by adding whey powder. *Meat Science,* 72, 155-163.

Singer, N. S. (1996). Microparticulated proteins as fat mimetics. In *Handbook of Fat Replacers.* S. Roller and S. A. Jones (Editors). CRC Press LLC., New York, USA.

Singer, N. S.; Yamamoto, S.; Latella, J. (1988). *Protein product base. European Patent Applied* N° 0.250.623.

Spiegel, T. (1999). Whey protein aggregation under shear conditions - effects of lactose and heating temperatures on aggregate size and structure. *International Journal of Food Science and Technology,* 34, 523-531.

Sullivan, S. T.; Khan, S. A.; Eissa, A. S. (2008). Whey proteins: functionality and foaming under acidic conditions. In *Whey Processing, Functionality and Health Benefits.* Ch. L. Onwulata and P. J. Hulth (Editors). John Wiley & Sons, Iowa, USA.

Torres, I. C.; Janhøj, T.; Mikkelsen, B. Ø.; Ipsen, R. (2011). Effect of microparticulated whey protein with varying content of denatured protein on the rheological and sensory characteristics of low-fat yoghurt. *International Dairy Journal,* 21, 645-655.

Walstra, P.; Wouters, J. T. M.; Geurts, T. J. (2006). *Dairy science and technology.* CRC Press, Boca Raton, USA.

Yazici, F.; Akgun, A. (2004). Effect of some protein based fat replacers on physical, chemical, textural, and sensory properties of strained yoghurt. *Journal of Food Engineering,* 62, 245-254.

Zalazar, C. A.; Zalazar, C. S.; Bernal, S.; Bertola, N.; Bevilacqua, A.; Zaritzky, N. (2002). Effect of moisture level and fat replacer on physicochemical, rheological and sensory properties of low fat soft cheeses, *International Dairy Journal,* 12, 45-50.

Zoulias, E. I.; Oreopoulou, V.; Tzia, C. (2002). Textural properties of low-fat cookies containing carbohydrate- or protein-based fat replacers. *Journal of Food Engineering,* 55, 337-342.

In: Whey: Types, Composition and Health Implications   ISBN: 978-1-61942-862-1
Editors: Rafael M. Benitez and Gustavo M. Ortero   © 2012 Nova Science Publishers, Inc.

Chapter 9

AN OVERVIEW OF THE BIOLOGICAL ACTIVITIES OF WHEY PROTEINS AND PEPTIDES

Lubna Ahmed * *and N. N. Misra*

School of Food Science and Environmental Health,
Dublin Institute of Technology,
Sackville Place, Dublin, Ireland

ABSTRACT

Whey proteins and their associated peptides in addition to their nutritional and functional attributes possess immense potential as functional and nutraceutical food ingredients owing to their biological activities. These encompass their antioxidant, chelation, antihypersensitive, anticarcinogenic, hypolipidemic, immune system stimulition, ACE inhibition, antiviral and antibacterial activities. An upsurge in the research activities associated with the investigation of the bioactivity and further corroboration of proven bioactivities of whey proteins and peptides has been evidenced by the scientific community in recent times. Further, the data from clinical studies has already set the pace for use of whey proteins and their associated peptides as functional food ingredients/ nutraceuticals. The current chapter provides an overview of the developments with respect to the potentially beneficial human health effects of whey proteins and their peptides. The therapeutic benefits stemming out of the biological activities have also been emphasised with a discussion of the supportive clinical trials.

INTRODUCTION

Milk contains two primary sources of protein (milk has nearly 3.5% protein), viz. caseins (~80% of total proteins) and whey (~20% of total proteins). Whey is a protein complex derived from milk containing all the essential amino acids, with the highest protein quality rating among other proteins. Milk whey is an abundant by-product in cheese manufacture

---

*Corresponding Author: Lubna Ahmed, Phone: +35314024442, Fax: +35314024495, e-mail: lahmed@dit.ie

(8.5–9 L of whey are produced from 10 L of milk during cheese making), which makes it an inexpensive source of high nutritional quality protein for uses as a physiologically functional food ingredient. Apart from the fact that whey represents 85-90% of the total volume of used milk, it also becomes particularly relevant due to the fact that the whey retains around 55% of the original nutrients of the milk (Abboud *et al.*, 2010). The general composition of whey is 93% of water and 7% of solid matter, which is comprised of lactose (5-6%), proteins (0.8-1%), lipids, minerals and vitamins (Abboud *et al.*, 2010). The high lactose content is the main reason why whey is considered to be a highly pollutant product, with a BOD (Biological Oxygen Demand) of 50 g/L and a COD (Chemical Oxygen Demand) of 80 g/L. Whey was formerly considered as a waste emerging from cheese and curd manufacturing industries. This waste was either discarded or sold at low value as a feedstock or used as a fermentation feedstock for the production of organic acids acid, ethanol, and single cell proteins. These applications still do not utilize all the whey produced and new uses for this by-product are continually being sought. Whey contains many components which if utilised effectively could allow processors to recover much of its untapped potential. Ever since the discovery of its health benefits and nutritional properties, it has been assigned "functional food" status. The biological components of whey include β-lactoglobulin, α-lactalbumin, bovine serum albumin, lactoferrin, immunoglobulins, lactoperoxidase enzymes, glycomacropeptides, lactose, and minerals.

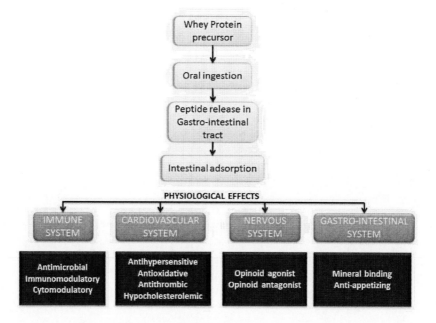

Figure 1. Physiological framework of bioactivity of whey peptides (Adapted from Madureira *et al.*, 2010).

Most of these components of whey demonstrate a range of immune-enhancing properties. Today, whey is a popular dietary protein supplement purported to provide antimicrobial activity, immune modulation, improved muscle strength and body composition, and to prevent cardiovascular disease and osteoporosis (Marshall, 2004). Hydrolysis of whey pro-teins is known to release bioactive peptides that can trigger a number of physiological effects in human body. Bioactive peptides have been studied by means of the following investigation techniques: establishment of an assay system to determine biological activity, hydrolysis of proteins by digestive enzymes, the isolation of peptides and the determination of the structures and synthesis of peptides for the verification of activity (Anne 2000). To exert physiological effects *in vivo*, bioactive peptides must be released during intestinal digestion and must then reach their target sites at the luminal side of the intestinal tract or after absorption in the peripheral organs (Anne, 2000). A physiological framework for the bioactivity of whey peptides is presented in Figure 1.

An Overview of Whey Proteins

The major proteins that have been identified in milk whey are β-lactoglobulin, α-lactalbumin, serum albumin, immunoglobulins and glycomacropeptide, while minor proteins include lactoperoxidase, lactoferrin, β-microglobulin, lysozyme, insulin-like growth factor (IGF), γ-globulins and several other small proteins. β-lactoglobulin is a major whey protein that corresponds to approximately half of the total whey proteins in bovine milk. It is a small, soluble globular protein with a variety of useful nutritional and functional-food characteristics that have made it an ingredient of choice in the formulation of modern foods and beverages. It exhibits a growing number of biological effects including anti-hypertensive, anti-cancer, hypocholesterolemic, opiodergic, and anti-microbial activities (Yalcin, 2006). α-lactalbumin is another major whey protein making up to 25% of total bovine whey protein. It is also a rich source of the amino acids - lysine, leucine, threonine, tryptophan and cysteine (Permyakov and Berliner, 2000). Both α and β-Lactoglobulin possess calcium binding ability. Lactalbumin is a protein specifically produced during lactation in mammary epithelial cells and it generally remains stable even after pasteurisation. Serum albumins in whey bind fatty acids and other small molecules. Immunoglobulins in whey include IgG1, IgG2, IgA and IgM. Glycomacropeptide, the glycosylated portion of casein-macropeptide, is present in sweet whey formed after cleavage of κ-casein by rennin (Brody, 2000). Whey peptides with molar masses in the range 1–2 kg/mol have been reported to possess biological activity and they are suitable for use in baby food due to their lack of allergenicity. Some of these peptides have been reported to naturally occur in whey, in addition to those cleaved from inactive protein precursors during milk processing (Clare and Swaisgood, 2000). A summary of the biological activities of milk proteins is presented in Figure 2. The biological activities of whey proteins have been discussed in the following sections and their therapeutic benefits also highlighted.

Lactoferrin and its peptide product, lactoferricin, demonstrate strong anti-microbial activity in tissue culture and animal studies. These compounds, in combination with lysozome, another element that can be isolated from whey, provide a "cocktail" with apparently synergistic protective activity against viral and bacterial organisms (Ha and Zemel, 2003). A number of short peptides with high bactericidal activity have been developed from the bactericidal domains of α-lactalbumin and β-lactoglobulin as well as lactoferrin. Immunoglobulins are the best-known of the whey components that provide antimicrobial action in the intestinal tract. IgG has been shown to bind the toxin produced by *Clostridium difficile*, thereby reducing the deleterious effects of infection (Warny *et al.*, 1999). Bovine milk/whey also contains significant amounts of nonproteic bioactive components, such as sphingolipids and fatty acids, which regulate diverse biological functions, even at low concentrations (Jensen, 2002).

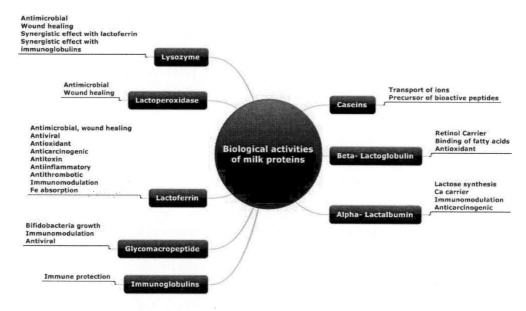

Figure 2. Summary of biological activities of milk proteins.Antimicrobial activity.

Antimicrobial activity has also been associated with the nonproteic bioactive components. Indeed, in vitro digestion products of whey-derived sphingolipids and triglycerides enriched in capric and lauric acids exhibit bactericidal effects and thus may protect against food-borne gastroenteritis. Whey antimicrobial peptides were reported to act against different gram-positive and gram-negative bacteria (*Escherichia, Helicobacter, Listeria, Salmonella* and *Staphylococcus*), yeasts and filamentous fungi (Rizzello *et al.*, 2005; Fitzgerald and Murray, 2006).

ACE Inhibitory Activity

Angiotensin I-converting enzyme (peptidyl dipeptide hydrolase, EC 3.4.15.1) is associated with the renin-angiotensin system, which regulates peripheral blood pressure. Angiotensin-I converting enzyme (ACE) raises blood pressure by converting the inactive decapeptide angiotensin-I, to the potent vasoconstrictor octapeptide angiotensin-II, as well as inactivating the vasodilating nonapeptide. Inhibition of ACE may exert an antihypertensive effect as a consequence of the decrease of angiotensin-II as well as increase of bradykinin. It has been reported that cheese whey digested with proteinase K has a depressive effect on systolic blood pressure (-55 mm Hg). Further, the tripeptide Ile-Pro-Ala (β-lg f(78–80)) has been associated with highest antihypertensive activity among the identified active peptides (Abubakar *et al.*, 1998). Powerful ACE inhibitory hydrolysates were obtained from whey protein after hydrolysis with trypsin (Ferreira et al. 2008) and α-chymotrypsin (Da Costaa *etal.*, 2007). Guo *et al.* (2009) investigated the effect of process conditions on the angiotensin-I converting enzyme (ACE) inhibitory activity of whey protein concentrate hydrolysed with crude proteinases preparation from *L. helveticus* LB13 using response surface methodology and obtained high ACE inhibitory activity close to 92.2% in optimal conditions (enzyme to substrate ratio at 0.60, pH at 9.18 and temperature at 38.9°C). Pan *et al.* (2012) found that the whey fraction with molecular weight of <6 kDa had the greatest ACE inhibitory activity. The authors then separated the <6 kDa fraction into four further fractions on a Sephadex G-25 for gel filtration chromatography and found that the highest ACE inhibitory activity of the four fractions were 72.31%. To this end, most studies on ACE-inhibiting activity of whey proteins have been conducted in vitro. It is worth mentioning that high ACE-inhibiting activity in vitro does not necessarily imply a high antihypersensitive activity in vivo.

Opioid Activity

Peptides such as enkephalins, which have an affinity for an opiate receptor as well as opiate-like effects, inhibited by naloxone are referred to as opioid peptides. Whey proteins contain opioid-like sequences in their primary structure, namely α-la, f (50–53) and β-lg (bovine) f (102–105). These peptides have been termed α- and β-lactorphins (Feeney et al., 1986). α- and β-lactorphin have been found to displace ^{3}H-naloxone from its binding sites at micromolar concentrations. β-lactotensin is yet another opioid peptide that has been identified in whey.

Thus, these peptides bring about a decrease of blood pressure by blocking opioid receptor antagonist naloxone. The peptide Albutensin exhibits opioid activity by complementing C3a and C5a receptor. Opiates are reported to influence gastrointestinal function in two ways: first, they affect the smooth muscles, which reduces transit time and second, they affect the intestinal transport of electrolytes, which explains their antisecretory properties (Anne, 2000).

In spite of these proven bioactivities based on in vivo studies, it should be noted that currently there is no evidence for the liberation of lactorphins or β-lactotensin during gastrointestinal digestion.

Immunomodulatory Activity

The role of human immune system is pivotal in defence against pathogenic micro-organisms. Some of the proteins isolated and purified from whey have been shown to be potent modulators of cellular immune function; these include lactoperoxidase, lactoferrin, and milk growth factor. Cross and Gill (1999) derived a modified whey protein concentrate (mWPC), as a by-product from the commercial manufacture of cheese and tested for its ability to modulate murine immune function in vitro.

They reported that the mWPC suppressed T and B lymphocyte proliferative responses to mitogens in a dose-dependent fashion. Additionally, this mWPC also suppressed alloantigen-induced lymphocyte proliferation during a mixed leucocyte reaction.

These results support the immunosuppressive activity of modified whey proteins. In addition to being sources of immunoglobulins viz. IgG1, IgG2, IgA and IgM and glutamine, whey may also provide other "immunonutrients" to protect against infection. Other whey based immune-modulating compounds include β-lactoglobulin, the major protein fraction of whey, β-lactalbumin, and their associated peptides (Walzem *et al.*, 2002). Bounous *et al.*

(1989) have shown that the immunoenhancing activity of the dietary whey protein concentrate is related, at least in part, to greater production of splenic glutathione in the "bioactive" whey-protein fed animals during the oxygen-requiring antigen – driven clonal expansion of the lymphocyte pool.

Antioxidant Activity

Dairy proteins and peptides have been associated with antioxidant activity since long. Some of the recent studies to isolate and identify antioxidant potential of proteins, peptides and hydrolysates derived from dairy sources has been summarised in Table 1.

Table 1. Recent studies on isolation and identification of antioxidant potential of proteins, peptides and hydrolysates derived from dairy sources

Source	Treatment(s)	Antioxidant activity	Reference
Whey protein concentrate (WPC) enriched in β-lactoglobulin	Corolase PP and Thermolysin	Radical scavenging potency (measured as Trolox equivalent)	Contreras et al. (2011)
Whey protein isolate (WPI)	Alcalase treatment at different concentrations and times	Radical-scavenging ability, greater Cu^{2+} chelating ability and improved reducing power; Superoxide and Hydroxyl radical scavenging activity	Peng et al. (2009); (2010)
Whey protein concentrate (WPC)	-No treatments-	DPPH radical scavenging activity and Fe^{2+} chelating capability; combination with Spirulina has synergistic effects	Gad et al. (2011)
Yoghurt peptides	Peptides are formed when milk is fermented to yoghurt	DPPH radical-scavenging activity, iron-chelating activity, and reducing power	Farvin et al. (2010)
Cheddar cheeses	Water extraction followed by fractionation	DPPH radical scavenging activity.	Pritchard et al. (2010)
Milk	Action of microbial proteases viz. validase from Aspergillus oryzae, alkaline protease from Bacillus licheniformis, and neutral protease from Bacillus subtilis	Oxygen radical absorbance capacity (ORAC, using Trolox); DPPH scavenging activity; Fe^{2+} chelating activity	Hogan et al. (2009)
Whey powder	Pepsin and Trypsin	Superoxide radical scavenging activity	Bayram et al. (2008)
Sodium caseinate	Alcalase treatment followed by chemical methods to obtain caseinophospho-peptides	Oxygen radical absorbance capacity (ORAC), reduction capacity and metal chelating activity	Kim et al. (2007)

Lactoferrin is only 8-30% saturated in its native state, which allows chelation of iron and subsequent inhibition of bacterial growth or oxidative reactions.

Further, whey enhances antioxidant capacity by contributing cysteine rich proteins which are lynchpin in the synthesis of glutathione, a major intracellular antioxidant (Walzem et al., 2002). Previous studies have shown that whey contains a broad range of antioxidant activity in an iron-catalysed liposome oxidation system (Pena-Ramos and Xiong, 2003) or a copper-catalysed liposome emulsion (Colbert and Decker, 1991), depending on the proteases used. Casein phosphopeptides (CPPs), derived from casein, possess a potential cytoprotective effect against H_2O_2-induced oxidative stress by preserving cell biology and enzyme-mediated antioxidant systems (Laparra et al., 2008).

They have been shown to bind pro-oxidant metals, such as iron and to inhibit lipid oxidation as metal chelators (Kim et al., 2007). Therefore, they can be utilised as natural antioxidants in oil-in-water emulsions to decrease oxidative rancidity in foods (Diaz et al., 2004).

In addition, casein trypsin digests showed inhibitory properties in the oxidation of linoleate by lipoxygenase, peroxyl radicals and 2,20-azinobis-(3-ethylbenzothiazoline-6-sulphonic acid (ABTS) radical (Rival et al., 2001). (Mao et al., 2010) suggested that casein hydrolysate possesses free-radical-scavenging and anti-inflammatory activities, and thus it can possibly be used in the prevention of oxidative stress and inflammation related disorders.

Regulation of Food Intake and Satiety

Whey may offer a nutritional advantage towards achieving a desirable body composition beyond that of promoting lean body mass accretion.

Whey provides amino acids to promote muscle protein synthesis in combination with dairy minerals which can assist in limiting body fat accumulation and, therefore, may confer specific advantages towards optimizing body composition (Ha and Zemel, 2003).

The calcium and mineral content found in certain whey products can potentially mediate body composition by shifting nutrient partitioning from adipose to lean tissue. Certain amino acids and whey-derived bioactive compounds offer the potential to extend health benefits to active people beyond body composition.

Many of the functions associated with these amino acids and whey components involve the immune system and may therefore be of particular importance to athletes in intensive training, as several studies demonstrate an immunosuppressive effect of vigorous or excessive training (Nieman, 2000). Respiratory tract infections, gastrointestinal health, and free radical production are issues of concern given the evidence that implicates physical exertion as an influential factor in these conditions.

Promotion of Gastrointestinal Health

Whey peptides and amino acids including glutamine are generally believed to be associated with some functionality in the gut. The use of whey as a carrier for other probiotics has already gained place among the interests of supplement manufacturers.

There are four beneficial areas of intestinal health modification with whey components: prebiotic effects, antimicrobial and antiviral properties, anticancer properties and influences on immunity. Glycomacropeptide and lactoferrin in whey have been found to support the growth of Bifidobacteria and demonstrate prebiotic activity (Harper, 2004). IgG may withstand proteolytic degradation in the intestinal tract, which is useful for preventing gastrointestinal infections of newborns.

Table 2. Examples of biologically functional peptides derived from bovine whey proteins

Precursor protein	Peptide Name	Function	References
α-lactalbumin	α-lactorphin	Opioid agonist, ACE-inhibition	Antila et al., 1991; Mullaly et al., 1996
β-lactoglobulin	β-lactorphin, β-lactotensin	Non-opioid stimulatory effect on ileum, ACE-inhibition, Ileum contraction	Antila et al., 1991; Mullaly et al., 1996; Pihlanto-leppala, 1997
Bovine serum albumin	Serorphin, Albutensin A	Opioid, Ileum contraction, ACE-inhibition	Tani et al., 1994; Yamauchi, 1992
Lactoferrin	Lactoferricin	Antimicrobial	Bellamy et al., 1992

Use of Whey in Food as Antioxidant and Antimicrobial Agent

Whey proteins and peptides are commonly used in the food industry due to their wide range of chemical, physical and functional properties. The most important functional properties of whey proteins and peptides are viscosity, water holding capacity, viscosity and emulsification (Almecija *et al.*, 2007). Whey hydrolysates applied to cooked meat pork patties could suppress lipid oxidation (Pena-Ramos and Xiong, 2003). Hernández-Ledesma *et al.* (2005) reported that individually both hydrolysed lactalbumin and lactoglobulin could act as antioxidants. Coronado *et al.* (2002) used rosemary extract and whey powder for the oxidative stability of wiener sausages during 10 months frozen storage and they found improved sensory scores as compared to wieners without additional antioxidant. They suggested that whey powder could have acted as a potential antioxidant. Whey has shown to be a promising alternative to chlorine for decontamination of fruits and vegetables during storage (Ahmed *et al.* 2011a, b, c). This is especially important as the possible formation of carcinogenic chlorinated compounds in water (chloramines and trihalomethanes) has called into question the use of chlorine in food products (Alegria *et al.*, 2010). The authors have screened a number of whey permeates and identified delactosed permeate (DP) as the most efficient for the preservation of the physico-chemical and nutritional value of fresh produce. The optimum concentration of the DP treatment was 3%, as at this concentration tomato slices retained a good appearance and overall quality and sensory scores for aroma and colour attributes were not reduced (Ahmed *et al.*, 2011d, e). DP was also found to enhance the antioxidant compounds in canned tomatoes (Ahmed *et al.*, 2011f). Whey has also been successfully used as a natural sanitizing agent of fresh-cut lettuce and carrots (Martin-Diana *et al.* 2006).

Challenges and Future Needs

At present the main challenge in the production of bioactive peptides from milk whey by enzymatic hydrolysis in vitro is finding the suitable enzyme and hydrolysis conditions that enhance the bioactivity and yield in their production. Studies on investigation of the efficacy and safety of bioactive peptides by carrying out animal studies in order to verify the effects and clarify adverse effects must be emphasised in future studies. The hydrolysis of most food proteins, especially the hydrolysis of whey and casein containing products is known to generate bitterness.

This causes palatability problems particularly when attempting to formulate orally ingestible products incorporating milk protein hydrolysates as a source of bioactive peptides. Further research is required for the recovery and characterization of the low-molecular peptides of whey and on their impact upon human health – as these peptides may play important physiological functions, as well as modulates a few regulatory processes. Methods to isolate these compounds commercially are also needed in order to bring these bioactive peptides to the market.

Additionally, studies are needed on their use in the formulation of novel nutraceutical ingredients and functional foods.

REFERENCES

Abboud, M. M., Aljundi, I. H, Khleifat, K. M. and Dmour, S. (2010). Biodegradation kinetics and modeling of whey lactose by bacterial haemoglobin VHb-expressing *Escherichia coli* strain. *BiochemicalEngineering Journal*, 48, 166–172.

Abubakar, A., Saito, T., Kitazawa, H., Kawai, Y. and Itoh, T. (1998). Structural analysis of new antihypertensive peptides derived from cheese whey protein by proteinase K digestion. *Journal of Dairy Science*, 81 (12), 3131-3138.

Ahmed, L., Martin-Diana, A. B., Rico, D. and Barry-Ryan, C. (2011a). The antioxidant properties of whey permeate treated fresh-cut tomatoes. *FoodChemistry*, 124, 1451–1457.

Ahmed, L., Rico, D., Martin-Diana, A. B. and Barry-Ryan, C. (2011b). Optimization of application of delactosed whey permeate treatment to extend the shelf-life of fresh-cut tomato using response surface methodology. *Journal of Agricultural and Food Chemistry*, 59, 2377–2385.

Ahmed, L., Martin-Diana, A. B., Rico, D. and Barry-Ryan, C. (2011c). Quality and Nutritional Status of Fresh-cut Tomato as Affected by Spraying of Delactosed Whey Permeate Compared to Industrial Washing Treatment. *Food and Bioprocess Technology*, *DOI*: 10.1007/s11947-011-0623-6.

Ahmed, L., Rico, D., Martin-Diana, A. B. and Barry-Ryan, C. (2011d). Extending the Shelf-Life of Fresh-Cut Tomato Using By-Product from Cheese Industry. Journal of Food Processing and Preservation, *DOI*: 10.1111/j.1745-4549.2011.00562.x.

Ahmed, L., Martin-Diana, A. B., Rico, D. and Barry-Ryan, C. (2011e). The Impact of Whey Permeate Treatment on Shelf-life and Antioxidant Content of Strawberries. International *Journal of Food Science andTechnology* (accepted).

Ahmed, L., Patras, A., Martin-Diana, A. B., Rico, D. and Barry-Ryan, C. (2011f). The Effect of Delactosed Whey Permeate on Phytochemical Content of Canned Tomatoes. *Food Chemistry* (accepted).

Alegria, C., Pinheiro, J., Gonçalves, E. M., Fernandes, I. and Moldão, M. (2010). Evaluation of a pre-cut heat treatment as an alternative to chlorine in minimally processed shredded carrot. Innovative Food*Science andEmergingTechnology*, 11, 155–161.

Almecija, M. C., Ibanez, R., Guadix, A. and Guadix, E. M. (2007). Effect of pH on the fractionation of whey proteins with a ceramic ultrafiltration membrane. *Journal of Membrane Science*, 288, 28-35.

Anne, P-L. (2000). Bioactive peptides derived from bovine whey proteins: opioid and ace-inhibitory peptides. *Trends in Food Science andTechnology*, 11, 347-356.

Antila, P., Paakkari, I., Järvinen, A., Mattila, M. J., Laukkanen, M., Pihlanto-Leppala, A., Mantsala, P. and Hellman, J. (1991). Opioid peptides derived from in vitro proteolysis of bovine whey proteins. *International DairyJournal*, 1, 215–229.

Bayram, T., Pekmez, M., Arda, N. I. and YaleIn A. S. (2008). Antioxidant activity of whey protein fractions isolated by gel exclusion chromatography and protease treatment. *Talanta*, 75 (3), 705-709.

Bellamy, W., Takase, M., Wakabayashi, H., Kawase, K. and Tomita, M. (1992). Antibacterial spectrum of lactoferricin B, a potent bactericidal peptide derived from the N-terminal region of bovine lactoferrin. *Journalof Applied Bacteriology*, 73(6), 472–479.

Bounous, G., Batist, G. and Gold P. (1989). Immunoenhancing property of dietary whey protein in mice: Role of glutathione. *Clinical andInvestigative Medicine*, 12, 154-161.

Brody, E. P. (2000). Biological activities of bovine glycomacropeptide. *BritishJournal of Nutrition*, 84, 39-46.

Clare, D. A. and Swaisgood, H. E. (2000). Bioactive milk peptides (6). *Journalof Dairy Science*, 83,1187–1195.

Colbert, L. B. and Decker, E. A. (1991). Antioxidant activity of an ultrafiltration permeate from acid whey. *Journal of Food Science*, 56, 1249–1250.

Contreras, Md. M., Hernández-Ledesma, B., Amigo, L., Martin-Alvarez, P. J. and Recio, I. (2011). Production of antioxidant hydrolyzates from a whey protein concentrate with thermolysin: Optimization by response surface methodology. LWT - *Food Science and Technology*, 44 (1), 9-15.

Coronado, S. A., Trout, G. R., Dunshea, F. R. and Shah, N. P. (2002). Antioxidant effects of rosemary extract and whey powder on the oxidative stability of wiener sausages during 10 months frozen storage. *MeatScience*, 62, 217–224.

Cross, M. L. and Gill, H. S. (1999). Modulation of immune function by a modified bovine whey protein concentrate. *Immunology and cell biology*, 77 (4), 345-350.

Da Costaa, E. L., Da Rocha Gontijo, J. A. and Netto, F. M. (2007). Effect of heat and enzymatic treatment on the antihypertensive activity of whey protein hydrolysates. *International Dairy Journal*, 17, 632–640.

Diaz, O., Pereira, C. D., Cobos, A. (2004). Functional properties of ovine whey protein concentrates produced by membrane technology after clarification of cheese manufacture by-products. *Food Hydrocolloid*, 18, 601–610.

Farvin, S. K., Baron, C. P., Nielsen, N. S. and Jacobsen, C. (2010). Antioxidant activity of yoghurt peptides: Part 1-in vitro assays and evaluation in [omega]-3 enriched milk. *Food Chemistry*, 123 (4), 1081-1089.

Feeney, R. E., Whitaker, J. R., Arai, S., Watanabe, M., Hirao, N., Adler-Nissen, J., Chiba, H., Yoshikawa, M., Jimenez-Flores, R. and Kang, Y. (1986). Protein tailoring for food and medical uses. FSTA- *Food Scienceand Technology Abstracts*, pp 1-40.

Ferreira, V. O., Pinho, O., Amaral, M. and Martins, I. (2008). Application of blended-learning strategies on sensory analysis teaching. in M. Munoz, I. Jelinek, and F. Ferreira (Eds.). Proceedings of The Iask International Conference Teaching and Learning, pp. 262–270. Aveiro, Portugal.

Fitzgerald, R. J. and Murray, B. A. (2006). Bioactive peptides and lactic fermentations. International Journal of Dairy Technology, 59, 118-125.

Gad, A. S., Khadrawy, Y. A., El-Nekeety, A. A., Mohamed, S. R., Hassan, N. S. and Abdel-Wahhab, M. A. (2011). Antioxidant activity and hepatoprotective effects of whey protein and Spirulina in rats. *Nutrition*, 27 (5), 582-589.

Guo, Y., Pan, D. and Tanokura, M. (2009). Optimisation of hydrolysis conditions for the production of the angiotensin-I converting enzyme (ACE) inhibitory peptides from whey protein using response surface methodology. *Food Chemistry*, 114, 328–333.

Ha, E. and Zemel, M. B. (2003). Functional properties of whey, whey components, and essential amino acids: mechanisms underlying health benefits for active people (review). *The Journal of nutritionalbiochemistry*, 14 (5), 251-258.

Harper, W. J. (2004). Biological properties of whey components: a review: update 2004. American Dairy Products Institute, Chicago, IL.

Hernández-Ledesma, B., Dávalos, A., Bartolome, B. and Amigo, L. (2005). Preparation of antioxidant enzymatic hydrolysates from α-lactalbumin and β-lactoglobulin. Identification of active peptides by HPLC–MS/MS. *Journal of Agricultural and Food Chemistry*, 53, 588–593.

Hogan, S., Zhang, L., Li, J., Wang, H. and Zhou, K. (2009). Development of antioxidant rich peptides from milk protein by microbial proteases and analysis of their effects on lipid peroxidation in cooked beef. *FoodChemistry*, 117 (3), 438-443.

Jensen, R. G. (2002). Invited Review: The Composition of Bovine Milk Lipids: January 1995 to December 2000. *Journal of Dairy Science*, 85, 295–350.

Kim, G. N., Jang, H. D. and Kim, C. I. (2007). Antioxidant capacity of caseino-phosphopeptides prepared from sodium caseinate using Alcalase. *Food Chemistry*, 104 (4), 1359-1365.

Laparra, J. M., Alegria, A., Barbera, R. and Farre, R. (2008). Antioxidant effect of casein phosphopeptides compared with fruit beverages supplemented with skimmed milk against H_2O_2-induced oxidative stress in Caco-2 cells. *Food Research International*, 41, 773–779.

Madureira, A., Tavares, T., Gomes, A. M. P., Pintado, M. and Malcata, F. X. (2010). Invited review: Physiological properties of bioactive peptides obtained from whey proteins. *Journal of Dairy Science*, 93 (2), 437-455.

Mao, X-Y., Cheng, X., Wang, X. and Wu, S-J. (2011). Free-radical-scavenging and anti-inflammatory effect of yak milk casein before and after enzymatic hydrolysis. *Food Chemistry*, 126, 484–490.

Marshall, K. N. (2004). Therapeutic applications of whey protein. *AlternativeMedicine Review*, 9 (2), 136-156.

Martin-Diana, A. B., Rico, D., Frias, J. M., Mulcahy, J., Henehan, G. T. M. and Barry-Ryan, C. (2006). Whey permeate as a bio-preservative for shelf life maintenance of fresh-cut vegetables. *Innovative Food Science andEmerging Technology*, 7, 112-123.

Mullally, M. M., Meisel, H. and FitzGerald, R. J. (1996). Synthetic peptides corresponding to alpha-lactalbumin and beta-lactoglobulin sequences with angiotension-I-converting enzyme inhibitory activity. *BiologicalChemistry Hoppe-Seyler*, 377, 259–260.

Nieman, D. C. (2000). Is infection risk linked to exercise workload? *Medicineand Science in Sports and Exercise*, 32, 406–411.

Pan, D., Cao, J., Guo, H. and Zhao, B. (2012). Studies on purification and the molecular mechanism of a novel ACE inhibitory peptide from whey protein hydrolysate. *Food Chemistry*, 130, 121–126.

Pena-Ramos, E. A and Xiong, Y. L. (2003). Whey and soy protein hydrolysates inhibit lipid oxidation in cooked pork patties. *Meat Science*, 64, 259–263.

Peng, X., Xiong, Y. L. and Kong, B. (2009). Antioxidant activity of peptide fractions from whey protein hydrolysates as measured by electron spin resonance. *Food Chemistry*, 113 (1), 196-201.

Peng, X., Ma, J., Cheng, K-W., Jiang, Y., Chen, F. and Wang, M. (2010). The effects of grape seed extract fortification on the antioxidant activity and quality attributes of bread. *Food Chemistry*, 119 (1), 49-53.

Permyakov, E. A. and Berliner, L. J. (2000). α-Lactalbumin: structure and function. *FEBS Letter*, 473,269-274.

Pihlanto-Leppala, A., Paakkari, I., Rinta-Koski, M., and Antila, P. (1997). Bioactive peptide derived from in vitro proteolysis of bovine β-lactoglobulin and its effects on smoothmuscle. *The Journal of DairyResearch*, 64, 149–155.

Pritchard, S. R., Phillips, M. and Kailasapathy, K. (2010). Identification of bioactive peptides in commercial Cheddar cheese. *Food ResearchInternational*, 43 (5), 1545-1548.

Rival, S. G., Boeriu, C. G. and Wichers, H. J. (2001). Caseins and casein hydrolysates. 2. Antioxidative properties and relevance to lipoxygenase inhibition. Journal of Agricultural and Food Chemistry, 49, 295–302.

Rizzello, C. G., Losito, I., Gobbetti, M., Carbonara, T., Bari, M. de D. and Zambonin, P. G. (2005). Antibacterial activities of peptides from the water-soluble extracts of italian cheese varieties. *Journal of Dairy Science*, 88, 2348-2360.

Tani, F., Shiota, A., Chiba, H., and Yoshikawa, M. 1994. Serorphin, an opiod peptide derived from bovine serum albumin. In β-Casomorphins and Related Peptides: Recent Developments, edited by V. Brantl and H. Teschemacher, pp. 49–53. Wein-heim, Germany: VCH.

Walzem, R., Dillard, C. and German, J. (2002). Whey components: millennia of evolution create functionalities for mammalian nutrition: what we know and what we may be overlooking. *Critical Reviews in Food Science andNutrition*, 42 (4), 353-375.

Warny, M., Fatimi, A., Bostwick, E., Laine, D., Lebel, F., LaMont, J., Pothoulakis, C. and Kelly, C. (1999). Bovine immunoglobulin concentrate-clostridium difficile retains C difficile toxin neutralising activity after passage through the human stomach and small intestine. *Gut*, 44 (2), 212-217.

Yalcin, A. S. (2006). Emerging Therapeutic Potential of Whey Proteins and Peptides. *Current Pharmaceutical Design*, 12 (13), 1637-1643.

Yamauchi, K. (1992). Biologically function proteins of milk and peptides derived from milk proteins. *Bulletin of the IDF*, 272, pp 51–58.

INDEX

H

I

J

K

L

O

P

R

S

T